endorsed by

D0537206

BTEC Level 3 National Health and Social Care

Second Edition

Elizabeth Rasheed,
Alison Hetherington and
Jo Irvine

WITHDRAWN

DYNAMIC
LEARNING

HODDER
EDUCATION

866025

Orders: please contact Bookpoint Ltd, 130 Milton Park, Abingdon, Oxon OX14 4SB. Telephone: (44) 01235 827720. Fax: (44) 01235 400454. Lines are open from 9.00 – 5.00, Monday to Saturday, with a 24-hour message answering service. You can also order through our website www.hoddereducation.co.uk

British Library Cataloguing in Publication Data

A catalogue record for this title is available from the British Library

ISBN: 978 1 444 115 529

First Published 2010

Impression number   10 9 8 7 6 5 4 3

Year   2016 2015 2014 2013 2012

Copyright © 2010 Elizabeth Rasheed, Alison Hetherington and Jo Irvine

All rights reserved. No part of this publication may be reproduced or transmitted in any form or by any means, electronic or mechanical, including photocopy, recording, or any information storage and retrieval system, without permission in writing from the publisher or under license from the Copyright Licensing Agency Limited. Further details of such licenses (for reprographic reproduction) may be obtained from the Copyright Licensing Agency Limited, Saffron House, 6-10 Kirby Street, London EC1N 8TS.

Cover photo © Aflo Foto Agency/Alamy
Typeset by Fakenham Prepress Solutions, Fakenham, Norfolk NR21 8NN

Printed in Dubai for Hodder Education, an Hachette UK Company.

WIGAN & LEIGH COLLEGE
LEARNING RESOURCES
LOCATION:
COLLECTION:
WITHDRAWN
CLASS MARK: 362 1042 5 RAS
BARCODE No. 866025
DATE: 8·1·13   £24·99

Contents

Core units

Optional units

The following units are available online at www.dynamic-learning.co.uk (see inside front cover for access code):

Walkthrough

Prepare for what you are going to cover in this unit, and what you'll know by the end of it.

Learning outcomes:

On completion of this unit, you should:

1 Understand effective communication and interpersonal interaction in health and social care

Reinforce concepts with hands-on learning and generate evidence for assignments.

Activity 1

Find out what the service user/staff ratios are in your setting. Do they differ from setting to setting? Are they different for different age groups?

Understand how your learning fits into real life and working environments.

Case Study

Mary is 82 years old. For the past 20 years, she has made weekly visits to her local bingo hall, where she meets up with friends. As well as the socialising benefits, she enjoys the game because, as she says, it 'keeps her brain ticking over'.

A handy fact to impress people with and help you evaluate key points.

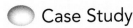

Did you know...

General practitioners already keep patient information on computer.

Key terms

Phenomenology – the philosophical study of lived experience.

Helps you reinforce and remember key concepts and information.

REMEMBER

Collect evidence as you go along. Don't leave it until the last month!

Revise all those new words and what they mean.

The comprehensive guide to what assessors will be looking for in your work.

Assessment and grading criteria

To achieve a pass grade the evidence must show that you are able to:	To achieve a merit grade the evidence must show that, in addition to the pass criteria, you are able to:	To achieve a distinction grade the evidence must show that, in addition to the pass and merit criteria, you are able to:
P1 outline the functions of the main cell components	**M1** discuss the role of energy in the body	**D1** analyse how two body systems interrelate to perform a named function/functions

You've just covered a whole unit, so here's a reminder of the key things you've learned!

Summary

There are many potential hazards within health and social care environments. Minimising the risks reduces the possibility of harm to service users, staff, visitors and property.

You'll often need to find further information for assignments, so here are some pointers to get you started

Resources

Taylor, T.J. and Cameron, D. (1987) *Analysing Conversation: Rules and Units in the Structure of Talk*, Oxford: Pergamon.

The internet's great for further research. These are pointers to some of the more useful information out there for assignments.

Weblinks

www.scie.org.uk:
Social Care Institute for Excellence

Author biographies

Elizabeth Rasheed is a qualified nurse and experienced teacher coordinating Health and Social Care including BTEC Health and Social Care at Dudley College. Elizabeth has taught in further education for over 15 years. She has a first degree in Social Sciences, a Post Graduate Certificate in Education and a Master's degree in Education. She is a Fellow of the Institute for Learning. In her spare time, she is an associate lecturer in Health and Social Care for the Open University. She would like to thank her husband Abu and children Leila and Shafiq for their patience and encouragement while she has been working on this book.

Alison Hetherington was born and educated in Sheffield. A qualified Registered Nurse, she worked for several years at the Royal Hallamshire Hospital in Sheffield. In 1985 Alison moved to Cheshire to begin her midwifery career at Leighton Hospital in Crewe, but following a guest speaker role at her local Further Education college continued as a part time lecturer and completed her Certificate in Education qualification. Up until 2000 Alison worked part time in both Midwifery and Lecturing and was then offered a full time post at Halton College in Runcorn teaching on health and social care and childcare courses. In 2004 she returned to Mid Cheshire College as a full time lecturer with the responsibility for coordinating BTEC Health and Social Care courses. She also works as an external verifier for a major awarding body. Alison would like thank her daughters Laura and Sally and her husband John who have always encouraged her next adventure. Alison would like to dedicate this book to her lovely dad, Stephen Fielding (1929–2008).

Jo Irvine has a great deal of experience in both BTEC and the Health and Social Care sector. Originally a Health Visitor, she has also worked as manager in the NHS and went on to manage a portfolio of Health and Social Care qualifications for a major awarding body. Since becoming an independent education consultant, Jo has been involved in the regulation of qualifications as well as developing a range of specifications in this field.

Photo credits

The authors and publishers would like to thank the following for permission to reproduce material in this book:

p22 © Julian Makey / Rex Features; p23 © John Phillips/EMPICS Entertainment/PA Photos; p50 © PAUL RAPSON / SCIENCE PHOTO LIBRARY; p54 © Health and Safety Executive; p76 © RUSSELL D. CURTIS / SCIENCE PHOTO LIBRARY; p81 © JOTI / SCIENCE PHOTO LIBRARY; p93 © DR P. MARAZZI / SCIENCE PHOTO LIBRARY; p103 (left) © PHOTOTAKE Inc. / Alamy; p103 (right) © PROF. P. MOTTA / DEPT. OF ANATOMY / UNIVERSITY "LA SAPIENZA", ROME / SCIENCE PHOTO LIBRARY; p104 (top) © INNERSPACE IMAGING / SCIENCE PHOTO LIBRARY; p104 (bottom) © CNRI / SCIENCE PHOTO LIBRARY; p137 © Ingram Publishing Ltd; p138, p140 (left), p140 (right) © Brand X/ Photolibrary Group Ltd; p141, p148, p160 © Ingram Publishing Ltd; p192 © ML Sinibaldi/Corbis; p193 © Bettmann/Corbis; p194 © OMIKRON / SCIENCE PHOTO LIBRARY; p200 © PHOTOTAKE Inc. / Alamy; p210 © Blend Images / Alamy; p213 © pixelcarpenter - Fotolia.com; p217 © George W. Hales/Fox Photos/Getty Images); p226 © 1997 David Toase / PhotoDisc / Getty Images; p231 © Ella - Fotolia.com; p244 © Alexander Raths - Fotolia.com; p253 www.CartoonStock.com; p262 (left) © BIOPHOTO ASSOCIATES / SCIENCE PHOTO LIBRARY; p262 (right) © US NATIONAL LIBRARY OF MEDICINE / SCIENCE PHOTO LIBRARY; p291 © TopFoto.

© Crown copyright material is reproduced with permission of the Controller of HMSO.

Every effort has been made to obtain necessary permission with reference to copyright material. The publishers apologise if inadvertently any sources remain unacknowledged and will be glad to make the necessary arrangements at the earliest opportunity.

1: Developing Effective Communication in Health and Social Care

Introduction

Effective communication is central to all work in health and social care. It is essential for practitioners working in social work, nursing, occupational therapy and many of the other professions in health and social care to develop relationships with the people they are caring for in order to understand their situation, their health issues and problems. Good interpersonal skills also help others feel valued, appreciated and listened to, so are just as important when working cooperatively with colleagues as they are when interacting with people using services.

This unit helps you to develop effective skills for interaction and communication. You are encouraged to examine factors that help or hinder communication and to look at what makes interpersonal skills effective in a work-related situation, including the barriers to effective communication and how these might be overcome. You will also reflect on your own performance and that of others.

Learning outcomes:

On completion of this unit, you should:

1 Understand effective communication and interpersonal interaction in health and social care

2 Understand factors that influence communication and interpersonal interaction in health and social care environments

3 Understand ways to overcome barriers in a health and social care environment

4 Be able to communicate and interact effectively in a health and social care environment.

1 Understand effective communication and interpersonal interaction in health and social care

Key term

Communication – an interactive, two-way process of giving and receiving a message, such as exchanging ideas or information.

Although communication involves interaction between people, the people do not have to be physically present. For example, when you listen to a favourite song, the singer is not there but you hear the message and respond emotionally to the words, so communication has taken place. Similarly, you may see a picture and respond to the message or you may respond to a good book by identifying with the character and feeling their emotions.

In health or social care, a great deal of communication is interpersonal – that is, between two people who are physically present – especially between those who are using services (patients, their relatives and friends) and professional health workers and care practitioners. However, while communication between professionals and practitioners may be interpersonal, it is possible for people who communicate frequently in the course of their work to have never met in person.

Key terms

Interaction – an exchange of communication between two people.
Interpersonal – between people.

The most common forms of communication are:

- verbal – speech, either face-to-face or by telephone
- written – including emails and text messages
- touch – hand-holding, patting, embracing, hugging and kissing

- artistic – abstract communication through music, drama, arts and crafts (e.g. sculpture).

Activity 1

Make a list or mind map of all the ways you communicated yesterday.

When you have finished, compare your list with another person's list. In pairs, see if you can work out which activities on your lists are examples of interpersonal communication and which involve interaction.

Your list for Activity 1 might include some of the following:

- Talking with friends in a group while waiting for class
- Talking to a relative
- Making a purchase in a store
- Reading
- Writing study notes
- Sending a text message
- Looking at a picture and thinking about the meaning of it
- Listening to music
- Producing a poster
- Word processing an assignment
- Sending an email.

These are the types of communication used every day, either consciously or unconsciously.

Contexts

Context refers to the circumstances in which you are communicating and with whom you are communicating. This will affect both the method of communication and the language you use. Communicating at work with your manager or other professionals is quite different from communicating with your family and friends. For example, the language you use and the grammar rules that are followed highlight the differences between formal and informal communication. Such rules are important in formal communication but may be deliberately flouted in informal communication, since many groups have their own words that are used in unusual ways to reflect shared meaning that is particular to the group. For example, groups of young people often have words and shared meanings that are not understood by their parents. This serves two purposes: firstly, it differentiates them from their parents and enhances their independence and, secondly, it obscures the meaning so that conversations can be kept private. For example:

Formal greeting: 'Hello. How can I help you?'
Informal greeting: 'Yo! What's up?'

Formal and informal language can also reflect, enhance or change power relationships, particularly when jargon or technical terms are used between professionals. In the same way that young people use terms not understood by their parents, professionals might use language that cannot be understood by the people using services, and this has the same effect – it obscures meaning, allowing the professionals to know things that the service user does not, which reinforces the relative powerlessness of those using services. This can have the effect of making people anxious – they sense the professionals are not telling them the whole story and they may feel that they are not being respected.

When you are communicating with just one person, it is quite different from communicating in a group. Communication with only one person is more personal because you each have the full attention of the other person and different rules apply. For example, you take turns to speak, having listened to what the other person is saying. The language you use will depend on whether this is a formal or informal situation and whether you are speaking about work or just having a leisurely conversation about your personal life.

When communicating in a group, the context is crucial. You may be with a group of friends, going to the cinema, for example. The conversation will be informal – several people may try to speak at once, the rules of the communication are much more flexible, there is likely to be laughter and spontaneity and it may be quite noisy as everyone tries to have their say! This is totally acceptable and desirable, as it demonstrates that the bonds between the group members are sufficiently strong so that individuals are not likely to be offended by breaking conversational rules of behaviour. However, it is not likely to result in effective communication because members of the group are not really listening to one another. They are more likely to be waiting for their opportunity to jump in with a contribution, interrupting someone or trying to listen to one person when several are speaking at once. Misunderstandings are therefore very common.

With formal groups, the situation is quite different. You are likely to have been brought together for a specific purpose – a meeting or training session, for example. It is likely that you do not know the other people in the group very well and may not even have met them before. In situations like this, effective communication can be difficult for a number of reasons. For example, you may feel shy and do not want to draw attention to yourself by speaking. You may not be clear about the purpose

Activity 2

Health and social care work involves a great deal of communication with others. Here are some examples of informal and formal interactions:

- **Discussing the resident's health and well-being with colleagues in the care home where you work**
- **Explaining a procedure to a patient in hospital**
- **Reporting and handing over care for residents in a home for people with learning disabilities to the night staff**
- **Talking to colleagues as you prepare snacks for residents in your care**
- **Giving a talk to a group of junior colleagues on an aspect of your work**
- **Speaking to patients as you help them with their personal care.**

Looking at these examples, work out which are formal and which are informal interactions.

of the group and are waiting for instructions. You may feel inhibited by the others in the group, especially if they seem to know each other or they seem confident and knowledgeable.

In formal groups, communication is usually 'regulated' – for example, if it is a formal meeting, there is likely to be a chairperson who is leading the meeting and through whom all questions and contributions should be addressed. It is up to the chairperson to ensure that everyone has an opportunity to speak and contribute. If it is a training group, the person leading will be the trainer or facilitator. Depending on the nature of the training, they may be standing up to teach and give information, or they may facilitate members of the group to work in pairs or small groups. Effective communication will depend on the trainer's skills in engaging the group.

Dr Bruce Tuckman researched the way that groups develop and operate. In 1965, he suggested that when groups work together they go through a series of processes or stages as they become more effective. This is a helpful way of thinking about team development and behaviour since much of the work in health and social care involves working in teams. As the group moves through the stages, the team or group leader needs to change their style of leadership to accommodate the group's progress towards effectiveness. This is called Tuckman's sequential theory of group development.

The stages that Tuckman identifies are as follows:

- **Forming** – establishing the purpose of the group, the expected outcomes and the relationship of the group with the wider organisation. Individual roles and responsibilities are not yet clear and processes are often ignored as members work at getting to know each other. Very little progress is made towards the goal and the leader needs to be directive and prepared to answer questions as members test them out.
- **Storming** – during this stage, members of the group compete with each other, and often with the leader, to establish their position. Sub-groups and factions may be present as

power struggles persist. Decisions are hard to confirm because this requires compromise. Clear direction and purpose can be obscured. The leader should be coaching.

- **Norming** – agreement begins to appear amongst team members. Roles and responsibilities are allocated and accepted, and big decisions are made collectively as the team establishes processes, working styles and methodologies. There may be some socialising and enjoyment of each other's company. The leader facilitates and enables the group to work together.
- **Performing** – the group finally begins to make progress towards achieving goals and objectives. There is a high degree of self-direction and autonomy and any disagreements are usually sorted out within the team. The leader needs to delegate tasks and projects, overseeing without interfering.

Tuckman later added a final stage:

- **Adjourning** – this is when the goals are achieved, tasks completed and the group is ready to break up and move on. This stage can engender some sadness and feelings of loss if members have bonded successfully. However they can feel good about their achievements.

If you join an existing group, you may find that Tuckman's sequence is not as obvious, so some theorists focus on the processes and purpose of the group rather than stages of development. For example, Robert F. Bales (1970) put forward a theory of 'task and maintenance' activity within a group, arguing that there needs to be a balance within the process between achieving the task and meeting the social and integration needs of the group members. He suggested that by observing behaviour using *interaction analysis*, which classifies individual behaviour within the group, observers are able to understand how a group moved between the task activities and the social activities. For example, see Table 1.1.

Key term

Interaction analysis – the assessment of a communication exchange to see if meaning has been shared.

Table 1.1 Processes within a group

Group task (work activity)	<ul><li>Gives suggestion (including taking the lead)</li><li>Gives opinion (including feelings and wishes)</li><li>Gives information (including clarifying and confirming)</li><li>Asks for information</li><li>Asks for opinion</li><li>Asks for suggestion</li></ul>
Group maintenance (social–emotional activity)	<ul><li>Seems friendly</li><li>Dramatises</li><li>Agrees</li><li>Disagrees</li><li>Shows tension</li><li>Seems unfriendly</li></ul>

Activity 3   P6

Take a group of six people and arrange them in two circles – the inner three people should be seated facing each other and the outer three people placed where they can see the faces of the inner circle, as shown in the diagram below.

The inner circle of three are given a task to discuss, plan and prepare to carry out – for example, planning a patient discharge from hospital or planning how to staff a residential home to meet the needs of the residents. You can think of your own task if you prefer.

Using the chart below, and based on Bales theory, identify the task and maintenance behaviours occurring minute by minute by putting the contributing person's initial in the relevant box. You will need to be able to see a clock or use a stopwatch.

Minutes	1	2	3	4	5	6	7	8	9	10
Group task										
Starting discussion										
Giving information										
Asking for information										
Clarifying discussion										
Summarising discussion										
Group maintenance										
Humour										
Expressing group feelings										
Including others										
Being supportive										

Each person in the outer circle should complete his or her own chart. Once you have done this, compare your charts and discuss your findings within the whole group.

Communication forms

As well as the context in which communication occurs, choosing the right form or method of communication is equally important for communication to be effective. For example, there have been instances of people being dismissed from their job and informed by text message not to turn up for work the following day. This gives out the message that the person is not important enough to waste time speaking to face-to-face. The person receiving such a message is likely to feel angry for being dismissed in such a disrespectful and unprincipled way. Can you think of examples when text messaging is the most appropriate way to communicate?

Once you have decided you need to communicate with someone, it is helpful to think about the communication cycle. This is a commonly used theory of communication first developed by Charles Berner in 1965 and modified by Michael Argyle, a social psychologist, in 1972. Simply put, the communication cycle is when someone decides to communicate, takes action (message sent), which is received by the other person (message received), who then works out the meaning (message decoded) and lets the other person know they have understood (feedback). The feedback is the response to the message and then the whole cycle may start again.

> ### Key term
>
> **Communication cycle** – the sending, receiving and decoding of messages.

How do we choose which method of communication to use? Firstly, we need to think about the purpose of communication – is it to find out information, or to reassure and comfort someone who is distressed? Perhaps you need to get to know someone, or you want to exchange ideas and thoughts. Maybe you are responsible for informing and instructing others. Don't forget, *the meaning of the message is the responsibility of the* **sender***, not the recipient.*

However, when communicating in health or social care, it is helpful to think about your service users and their needs, since the core of your job role is likely to be helping people. Not all service users are the same and certainly do not present with the same needs. So the purpose of the communication is to establish what an individual requires from you that will help them feel better.

Two effective ways to consider service users' needs are:

- Maslow's hierarchy of needs
- PIES – physical, intellectual, emotional and social.

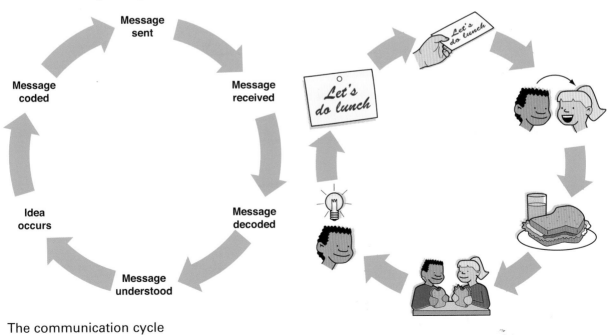

The communication cycle

Maslow's hierarchy of needs

This is a theory put forward by Abraham Maslow (1908–1970), who suggested that people continue to develop throughout their lives. He suggested that the ultimate goal in human life is to maintain personal growth to reach fulfilment, which he described as self-actualisation. In order to meet that ultimate goal, basic needs must first be met. These range from the things needed for basic physical survival to higher-level intellectual needs. To aid service users to meet their needs and to work towards this goal, good communication is essential.

> ## Key term
>
> Self-actualisation – self-fulfilment, meeting one's full potential.

Level 1: Meeting physical and biological needs

A person will experience stress and their health will suffer if they do not have these needs met. Poor and inappropriate communication can cause stress. For example:

> Mrs Healy: 'Can you help me to the toilet, please?'
> Care worker: 'Just a minute, Mrs Healy.'
> Mrs. Healy (sounding anxious): 'I really need to go. Can you help me, please?'
> Care worker (sounding irritated): 'I said, in a minute.'

What do you think would have improved this communication? What if the care worker had said, 'I'm just going to put this in the laundry room and wash my hands and I'll be right with you'? This would have demonstrated that the care worker had heard and understood Mrs Healy's request.

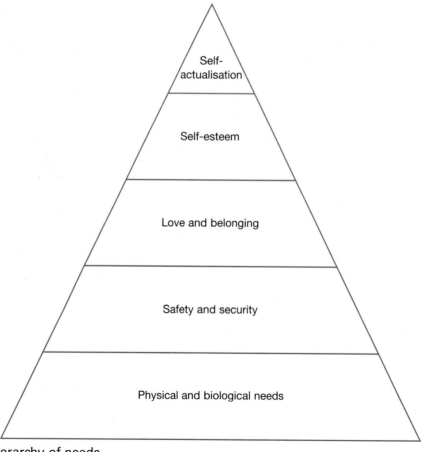

Maslow's hierarchy of needs

Level 2: Ensuring that the person feels safe and secure

If a person is unable to make their needs understood or others are not listening to them, they are likely to feel physically unsafe and emotionally threatened. For example:

> Mr Barnes: 'I don't think I can walk to the ambulance – my feet are very painful.'
> Care worker: 'It's only a short way. You'll be fine.'
> Mr Barnes: 'I really could do with a wheelchair.'
> Care worker: 'Nonsense. You can hold onto my arm if you must.'

Mr Barnes is likely to feel unsafe because he is frightened of falling. His needs have been ignored and his wishes invalidated, which is emotionally damaging.

Level 3: Enabling individuals to comfortably express their emotions and show affection to others

Communication barriers can create a sense of isolation and exclusion. For example, Mr Lewis has recently had a stroke, which has affected his speech. He is embarrassed about this and the fact that he is unable to close his mouth properly. He is reluctant to leave his room and has stopped trying to communicate with the care workers. He pretends to be asleep when his wife visits.

It will be important for care workers to try hard to find an acceptable method for interactive communication with Mr Lewis so that his mental health does not deteriorate.

Level 4: Promoting self-esteem

Positive communication enables people to have their say and feel valued and listened to. Listening skills are very important so that you can respond appropriately when people tell you something that means a lot to them. Listening is a communication skill.

Level 5: Enabling individuals to share ideas

Effective communication will enable individuals to share ideas and become equal partners in their own care. You can discuss and agree any changes to their care according to preferences and circumstances.

Maslow's framework is useful because it helps us to consider forms of self-expression, such as dance, drama, music, artistic expression and handicrafts as forms of communication.

PIES

The PIES framework is helpful for thinking about the needs of others in a structured way:

- Physical – the need for food, water, warmth and shelter, sex and reproduction.
- Intellectual – the need for babies and children to develop concepts such as language, a sense of 'me', and the idea of colours, sizes, shapes and numbers. In adults, it is intellectual challenge and stimulation from work, activities and competitive games, puzzles and crosswords, reading and artistic interpretation, discussions and involvement in societies, hobby clubs or politics, for example.
- Emotional – the need to belong and to be loved, to be valued and appreciated.
- Social – the need for friendship and companionship with like-minded people.

When working with individual people to establish their needs, you are most likely to be using verbal communication. However, if you were reporting back to your manager or recording your conversations with those using services, you would usually use written forms of communication.

It is important to remember that records are formal documents of the care given to those using services and, as such, they could be used as evidence in situations where there might be a dispute about the care provided to someone. It is very important to write exactly what you have done and what you have observed in case the records need to be used in court. For example, you cannot write, 'Mrs Jones fell out of bed' if you didn't actually see this happen. You could write, 'Mrs Jones had some cuts and bruises, consistent with a fall.' You could also write, 'Mrs Jones told me she had fallen out of bed', but you cannot state it as fact if you did not observe it yourself.

Interpersonal interaction

'Inter' means between, so 'interpersonal' means between people. Interaction is action between people. There are many ways of interacting with others; we do this on a daily basis. The role of communication in building relationships is crucial. Communication is about the way we send and receive messages, so in order for it to be effective, there must be mutual understanding. Interpersonal interaction involves applying the communication cycle in ways that ensure your message has the best chance of being understood. Communication goes both ways. Below is a sample of questions to consider before communicating.

- What do I want to communicate?
- Why do I want to communicate this?
- Who am I communicating with?
- What is the best way to communicate my message?
- How can I get the person's attention?
- Would it be better presented orally or in writing?
- Will I need to use pictures, symbols or translators?

Working within a health or social care setting, you will come across people from all walks of life and you need to be able to adapt your communication so that you can interact with them appropriately. Many of the people you meet will be quite different from you. There are cultural differences in the way we communicate that may or may not include speaking a different language.

Effective interactions involve the whole person, since one of the most important aspects of interactive communication involves body language. It has been suggested that up to 70 per cent of meaning is conveyed through body language, or non-verbal communication, rather than speech. External appearance – our clothes, hairstyle and general appearance – also sends signals that help someone form an opinion about us before we have even spoken. This means that, although what you say is important, it is not as important as how you behave and appear to the other person.

Types of non-verbal communication include the following:

- Facial expression – this tends to indicate a person's emotional state. For example, someone who is sad may be 'down in the mouth' literally; the corners of the mouth will be turned down and they may have a slight frown.
- Tone and pitch of voice – tone, or intonation, refers to the way our voice sounds as the vocal chords vibrate. Pitch refers to how high or low on the register the voice becomes. For example, a loud, fixed tone can indicate anger; a high-pitched, sharp tone may indicate irritation; a faint or quiet tone can indicate shyness. Normal tone is mid-range and even.
- Pace of speech – pace of speech is often used to express emotional reaction; excited, nervous or agitated people speak faster than normal. Fast speech can also indicate anger or that the person is seeking to dominate or impress. Pace of speech is inseparable from tone when interpreting body language and people have their own individual speaking styles. Radio and TV presenters have an ideal pace, tone and pitch for presenting information clearly.
- Eye contact – in normal interaction (in the UK – be aware that there are cultural differences in this area) people will look briefly into the other person's eyes, then look away. When a person does not make eye contact they may be shy, or they may be evasive. A fixed stare or glare is part of an angry expression, whereas looking away may indicate boredom or disinterest in what is being said. Pupils get bigger when people are excited or attracted to someone and narrowing of the eyes, where the lids come together slightly, indicates distrust.
- Posture – this refers to the way we sit, stand and hold ourselves. For example, sitting back in a chair with crossed arms and legs is called a 'closed' posture and indicates that the person does not want to listen or engage in conversation. They are not prepared to hear anything you have to say. Leaning back is a relaxed or bored posture, whereas leaning forward is engaged or intense. Head down indicates shyness.
- Gestures – these are used for emphasis, so someone who is excited and telling a tale may use lots of gestures to enhance the story. Gestures can be important in promoting effective communication. However, be aware that there are many gestures that mean one

thing in one culture but something entirely different – and sometimes offensive – in another!

- Muscle tone – clenched muscles are a sign of tension, stiff facial muscles make it difficult to smile and clenched fists is a sign of anger.

These aspects of our behaviour send messages to the other person and let them know our true feelings. Adults can be very good at trying to hide their feelings but body language often gives them away by revealing their true feelings – most of us can recognise a fake smile, for example. People vary in their ability to 'read' body language and some people are more sensitive to it than others. It is a really useful skill to practise as a care worker.

There are also other factors involved in communication, as outlined below.

Touch

Many people who use health and social care services are in crisis in their lives, usually because of factors outside their control. They are most likely to be feeling vulnerable and emotional and appropriate touch, such as holding a hand or patting an arm, can be reassuring. However, it is important to recognise that there are cultural differences in whether touch is seen as acceptable. For example, because touch can also express sexual interest or power relations (e.g. someone grabbing your arm and pulling you against your will), touch is seen as inappropriate between unrelated men and women in some cultures.

Proximity

This is how close you get to someone physically when you are communicating. Each of us has a 'personal space' – an invisible zone around us that we do not like to share. If someone encroaches into this space, we feel uncomfortable. Again, the size of this 'proximity zone' varies from person to person and culture to culture; in some cultures people in conversation may stand close. In other cultures, people prefer a greater distance between them and another person. As a general rule, the closer the relationship, the closer we allow people to be – physically and emotionally. Similarly, the more crowded the environment, the more people are able to deal with a smaller proximity zone. For example, people using the London Underground

are forced to share their personal space with strangers; consequently, they adopt a number of strategies to enable them to cope. For instance, they rarely speak to each other or acknowledge other people. Many passengers will be reading or listening to music – in effect, pretending they are alone!

Listening

Since communication is a two-way process, it is essential that you are able to receive the message, and in order to do this effectively and obtain the maximum information from the person you are speaking to, you must be able to listen fully to them. It has been said that, since we only have one mouth but two ears, we should listen twice as much as we speak! Listening properly (active listening) means letting the other person know we are fully attending to what they are saying by regularly checking our understanding. When someone speaks, we create a mental picture of what they are telling us, which we need to think about and check out. We can do this by re-phrasing what has been said to us in the form of a question. For example, 'So you are often on your own for several days at a time?'.

Asking questions

There are a number of reasons you might want to ask questions; you may need to find out practical information, or you may want to find out about a person's lifestyle, family and friends. You may want to know and understand how they are feeling in order to help meet their needs.

There are several ways of asking questions depending on the purpose. For example, open questions such as 'How do you feel about the food here?' encourage the person to think about the food and form an opinion. On the other hand, if you ask 'Do you like the food?', the person can just say yes or no, without giving you any information about their likes, dislikes or preferences. This is called a closed question. Another questioning technique is called 'funnelling', which involves asking general open questions, then narrower questions, then closed questions. Doctors often use funnelling when diagnosing an illness to establish which part of the body is the cause of the problem. Probes and prompts are also used to tease out more information; probes are short questions following on from the previous answer, when that answer hasn't been sufficiently satisfactory. For example, 'Can you tell me more?'. Prompts are used to encourage a fuller answer. For example, 'Would you go there again?'. Questions can be very useful in keeping a conversation going.

Silence

Silence also has a role in communication. It can indicate empathy and concern for another's feelings, especially when accompanied by touch. Silence can also be used to encourage people to talk as it can make them want to fill in conversational gaps to stop feeling embarrassed. However, this is not a good tactic as it can appear as if you weren't listening or interested, or it can seem manipulative and controlling. Silence is best used sympathetically.

Activity 4 — P5

Working in pairs, hold a conversation on an agreed topic, e.g. hobbies. Decide who is to ask the questions first and hold a one-to-one conversation for five minutes. Practise using body language and all the skills and techniques discussed so far (body language, active listening, questions, probes and prompts). Either video the conversation and review it together, making a note of how you have used the different techniques, or have an observer note these down. When you have finished, you may swap over and change roles.

Communication and language needs and preferences

Much work in health and social care can be described as 'emotional work'. This is because people using health and social care services are often in crisis, sick and therefore emotionally vulnerable. Because of this, you need to establish a trusting relationship in order to help them, so it is important not to judge or make assumptions about the people you are dealing with. Using the communication skills discussed earlier, you will be able to show warmth, sincerity and understanding towards people, creating a supportive environment, which will enable them to express their needs. In getting to know people, you need to understand how age, gender, disability, social class, ethnic origins and religion influence a person's life. You may find that this challenges your own beliefs, values and assumptions and you will need time to reflect on and absorb what this means for you. You may find that you need to seek out information to help you respect other cultures. Any possible misunderstandings are more easily resolved when respect is demonstrated.

Eminent theoretical physicist Professor Stephen Hawking, who has motor neurone disease (see the case study below), said, 'One's voice is very important. If you have a slurred voice, people are likely to treat you as mentally deficient.'

It is increasingly common to meet individuals in care settings who are unable to communicate effectively, so it is vital that we recognise this and assist them appropriately. Individuals may have specific communication needs. For example, they may:

- speak a language other than English as their first language, or may not speak English at all
- be suffering from a condition that affects their speech, e.g. stroke, motor neurone disease, cancer of the throat, cerebral palsy
- have cognitive difficulties that make it difficult for them to understand or respond to you, e.g. post-traumatic brain disorder (following head injury), severe learning difficulties, autistic spectrum disorders
- have sensory difficulties, such as deafness or blindness.

Case Study

Stephen Hawking, born in 1942, is now a famous scientist who was diagnosed with motor neurone disease at the age of 21. Limited mobility in all his limbs means that he is confined to a wheelchair, but although his voice was affected and he uses a voice synthesiser to communicate, he still writes books and scientific papers and delivers lectures at universities.

Visit his website – www.hawking.org.uk – and find out how he used to communicate before he used the synthesiser. Follow the disability link.

2 Understand factors that influence communication and interpersonal interaction in health and social care environments

Theories of communication

Communication studies is a large area of study, which overlaps with other disciplines, such as social psychology, media studies and sociology. Theories such as Argyle's stages of communication theory and Tuckman's theory of group formation are useful as a framework through which to better understand how communication works. However, there are other theories that are particularly relevant to health and social care because they attempt to explain some aspects of behaviour, and communication behaviour in particular, and are useful when aiming to put across health messages.

Cognitive dissonance theory (first developed by Leon Festinger, 1951)

'Cognitive' is concerned with intellectual and thinking behaviour and 'dissonance' refers to conflict or discord. This theory is concerned with communication's social influence and is adapted from social psychology. It suggests that cognitive dissonance occurs where there is a contradiction or conflict in a person's beliefs. This makes people uncomfortable and they strive to reconcile these conflicting ideas.

For example, you may believe that the death penalty is wrong, but you also believe that individuals who commit acts of terror that cause many people to die should receive severe punishment that does not cost society financially. In this situation, you may believe that, logically, they should receive a death sentence, even though you think it is morally wrong. Similarly, you may believe in a woman's right to choose whether or not to have a baby, but feel strongly that abortion violates the right to life of the unborn child.

Cognitive dissonance also occurs when your experience does not match the research findings or respected sources. For example, if several members of your family have lived into their eighties and died of natural causes, despite being smokers, you may not believe that smoking causes cancer, even though research proves that it does.

People may respond to cognitive dissonance by justifying their views – for example, by stating that terrorism is an exceptional crime and therefore the death penalty should apply, but only to terrorists. People suffering from cognitive dissonance will avoid facing up to information that challenges their conflicting views. If a person is suffering cognitive dissonance, it will be much harder to persuade them to act, for example, to give up smoking (as in the example above). This has implications for health promotion programmes.

Conversational studies (Grice, 1968; Taylor and Cameron, 1987)

This theory is concerned with what happens during conversational speech. It suggests that meaning within conversation is created between speakers and hearers through dialogue and negotiation. In other words, it is the interaction between people that generates shared meaning. Grice proposed that conversations are organised around a number of unspoken rules. For example:

● Make your contribution as informative as required to meet the purpose of the conversation.

- Do not give more information than necessary.
- Do not say what you don't believe to be true.
- Don't state things as true when you have no evidence.
- Be relevant.
- Be clear, not obscure.
- Do not be ambiguous (vague).
- Be brief.
- Be orderly.

These points are important to bear in mind when interacting with people in health and social care, since you are likely to have more knowledge of the situation or their condition than them and it is important that meanings are clearly understood and agreed.

Fear appeals (Witte, 1992)

These are persuasive messages communicated to individuals in order to encourage them to change their behaviour by frightening them over the consequences of not complying with a particular message. Health promotion adverts sometimes use this model of communication. For example, drink-driving adverts and adverts showing the consequences of drunken behaviour or drugs.

Activation theory (Lewis Donohew, Phillip Palmgreen and J. Duncan, 1980)

This theory explains how people seek out messages that meet their need for intellectual stimulation and entertainment as well as information. Any health messages must appeal to both the intellect and the emotions, being sufficiently interesting to hold people's attention long enough to get the message across.

Health belief model (G.H. Hochbaum, 1958)

This is used in discussions with individuals when trying to influence behaviour change. Essentially, people will evaluate the perceived benefits of changing their behaviour against the perceived cost or effort of changing and the barriers in the way of change.

When interacting with people for the purposes of discussing health, you need to be aware of the issues that might affect your interaction. Theories are helpful in making you aware of some of the ways in which individuals are likely to receive information, accept it or reject it. Other factors that can affect your interaction and whether your message gets across can be found in the external environment.

Environment

The environment refers to the external surroundings in which communication and interaction take place, and it is central to the effectiveness of communication. If you want to tell someone something important, you will probably consider when and where you will have the conversation. It is unlikely that you will use a mobile phone as you walk round the supermarket to tell someone your important news. Similarly, if you have ever tried to hold a conversation on a mobile phone in the street or other public place, you will know that it can often be too noisy to make yourself understood.

In hospitals and other health or care settings, consultations with the doctor usually take place in a private room so that there are no distractions, such as phones ringing or people walking in and out.

If you are someone with a hearing difficulty, who relies on lip-reading and body language to communicate, the room needs to be well lit and the person with whom you are interacting needs to be facing you so that lip-reading can take place.

Barriers

Other barriers to interactive communication can occur when the information you need to pass on is difficult or sensitive and you are aware that it may not be received well. In such cases, you need to think about how to apply communication theories and ensure that you approach the discussion in a planned way, using all your communication and listening skills to create empathy and demonstrate your understanding.

Emotional states, such as anxiety or depression, affect people's ability to hear the message and understand it. In addition, people may make assumptions or judgements about you, affecting their perception. It is important that you are able to develop a sympathetic attitude and confidence in your communication skills. This will need practise.

3 Understand ways to overcome barriers in a health and social care environment

There are a number of ways that an organisation can help to promote effective communication and overcome barriers.

Communication and interpersonal interaction

Because people using health and social care services are often in a stressful situation, they sometimes do not behave as they would normally. Also, if people are feeling ill or unwell, they may be unable to interact effectively because they cannot think about anything except how poorly they feel. In these situations, it is up to the practitioner to make sure that effective communication takes place.

Effective communication depends on good, trusting relationships developing. This means always making sure you find out what the person needs and putting their interests first. You can do this by adopting a sympathetic approach, ensuring that the person feels comfortable and that you are practising active listening, making sure the time and place are right for the conversation to take place and using appropriate body language. You need to focus on building the person's confidence in you, so be clear about confidentiality and explain the limits of this to the person. For example, if someone confides in you that they are not taking their medication because it makes them feel strange, you have to try and tell them that you cannot keep secrets.

Objects of reference

Sometimes it is necessary to encourage people to talk about themselves. Many people who need to be away from home for some time will like to have with them 'objects of reference'. These are objects that are special to the person in some way; they have meaning and significance. To the individual, they are 'treasures'. Examples of objects of reference are:

- photos of special occasions, e.g. wedding photographs
- photos of children and family
- baby's first tooth/shoe/lock of hair
- ornaments bought to commemorate something or gifts from a special person
- a handkerchief.

Objects of reference help to remind the person of who they are, of their life story, and this helps them maintain their individuality. They also help the person to feel secure by reinforcing their sense of self, which is especially important when in a strange and unfamiliar place with people you don't know.

Assertiveness skills

Fear and aggression are two basic emotions that are linked. When people are frightened, they sometimes become aggressive as a defence mechanism to diffuse their fear. The opposite of aggression is submission and some people will be submissive because they are frightened. As a health or social care practitioner, you need to be able to recognise and deal with these situations. To do this, you need to practise being assertive. Being assertive means being able to control your emotions so that you can think more clearly and use negotiation and problem-solving skills. Being assertive is not the same as being bossy or aggressive; it is about trying to reach a win–win solution in which no one feels put down. Assertiveness skills also help you deal with situations in which others are being aggressive with you, over-riding your rights and making unreasonable demands on you. Assertive behaviour requires you to:

- be calm and use open body language; breathing deeply steadies nerves and calms the emotions
- try to understand the situation in a practical, factual way and consider other people's perceptions
- keep your tone of voice level, even and calm; repeat your position as often as necessary in the same tone of voice until your message has been heard and acknowledged
- use the right words and verbal behaviour to diffuse the situation, acknowledging the other person's point of view, while not necessarily agreeing with it.

The difference between aggressive behaviour, assertive behaviour and submissive behaviour is summarised in Table 1.2.

Table 1.2 Aggressive, assertive and submissive behaviour

Aggressive	Assertive	Submissive
Main feature is anger: ● Making demands ● Not listening to others – talking over them ● Insulting people and putting them down ● Wanting own way ● Shouting or talking loudly. Body language: ● Fixed eye contact – glaring ● Clenched fists, maybe shaken as a gesture ● Waving hands or folding arms ● Angry, frowning expression.	Main feature is to stay in control of emotions: ● Negotiation ● Trying to solve problems ● Acknowledging other's feelings ● Listening ● Showing respect for others ● Keeping calm and speaking clearly. Body language: ● Variable eye contact ● Relaxed facial muscles ● Keeping hands and arms still at the sides ● Upright posture, shoulders back.	Main feature is feeling fear: ● Agreeing with others against one's will ● Not putting one's views across ● Speaking quietly or not at all ● Looking down and not making eye contact ● Frightened expression. Body language: ● Tense muscles ● Not engaging with anyone ● Clasping or wringing hands ● Slumped posture ● Tense, frightened expression.

Aids to communication

There is a whole range of communication aids and initiatives designed to facilitate communication with people who have difficulties. These are briefly summarised below:

● Interpreters are employed as required to translate for people who don't speak English. It is important to have an independent interpreter, rather than a family member, to maintain professional distance and minimise any embarrassment for the individual. It also prevents any possible mis-interpretation or interference from family members (e.g. they may not wish to upset their relative and so don't pass bad news on fully). Advocates are trained to speak on behalf of the individual. However, advocates must be confident that they know what the person actually wants and needs, rather than guessing or assuming.
● Sign language – this is where signs, facial expressions and gestures are used to convey meaning visually instead of orally (e.g. British Sign Language, finger spelling).
● Pictures and symbols of common or everyday objects and situations allow people with compromised speech to point at what they need, e.g. flash cards, Makaton.
● Braille is an alphabet made up of a system of raised dots, which can be 'read' with the fingers. Your telephone keypad and TV remote will have a raised dot on the central button for visually impaired and blind people.
● Communication passports are person-centred documents for those who cannot easily speak for themselves. Sally Millar invented them in 1991 as a communication support aid. They are a way of recording important information about a person, such as the most effective way to communicate with them, their personal history, likes and dislikes, sense of humour, etc. Communication passports can be made in different formats, such as booklets, wall charts, laminated sheets, packs of cards and place mats. They can include photos and pictures.
● Technology can be used to assist people with communication difficulties. For example, a voice synthesizer (Voice Output Communication Aid – VOCA); personal digital assistant (PDA); computers activated by a range of different means, e.g. touch,

Key term

Makaton – a system of symbols and pictures that works like a language to help people make themselves understood.

puff, movement, tongue; software that allows speech. Hearing aids, text phones, loop systems (see www.deaftech.force9.co.uk for more information) and minicom are all technological aids for people with hearing problems. For example, minicom records the conversation, which can then be read and printed out. It looks a little like a fax machine.

Activity 5   P1   P2   P3   M1

Consider the case studies below. Referring to the theories of communication, explain what factors may be affecting communication, what you need to be able to do and what action you would need to take in order to communicate effectively in each situation.

Why is it important to communicate effectively and what are the consequences of not doing so? You need to think about your role, the skills you will need, why they are important and what aids you might use to overcome the barriers to communication.

Case Study 1

You are caring for Mr Johnson, who is 78 years old and is recovering from a stroke. His speech is slurred and difficult to understand. This is making him frustrated, anxious and occasionally short-tempered.

Case Study 2

In the GP surgery, Mrs Iqbal has brought her son for his immunisations but is unsure about the programme on offer. She speaks very little English as it is her second language.

Case Study 3

In a school placement, you are helping the class teacher support Molly, who has a hearing impairment and has had a cochlear implant. She has some hearing but not a full range of sounds.

Case Study 4

You are a social care support worker attending a weekly multi-disciplinary meeting to discuss the care plans for three patients being discharged from hospital. You will be responsible for one of the patients and will have to report back to your supervisor. Describe how the group will work together and how you will present your report.

4 Be able to communicate and interact effectively in a health and social care environment

In order to become a good communicator, you need to practise. Everyone communicates, but the particular skills needed for effective communication in health and social care settings are either not used on a daily basis or not used at all. You need to become a conscious communicator before you are able to use these skills automatically and in the right context. Take every opportunity to practise and you will soon be proficient!

Evaluation

In order to know if your communication has been effective, you will need to think about how to evaluate it. Of course, you can always check with the other person whether they feel that the communication was satisfactory. However, while feedback is important, you also need to carry out your own review and evaluation to see if you met your objectives and the purpose for the communication was achieved in the best way possible.

This is called 'reflective learning', which involves using theory and experimenting. See the diagram below.

Once you have completed the cycle, you can start again. It might be useful to keep a notebook of what you have done.

1. Conversation with others

2. Think: What was effective? What could be improved?

3. Use theory to explain what happened. Which concepts explain other's reactions?

4. Think of ideas for improving your skills

5. Plan how you could practise the skills, e.g. role-play or in your work

6. Try out new ideas

Activity 6

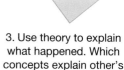

P4 · M2 · M3 · D1 · D2

In pairs, decide what skill you want to practise, e.g. active listening or assertiveness, and develop a list of criteria against which you can measure yourself, e.g. body language. Role-play a situation that you have agreed with your partner. Video or tape-record your role-play conversation and interaction. Get someone else – another colleague or your tutor – to evaluate you against your criteria. Discuss how this felt and ask them what went well and what you need to practise.

You could use the following criteria:
- Very effective and appropriate use of skill
- Some appropriate use of skill
- Ineffective use of skill
- Inappropriate behaviour
- Area not relevant or applicable
- Generally ineffective or inappropriate use of skill.

Summary

In this unit, you will have had the opportunity to start developing advanced skills in communication and interaction, which you can use in your everyday life as well as in preparation for work in the health or social care sector.

You will understand the difficulties some people have in communicating because of their condition or illness, or because they are unhappy. You will be able to think about this and consider the range of communication support aids you can use to communicate, interact and develop relationships with a range of different people.

You will have gained some insight into the theoretical approaches to communication and learnt about human interaction. You will be able to spend many happy hours 'people watching' to try and work out how they feel and what they are saying unconsciously through their body language

Assessment and grading criteria

In order to pass this unit, the evidence that the learner presents for assessment needs to demonstrate that they can meet all the learning outcomes for the unit. The assessment criteria for a pass grade describe the level of achievement required to pass this unit.

To achieve a pass grade the evidence must show that the learner is able to:	To achieve a merit grade the evidence must show that, in addition to the pass criteria, the learner is able to:	To achieve a distinction grade the evidence must show that, in addition to the pass and merit criteria, the learner is able to:
P1 explain the role of effective communication and interpersonal interaction in a health and social care context	**M1** assess the role of effective communication and interpersonal interaction in health and social care with reference to theories of communication	**D1** evaluate strategies used in health and social care environments to overcome barriers to effective communication and interpersonal interactions
P2 discuss theories of communication		
P3 explain factors that may influence communication and interpersonal interactions in health and social care environments	**M2** review strategies used in health and social care environments to overcome barriers to effective communication and interpersonal interactions	

To achieve a pass grade the evidence must show that the learner is able to:	To achieve a merit grade the evidence must show that, in addition to the pass criteria, the learner is able to:	To achieve a distinction grade the evidence must show that, in addition to the pass and merit criteria, the learner is able to:
P4 explain strategies used in health and social care environments to overcome barriers to effective communication and interpersonal interactions		
P5 participate in a one-to-one interaction in a health and social care context	**M3** assess their communication and interpersonal skills in relation to each interaction.	**D2** evaluate factors that influenced the effectiveness of each interaction.
P6 participate in a group interaction in a health and social care context.		

Resources

Bales, R.F. (1970) *Personality and Interpersonal Behavior*, New York: Holt, Rinehart and Winston.

Donohew, L., Palmgreen, P. and Duncan, J. (1980) 'An activation model of information exposure', *Communication Monographs*, 47: 295–303.

Festinger, L. (1957) *A Theory of Cognitive Dissonance*, Evanston, IL: Row, Peterson.

Grice, P. (1968) 'Utterer's meaning, sentence meaning and word meaning', *Foundations of Language*, 4: 225–242.

Hochbaum, G.M. (1958) 'Public participation in medical screening programs: a sociopsychological study', PHS publication no. 572, Washington, DC: US Government Printing Office.

Taylor, T.J. and Cameron, D. (1987) *Analysing Conversation: Rules and Units in the Structure of Talk*, Oxford: Pergamon.

Witte, K. (1992) 'Putting the fear back into fear appeals: the extended parallel process model', *Communication Monographs*, 59: 329–349.

Weblinks

www.scie.org.uk:
Social Care Institute for Excellence
www.mindtools.com:
Mind Tools

Search for videos on effective communication skills on the following websites:
www.youtube.com:
YouTube

2: Equality, Diversity and Rights in Health and Social Care

Introduction

Effective health and social care work depends on practitioners being able to understand the great diversity amongst people within British society, and how good health and social care practice both recognises and accommodates this diversity, so that everyone is able to benefit equally when they need to use the services.

This unit looks at how equality, diversity and upholding rights are fundamental for the effective delivery of health and social cares services. It looks at discriminatory practice and its effects and how anti-discriminatory practice can be promoted.

Learning outcomes:

On completion of this unit, you should:

1 Understand concepts of equality, diversity and rights in relation to health and social care

2 Know discriminatory practices in health and social care

3 Understand how national initiatives promote anti-discriminatory practice

4 Know how anti-discriminatory practice is promoted in health and social care settings.

1 Understand concepts of equality, diversity and rights in relation to health and social care

Britain has a long history of being multi-cultural, with many customs, cultures and beliefs existing together. As a result, we live in a diverse society, which, in order to function smoothly, needs to ensure that all these different groups are able to get along together so that society can remain stable

The principles of equality, individual rights and choices are fundamental values that underpin British society. They encompass ideas of 'fairness', but are much more than this. They are about everyone having basic rights as a human being, being treated as valuable, having the opportunity to live peacefully, to earn a living and to be protected, as necessary, from those who would override individual rights for personal or economic gain – exploitation. These principles are a key aspect of a democratic society and have resulted in laws being passed by Parliament to enshrine these principles in law, influencing how Britain functions and develops.

In the health and social care sector, practitioners must uphold these principles as part of their job. They are considered to have a 'duty of care' to those they look after. This means that they have clear responsibilities to the users of the services, which are enshrined in law and reflected in the policies and practices of health and care organisations.

Benefits of diversity

There are many benefits to a diverse society. Britain has benefited enormously from the enrichment of society that a diverse culture brings. Examples include the following:

Brick Lane author Monica Ali

- Music – musicians have always collaborated with each other across cultural, racial and ethnic boundaries and new musical forms have evolved and continue to evolve as a consequence. Gospel music and 'negro' spirituals evolved into blues, soul, R&B, reggae and rap. Jazz also evolved from blues but went in a different direction. Bands are constantly experimenting, blending traditional folk music with Indian rhythms, Celtic roots with African beats. British music has benefited from exposure to all these different influences that people coming to live in Britain have brought with them.
- Sport – people born in Britain from immigrant parents bring with them the biological diversity that helps to promote excellence across a broader range of sports.
- Books – people from different backgrounds writing about their experiences helps to promote understanding and tolerance. For example, *Small Island* by Andrea Levy and *Brick Lane* by Monica Ali demonstrate what life was like for immigrants to Britain.
- Painting and art – different colours, textures and perspectives are provided by artists from

other cultures, e.g. Turner Prize winner Chris Ofili.
- Language – language is constantly evolving. The English language is full of words from other cultures. For example, from France, rapport, charlatan, ballet; from Germany, hamburger, lager, muesli; from India, bungalow, pyjamas, chai; and patois from Jamaica.
- Design – Swedish design, African colours, Indian paisley.
- Food – Britain now has the benefit of being able to enjoy food from all over the world, from French haute cuisine and Italian pizza to Indian curries and Japanese sushi.
- Economic – there are huge economic benefits to Britain of attracting people into Britain to study and work. The world's current third richest person, Lakshmi Mittal, is a British citizen of Indian descent. It also allows for

Activity 1

Pick one of the areas in the list above. Research the contribution made in each field by people from different backgrounds.

Lakshmi Mittal

Key term

Tolerance – broadminded acceptance (of difference).

Respecting diversity means an appreciation and acceptance that all individuals are different. This leads to promoting fair and equal opportunities.

Terminology

There are many key terms used to describe and express concepts of equality and diversity within health and social care. It is necessary to understand these concepts to be able to discuss the importance of equality and diversity and the issues surrounding these.

Discrimination against specific groups has its own terminology. This includes racism – discrimination based on race, ethnicity or skin colour; sexism – discrimination on the basis of gender; religious discrimination and discrimination on the basis of sexuality, including transgendered individuals. When individuals in any of these specific groups are victims of crime, it is known as hate crime. Hate crime is defined as:

'any criminal offence that is motivated by hostility or prejudice based on disability, race, religion or belief, sexual orientation or transgender.'

a flexible workforce as religious festivals are staggered and hospitals and care facilities can stay open. Britain benefits from the contribution different people offer.

Tolerance is important to ensure that everyone has equal opportunities. It is recognition of the fact that everyone is different. Tolerance leads to social cohesion, which means that groups within society get along together and share the things they have in common, while respecting each other's difference.

Case Study

Debbie and Asima are walking their children to school and chatting about their plans for the evening. It is Friday and Debbie tells Asima that she is looking forward to going to the cinema this evening. Asima asks who will look after the children. Debbie replies that her mother always comes on Friday to babysit so they can go out. Asima says that her mother also comes on Friday to babysit so that she can have her driving lesson while her husband is at Friday prayers. They both agree that it's nice to have a break from the children and that their respective mothers really enjoy time alone with their grandchildren.

Debbie and Asima share several things – they are both young mothers, they like to socialise and learn new things and they both recognise that time to pursue one's own interests is important but that, because they have their children's interests and well-being at heart, they need to have support from their families in the care of their children.

Key terms

Equality – this is about ensuring that people have equal opportunities in life and a fair chance to fulfil their potential. In health and social care, equality is focused on equal access to health and social care and equal treatment for everyone, irrespective of race, ethnicity, sex, gender, religion, social class, age or any other difference.

Equity – this is a principle that all people should be treated fairly and impartially (in an unbiased way). This is not about everyone having the same wealth or power but about ensuring that everyone has the same rights under the law. It also means that individuals should not be discriminated against. It is based on a moral right that individuals have the right to be treated equally.

Diversity – this is about accepting that everybody is different. We all have the right to different views and opinions and these must be respected. It is not just about being politically correct or being a good society; it is about creating social cohesion and harmony through challenging and changing people's attitudes towards different cultures.

Rights – everyone has a right to care and practitioners have a duty and responsibility to uphold this right, otherwise you are not giving appropriate care. By not accepting that all people have the same rights, they are being denied their rights as human beings.

Opportunity – if equality and diversity are enshrined within society, discrimination will eventually be eradicated and everyone should have an equal chance to achieve his or her potential in society.

Difference – this is the quality that makes someone unlike someone else.

Direct (overt) discrimination – this is one of two forms of discrimination. It is when you knowingly treat someone unfairly on the basis of race, gender, etc.

Indirect (covert) discrimination – this type of discrimination tends to be subtler – for example, applying criteria that only some people are able to meet. Although it may be unintentional, it is still unlawful.

Stereotyping – this is based on prejudice (pre-judging) and means holding beliefs that all members of a group are the same. This information is often based on negative beliefs and is inaccurate. The person is not seen as an individual. Stereotypical remarks often start with 'They all....'

Labelling – by labelling someone, you are applying a stereotype to him or her. People are not seen as individuals but seen as whatever is implied by the label. For example, 'hoodie', rather than someone's older brother, 'queer', rather than a good worker, etc. From this, discrimination results. It is used to 'put people down'. Individuals or groups who fall within a negative stereotype start from a disadvantaged position and thus lack power and influence.

Prejudice – this means having a pre-conceived idea about somebody or a group of people. Prejudice can take many different forms; it is often deep-seated and can lead to discrimination, preventing people having their needs addressed and, in extreme cases, can result in bullying and abuse. It is based on fear or lack of knowledge and can be a feature of unequal power relations.

Disadvantage – this is a situation in which an individual is in a position of weakness relative to someone else. A disadvantage is something that will count against someone and put him or her in a weaker situation than someone else.

Beliefs and values – these are things you hold to be true. They inform your attitude and how you live your life – your values. They are important to a person and are generally based on what was learnt during someone's upbringing or through experience. It is important to remember not to treat someone differently because they do not share your views. Beliefs and values help to inform a person's sense of self.

Vulnerability – this is a psychological state of mind that can make someone more likely to suffer from danger, harm or abuse. Many people who use services are vulnerable because they are in a stressful situation as a result of ill health or an unforeseen crisis.

Abuse – a violation of an individual's human and civil rights by any other person or persons. It can be the neglect or mistreatment of individuals, generally those who are vulnerable, and can be sexual, physical, emotional or financial.

Empowerment – one of the fundamental principles of care work, empowerment is about enabling people to take control over their lives through choices and be as independent as possible.

Independence – this means that someone has the freedom to choose how they live their lives, to not be dependent or controlled by someone else, an organisation or the state.

Interdependence – this is when people are dependent on each other. This may be through mutual assistance or cooperation.

Hate crime infringes human rights and causes greater psychological damage than similar crimes without prejudiced motivation.

Settings

The locations in which health and social care take place are called settings. For example, a hospital is a healthcare setting. There is a wide variety of settings – however, each of them will have policies and practices in place to protect the rights of those who use services. Such policies are in place to make sure that the organisation and staff comply with the law in relation to equality and diversity. Staff have a responsibility to follow the policies and ensure they do not break the law

Activity 2

Take a flip chart and divide it into two. Divide into two groups.

Group 1 should write the names of different groups of people within society in Column 1.

Group 2 needs to think of all the names and descriptions they have heard used in relation to these groups and write these in Column 2.

Swap over. At the end of the session, discuss where your information about these groups has come from. Does anyone have any evidence that this information is correct or incorrect? Here are some groups to start you off:

- Homeless people
- Mental health patients
- Pensioners
- Single mums.

Try to answer the following questions:

- Where do our prejudices come from?
- How do we form our ideas of groups of people?
- How could you challenge your prejudices?

by doing something which might discriminate against an individual or group of service users.

Activity 3 — P3 M1

Look at the groups you have identified in Activity 2. In pairs, choose one group and write down:

- how these people might be discriminated against in health and social care

- how this might affect them and how they would feel.

Compare your answers and make a list of the effects.

Active promotion of equality and individual rights in health and social care

In all care settings there should be an 'active promotion' of equality and individual rights. This means making sure that equality and rights are clearly understood by all within the workplace, and that the rules put in place to ensure equal treatment are followed, including challenging discriminatory words and actions. It also means that an individual's rights must be respected, as long as this doesn't affect other people's fundamental rights.

However, it is important to recognise that rights have corresponding responsibilities. For example, it is your right as a practitioner to work in a safe environment. Your corresponding responsibility is to follow the safety rules that the organisation has written into policies and procedures. An example might be a policy that states that it is the responsibility of the individual using lifting equipment to check that the equipment is in good working condition and to report any faults immediately to the person in charge of the setting. If someone is hurt because these rules have not been followed, it could be considered negligent on the part of the person who last used the equipment or who failed to report a fault.

Although the issues of individual rights and equal opportunities can be addressed through organisational policies and procedures that enable legislation to be put into practice, there may be dilemmas and conflicts of interests, particularly in group settings.

Within health and social care, practitioners should behave ethically; they are encouraged to adopt an ethical code of practice, previously known as the care value base. This ethical approach has informed the development of formal standards of care that practitioners should use to ensure they promote equality and individual rights within their work.

The three key principles that inform this ethical approach are outlined below.

To maintain confidentiality

This means not divulging information to anyone who does not have the right to that information. There are a few exceptions when you can break confidentiality. These are when the person is at risk to themselves or to others, or if they are at risk from abuse. Confidentiality can be maintained in a number of ways, such as not talking to or about people you are caring for in a public place, making sure records are marked 'confidential' and read only by those who should read them and ensuring that computer records have passwords. Confidentiality is important as it builds trust between individuals and staff members and can protect both groups. The principles of confidentiality should be reflected in policies, procedures and guidelines.

To foster equality and diversity

This is all about understanding and recognising the implications of prejudice, stereotyping and labelling on an individual's psychological health and well-being. It is also important to recognise, understand and appreciate your own beliefs and assumptions about diversity and acknowledge how these may impact upon practice. It is important to remember the benefits that diversity has on society and ensure that everyone is treated as an individual.

Activity 4   P2   P3

Which of the care values are not being observed in the following case study? What should be done instead and what would you do to challenge the situation if you were the manager? What is the likely effect on Mr Newman?

To promote rights and responsibilities

People have many rights within health and social care. These include the right to be different, to have choice and dignity within health and social care and to be safe and secure. Care workers have the responsibility to adhere to these rights, but also have their own rights. These include working

Key term

Putting the patient/service user at the heart of service provision – this means to focus on what the person needs and provide it, giving them control and power over their lives, rather than telling them what services are available. People should be involved in decisions over things that affect their lives, so that they are as independent as possible.

in a safe environment and not being subject to abuse.

Actively involving the individual service user leads to empowerment. You can empower the service user by making sure that you help them do the things that they want and feel able to do, rather than doing things for them. Centres can ensure the participation of service users within provision, such as involving them in the running of the centre, helping to organise trips and promoting individuals' rights, such as giving a choice of food at meal times.

Look again at Activity 4. In what way is Mr Newman being empowered? How would you change the behaviour of the staff to empower the people they look after more effectively?

Sometimes there may be tensions between rights and responsibilities and this may mean that a service user's rights may be compromised; however, in situations where conflict arises, sensible negotiation and compromise can usually be achieved if it is clear that you are being fair and not showing preference for one individual. When there is likely to be a conflict of interests and there is an ethical decision to be taken, a few key principles will help to ensure fairness.

- Gather the facts. Decisions depend on all relevant details being available – for example, the individual's clinical and psychological needs and legal rights.
- Consider the extent to which a decision will have a favourable outcome for everyone.
- Consider the fairness and consistency in

Case Study

Sheila works in a care home for older people with dementia. She sees Carla, another assistant, dress Mr Newman. Carla chooses the clothes that he should wear without consulting Mr Newman. After he is dressed, Mr Newman comes down for his breakfast. He is a strict orthodox Jew. The new care assistant, Tim, is giving Mr Newman his breakfast of bacon and eggs and has not been told about any dietary needs that Mr Newman has. Mr Newman requests a visit to the synagogue and this is denied.

Carla, Tim and Sheila then write up the notes from the shift. Sheila finishes her section and leaves Carla and Tim to finish their section. Carla and Tim forget to put their notes away and are still talking about the shift and the demands of Mr Newman when they go for a drink after work.

Key term

Anti-discriminatory practice – discrimination is against the law and, as a care worker, it is essential not only that you uphold the law yourself, but that you ensure the service users you deal with are not subjected to discrimination or unfair practice from others. This may mean challenging others if you witness discriminatory behaviour, either by other service users or by colleagues. Discriminatory practice means treating someone unfavourably compared to others in relation to the provision of goods or services, buying, renting or selling land or property or within employment.

the decision – people have a right to equal treatment and must not be discriminated against.

- Consider whether the decision empowers the individual and increases their control over their own circumstances.

Examples of anti-discriminatory practice could include:

- making sure all areas of the setting are accessible to everyone, e.g. having wheelchairs available to borrow
- providing aids for people with sensory difficulties, e.g. providing a minicom or hearing loop
- ensuring staff and service users are represented at meetings
- making sure that policies and procedures are available to all, including in different languages

- monitoring the equal opportunities policy
- having a suggestion box for improvements
- having an induction programme for new staff and regular staff training and development sessions.

Individual rights

Everyone, including service users, have rights as human beings, which should be respected within health and social care settings. Treating people well and respecting their rights and feelings encourages psychological well-being and has a beneficial effect on health and healing. Rights are often protected by legislation. Some of these rights are explained in Table 2.1.

Table 2.1 Individual rights

Right	How this right can be demonstrated
To be respected and treated as an individual	Through effective communication that makes sure individuals are able to make choices and act in their own interests. By showing interest and respect for service users and their experiences, valuing them as people. By ensuring that the dignity and privacy of service users is maintained.
To be treated equally and not discriminated against	By ensuring that all service users have their needs and requirements assessed so they can have equal access to services. Through recognising that people are not the same and should not be treated as if they were. By involving people in decisions, attempting a redistribution of power.

Right	How this right can be demonstrated
To be treated in a dignified way	By making sure you ask the individual how they prefer to be addressed. By speaking and communicating with them in a respectful, adult manner. By making sure you protect the individual's self-esteem and self-respect during conversation and caring activities. By making sure the person is being neither humiliated nor embarrassed. By treating service users as you would expect to be treated yourself, or as you would expect a family member to be treated.
To privacy	By making sure the person has a private space that can only be entered by invitation, by consent. By recognising that people may need assistance with personal hygiene, which is a private matter and should be attended to practically and with respect. By maintaining privacy through simple actions, such as ensuring that a door is closed when carrying out personal hygiene tasks.
To be safe and protected from danger and harm	By carrying out risk assessments to ensure the environment is safe and secure. By making sure that the person's possessions are accounted for and valuable items are stored in a safe and secure place. By making sure people's relationships with others are a positive choice, rather than being the expected thing to do. By carrying out checks on visitor identities and providing identification.
To be allowed access to information about themselves	By providing mechanisms to ensure service users are involved with meetings or discussions about things that affect them. By discussing notes with service users before writing them up.
To be able to communicate using their preferred methods of communication and language to express themselves	By ensuring that service users who require appropriate communication methods, such as communication passports, advocates or sign language, are accommodated within the setting. By using active listening and other effective communication and supportive techniques.
To be cared for in a way that meets their needs	By making sure there are effective processes in place for assessment and monitoring of service user's needs. By ensuring services put the individual at the centre of the process and ensure all needs (physical, emotional, social, intellectual, cultural) are taken into account.
To exercise personal choice	By ensuring the service user is at the centre of any planning (person-centred planning) and is able to contribute and make their views known. By making sure service users have as many options as possible – for example, what time to get up or go to bed or what treatment they receive. By providing choices that are realistic.

Activity 5   P1

Read the following case study and decide where the tensions are and what you would do in the situation. Compare your views with someone else's.

◯ Case Study

Tim works in a residential home for people with learning disabilities. A service user, David, has suddenly decided he wants to go to the shops. However, if David goes out, it will mean leaving the other service users with one member of staff.

Now make up your own case study illustrating some of the tensions between rights and responsibilities. What would you do in the situation?

2 Know discriminatory practices in health and social care

Basis of discrimination

Discrimination has its roots in people's early learning experiences. Although children are aware of differences from a very early age – young children can usually tell you from about the age of two or three whether they are a boy or a girl – at that time, there is little meaning attached to the label 'boy' or 'girl'. Meanings have to be learnt from the adults around them. If children hear the adults around them express negative comments, prejudiced attitudes and hostility to particular individuals or groups in society, they will come to share those views. This is because, in a child's early life, the parents are the main source of knowledge and information. It is parents that help children make sense of the world before they move into the wider world of school. This process is commonly known as socialisation.

Parents can also affect a child's resilience and sense of self if they have unrealistic expectations of the child or are too ready to criticise. Socialisation continues throughout life, as people learn from their experiences and are influenced by the media, education, work colleagues and others with whom they come into contact.

This poem by Dorothy Law Nolte clearly explains how the way a child is treated can affect them:

If children live with criticism
    They learn to condemn
If children live with hostility
    They learn to fight
If children live with ridicule
    They learn to be shy
If children live with shame
    They learn to feel guilty
If children live with tolerance
    They learn to be patient
If children live with encouragement
    They learn to be confident
If children live with praise
    They learn to appreciate
If children live with fairness
    They learn justice
If children live with security
    They learn to have faith
If children live with approval
    They learn to like themselves
If children live with acceptance and friendship
    They learn to find love in the world.

Discrimination is more common amongst certain groups of people, although it is helpful to remember that not all members of a group will be discriminated against. Factors that form the basis of discrimination are outlined below.

Culture

People from cultures that are in a minority in the local community can be discriminated against in a number of ways. For example, they might not speak English well or they might have a strong regional accent; children can be teased and bullied at school and people can be denied job opportunities as a result. People from other cultures are also from different countries and may wear different clothes and eat different foods.

Age

Older people and younger people are the most likely to be discriminated against. Older people might be discriminated against because they are no longer economically active and some people may see them as a financial burden on society, despite the fact that older people are likely to have saved for their pensions all their working lives. They may have been professional people, such as barristers or managing directors, but they may still be seen as 'just' an old person. Younger people can be discriminated against because they are portrayed in stereotypes as either likely criminals or victims. They are unable to challenge these views due to their relatively powerless position in society. The government introduced legislation, such as the Age Discrimination Laws in 2006, to prevent discrimination against older workers.

Social class

This is discrimination based on wealth and the perceptions of higher status that this brings. Discrimination can occur when people do not appear to have the material goods and benefits of an affluent society. The media promotes images of success based on material wealth and expensive consumer goods, which are beyond the aspirations of most people. People who live in supported housing or who are receiving welfare benefits because of their circumstances can be the focus of stereotyping and subsequent discrimination, including bullying.

Gender

It is important to recognise that sex is a biological difference, whereas gender is socially determined: a product of socialisation that what it means to be a boy or girl as gender roles are learnt. In society, there are expectations of these gender roles and associated stereotypes that, in the past, have prevented women from accessing certain professions or taking on employment traditionally seen as for men. Similarly, men have been allocated the role of provider and can be discriminated against if they stay at home to look after the children. These gender roles are being challenged.

Although it is against the law to discriminate on the basis of gender, it is still common for women not to earn the same as men for comparable jobs.

Sexuality

According to Stonewall, a campaign group that works for equality and justice for lesbians, gay men and bisexuals, the government's figures show that 5–7 per cent of the population is lesbian, gay or bisexual (source: www.stonewall.org.uk). In the past, lesbian, gay and bisexual people have not had equal access within society. This can lead to both discrimination and people not feeling comfortable about being open about their sexuality for fear of discrimination. There are many sportsmen who fear the repercussions of revealing that they are homosexual, for example.

Health status

A person's health status may cause them to be subject to discriminatory practice. This could include people who are HIV positive, who may be seen as a risk to others, especially if they are also homosexual. People with mental health conditions may also experience discrimination and prejudice. This is often based on people not understanding the causes and conditions and not having much experience of people with such conditions.

Family status

Due to the prevalence of stereotypes, often built up through sensational media reporting, single-parent families are frequently portrayed in a negative way as 'benefit scroungers' or young women who get pregnant on purpose in order to get access to housing. In reality, most single-parent families are the result of divorce and often women are left with responsibility for childcare. Since women tend to earn less than men, they are financially disadvantaged as well. Families with a lot of children can also be discriminated against, as large families were not common in the UK in the twentieth century, although this may change due to the frequency of re-marriage, when both partners may have children from previous relationships. This situation was not uncommon in Victorian times, however, since many women died in childbirth, so men remarried and went on to have more children.

Cognitive ability

Children and adults with learning disabilities are often discriminated against and, in some cases, have been the victims of hate crime. For example, a man with learning disabilities was abducted by two people who lived nearby, kept in a garden shed and tortured to death. In another case, several youths threw a firework through the letterbox of a young man with learning disabilities who lived with his mother, setting the house on fire. The mother, a middle-aged woman, died after she was overcome by smoke helping her son climb out of a window. These are extreme cases that had a high media profile, demonstrating their unacceptability. The perpetrators were caught and brought to justice.

Discriminatory practice

Discriminatory practice can occur on three levels, which are not mutually exclusive and can be the cause or effect of each other.

Discrimination on an *individual* basis happens as a result of the prejudice of others. This may include exclusion, insults or violence, as in the cases described above. An individual may be singled out and treated differently; bullying in school is the result of an individual being singled out in this way.

Discrimination at an *institutional* level occurs, for example, through an organisational culture that fails to adequately implement and monitor anti-discriminatory policies and practice. When such an organisation is providing public services, the results can be extremely serious. Organisational culture is expressed through an organisation's rules, regulations and practices.

Discrimination on a *structural* level occurs when whole communities and societies have discriminatory views or beliefs about certain people. A whole community can pass on discrimination. People see the world from their culture and this is a reflection on society.

The way in which discriminatory practice is displayed can be either direct (overt) or indirect (covert). Direct discrimination is usually quite clear and obvious – for example, if someone was refused a job opportunity because of his or her age or racial origin. There does not have to be

an intention to discriminate; for the law to be broken, it is sufficient if someone suffers from discrimination.

Indirect discrimination, on the other hand, is much more subtle and difficult to prove; it may occur when people seem as though they are being treated alike. Indirect discrimination often occurs when a condition is applied that is much harder for one group to meet than another and where there is no basis for it. For example, giving less favourable terms for a pension scheme to part-time employees would be indirect discrimination against part-time workers and, because women make up the majority of part-time workers, these terms could also be indirectly discriminating against women.

Other types of discrimination include victimisation – for example, if someone won a tribunal case against their employer for discrimination

Case Study – direct discrimination

Andrew is black and comes from Newcastle, where he has lived all his life. He speaks with a broad accent. He has found a job vacancy that he is interested in and phones to enquire. He is asked to attend an interview the following day and takes his CV with him. When he arrives, the receptionist asks him to wait and disappears. When she comes back, she informs him that the job has been taken.

Andrew suspects that this is not true and that he has been refused the interview on racial grounds and that he would not have been asked for interview if the employer had known that he was black. He asks his friend Paul to telephone and make enquiries and, sure enough, Paul is told the job is still available.

Andrew takes advice from a lawyer at the Citizen's Advice Bureau and decides to take the employer to an employment tribunal.

Case Study – indirect discrimination

Susie is a single parent who has worked for the same company, making car parts, for several years. When she got divorced, she was able to keep her job because the working hours fitted in with her childcare arrangements. However, a new director has recently been appointed and has reorganised the workforce and changed the shift patterns, making it difficult for Susie to collect her children from school.

Susie goes to see her employer and explains the situation. However, he tells her that there are more people to consider and the economic situation means he has to change shift patterns. Susie has been obliged to give up her job. She takes her case to a tribunal, arguing that it is indirectly discriminating against women because they are more likely to have childcare responsibilities. Her employer is told he must adopt family-friendly policies, including offering job share and flexible working arrangements.

Other types of discriminatory practices include:

- physical assault of people who are different
- verbal abuse towards people who are different
- excluding people from activities
- avoiding people because they are different
- negative non-verbal communication, such as not looking at people directly
- making assumptions, e.g. that everyone should be treated exactly the same
- devaluing people by treating their needs and interests as less important than others, including your own.

For further information and general examples, go to the Citizen's Advice website at www.adviceguide.org.uk. You can access information in relation to Northern Ireland, Wales and Scotland from the same site.

Effects

Most of us have experienced discrimination at some point in our lives, such as not being picked for the sports team or being insulted. Single experiences do not make a big difference to our health and well-being overall, unless we are subjected to a targeted violent physical assault or hate crime. It is systematic and consistent discrimination that is most harmful.

Minority groups can be marginalised and isolated. They may feel oppressed. Low self-esteem, poor self-image, negative self-worth and low self-confidence can have a lasting effect on educational achievements and progress at work, leading to a loss of motivation to achieve. Stress itself has a number of consequences, such as tiredness. People can develop mental illness, such as anxiety and depression, as a consequence of stress related to discrimination.

Groups or individuals who are discriminated against or marginalised effectively lose their rights as citizens under human rights legislation.

and they were subsequently dismissed, they could argue that they had been victimised because of their action in bringing a case against their employer.

Sexual and racial harassment are also forms of victimisation and are unlawful under legislation. Harassment means subjecting someone to unwanted sexual advances or attention, forms of verbal racial abuse, such as jokes or bullying, or excluding people from social activities because of race or sex. Sexual harassment is more common where, for example, there are many more men working in a team than women, or many more women than men.

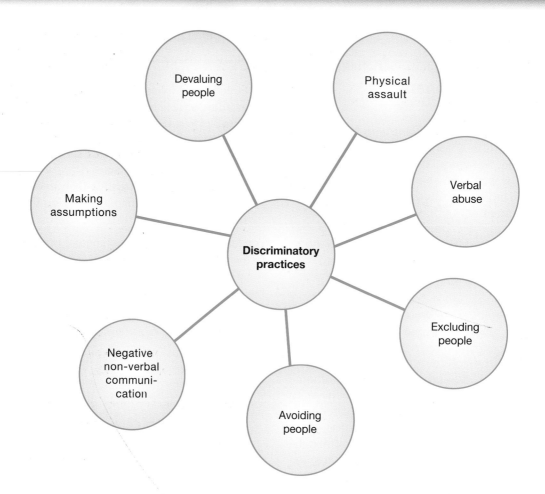

3 Understand how national initiatives promote anti-discriminatory practice

The principles of democracy, individual rights, equality and choice have resulted in legislation – laws and regulations passed by government – that promote these values by making anti-discriminatory action illegal. In other words, in Britain, it is against the law to discriminate against another person or group of people because they are different from you.

Did you know...

In 1964, people letting rooms in London displayed signs saying: 'No Blacks, No Irish, No Dogs'. Women doing the same job as men were not paid the same wage. Women were discriminated against in employment just because they were female. For example, up to the late 1950s, women had to leave some professions, including nursing, if they got married.

Conventions, legislation and regulations

The purpose of legislation is to protect people from those who would do harm, ensuring that the citizens of the UK can get on with their individual lives without undue interference from others, including government. Where there are contradictions or conflicts of interest, the courts decide how the law should be interpreted. This is called case law and it sets a precedent or benchmark for other rulings or judgements of a similar nature. Conventions are an agreed set of principles to which others have to sign up, e.g. governments. Regulations state how a particular Act of Parliament should be interpreted in practice.

Legislation is frequently amended and updated to reflect changes in society and it is important to recognise that there are some laws which apply only to England and Wales and some which apply only to Scotland or Northern Ireland because each of the countries making up the UK has its own government. In addition to these laws, there are conventions, which are also a type of law.

Equalities legislation

There has been legislation protecting equality in the UK for over 30 years. For example:

- The **Sex Discrimination Act 1975** was passed to protect men, women and transgendered people from discrimination on the grounds of gender. This act made it illegal to refuse a job or training to someone because of gender.
- The **Race Relations Act 1976** made racial discrimination illegal and the Race Relations (Amendment) Act 2000 required public bodies, e.g. schools, local authorities and health bodies, to promote race equality.
- The **Disability Discrimination Act 1995** and **Disability Discrimination Act 2005** made it illegal to refuse employment to a disabled person on the grounds of their disability. The act gave people with disabilities rights in employment, education, access to goods and facilities and when buying land or property. Minimum standards were set requiring public transport to meet the needs of those with disabilities. Other changes included making it illegal for private clubs with 25 or more members to exclude disabled people and making it easier for disabled people to rent property. For the first time, the definition of disability was extended to cover hidden disabilities, such as HIV, cancer and multiple sclerosis.

All legislation has been subject to review and

amendment during this time, particularly to meet the requirements of European laws or directives about equal treatment for men and women. Compliance with equalities legislation has been monitored in order to ensure the law is working.

The **Equality Act 2010** aims to simplify the law, which, over the years, has become complex and difficult to understand. The act will update, simplify and strengthen all the previous legislation, setting out new laws, which aim to help

---

Activity 6 | P4 | M2 | D1

You are a social work assistant supporting people with their daily activities. First, research the Disability Discrimination Act 2005. Make a note of the key issues and the rights disabled people have under the act.

Next, take a walk around your local area and examine access to shops, restaurants, the local health centre, post office services and public transport for your two service users:

- Mrs Harris, who uses a wheelchair
- Mr Singh, who is blind.

See if you can interview people who work in two of the areas and ask them what provision they have for your two imaginary service users (e.g. access to toilets, help with forms, menus, money).

In relation to the Disability Discrimination Act (DDA), write a report of your findings and evaluate how influential the DDA has been in promoting anti-discriminatory practice. Do you think it has been successful? Explain and justify your answer in relation to your findings.

narrow the gap between rich and poor and create a more equal society.

This single act provides a framework of discrimination law, which incorporates much of the previous legislation designed to protect individuals from unfair treatment. See www.opsi.gov.uk for details of this act.

The Human Rights Act 1998

This is a significant piece of legislation that formally protects individual rights in law. It has its origins in the European Convention on Human Rights, drafted by the Council of Europe, which was set up in 1950 to unite Europe after the Second World War (not the same as the European Union). The council also set up the Court of Human Rights, based in Strasbourg, to which European citizens whose rights have been violated can appeal if all other attempts to redress the alleged wrongdoing have failed.

You can find out more about the Council of Europe and the Court of Human Rights in Strasbourg by looking on the following websites:

- http://conventions.coe.int
- www.echr.coe.int/ECHR
- www.justice.gov.uk/guidance/docs/act-study guide.pdf.

The body responsible for monitoring equalities legislation is the **Equality and Human Rights Commission**. This statutory body has the responsibility to protect, enforce and promote equality across the seven 'protected' grounds – age, disability, gender, race, religion and belief, sexual orientation and gender reassignment. It replaces the separate bodies – the Equal Opportunities Commission, the Commission for Racial Equality and the Disability Rights Commission.

Children's rights

Other important conventions include those adopted by the United Nations (UN). In 1989, the UN adopted the Convention on the Rights of the Child (UNCRC), which was the result of an international convention setting out the civil, political, economic, social and cultural rights of all children. Countries that ratify (sign up to) the convention are bound to it in international law and have to present a progress report to the United

Nations Committee on the Rights of the Child, the body responsible for monitoring compliance. The guiding principles of the Convention on the Rights of the Child are found in the following web link

- www.dcsf.gov.uk/everychildmatters/ strategy/strategyandgovernance/uncrc/ unitednationsconventionontherightsof thechild/life.

This has been generally adopted throughout the UK. For example, the Welsh Assembly Government was the first to adopt the UNCRC as the basis for all childcare provision in Wales.

The Children Act 1989

This is the key legislation concerning the welfare of children and includes important principles concerning children's rights, the most significant of which is the 'paramountcy principle', which means that the welfare of the child is the first and foremost consideration in any decisions affecting the child, over-riding the wishes of the parents if necessary.

> ## Key term
>
> **Paramountcy principle** – when dealing with children and young people, their welfare, needs and rights must come first, before those of adults.

Under the act, local authorities have a statutory general duty to safeguard and promote the welfare of children in need, commonly those children who have been maltreated or harmed or those in danger of harm or maltreatment and whose health, safety or development is likely to be impaired.

The **Children Act 2004** looks at improving children's lives. The aim is to encourage joint planning, commissioning and delivery of services. This should reduce duplication, improve multidisciplinary working and increase accountability.

Mental Health Act 1983

The Mental Health Act 1983 makes provision for the compulsory detention and treatment in hospital of those with a mental disorder. The Mental Health (Northern Ireland) Order 1986 makes similar provision in Northern Ireland. This act was amended in 2004 to clarify some issues.

The **Mental Capacity Act 2005** provides a statutory framework to empower and protect vulnerable people who are not able to make their own decisions. It makes it clear who can take decisions, in which situations, and how they should go about this. These acts have since been amended through the **2007 Mental Health Act**. See these amendments in part 1 of the document on weblink:

- www.opsi.gov.uk/acts/acts2007/pdf/ ukpga_20070012_en.pdf.

Data Protection Act 1998

The Data Protection Act 1998 came into force on 1st March 2000, replacing the 1984 Data Protection Act (see www.ico.gov.uk). The act applies to 'personal data', which is data about identifiable, living individuals, and covers both personal data held electronically and manual or paper data held in structured files or easily accessible systems.

The Data Protection Act gives rights to individuals about whom information is held. It also requires those who record and use 'personal information' to follow the eight principles of good information handling. The eight principles require that data must:

- be fairly and lawfully processed
- be processed for limited purposes
- be adequate, relevant and not excessive
- be accurate
- not be kept for longer than is necessary
- be processed in line with the data subject's rights
- be secure
- not be transferred to countries without adequate protection.

Processing may be carried out only where one of the following conditions has been met:

- the individual has given his or her consent to the processing
- the processing is necessary for the performance of a contract with the individual
- the processing is required under a legal obligation
- the processing is necessary to protect the vital interests of the individual

- the processing is necessary to carry out public functions
- the processing is necessary in order to pursue the legitimate interests of the data controller or third parties (unless it could prejudice the interests of the individual).

Further provisions relating to the processing of sensitive data include data on racial or ethnic origin, political opinions, religious or other beliefs, trade union membership, health, sex life, criminal proceedings or other convictions. The Data Protection Act 1998 gives individuals the right of access to information held about them but forbids releasing that information to anyone else without permission, unless there is a legal requirement to do so.

The Freedom of Information Act 2000 (FOI Act)

This legislation gives individuals the right to obtain access to official information consistent with the public interest and the need to protect confidential information. Many journalists use this to uncover information which might not otherwise be brought to public notice.

The Care Standards Act 2000

The main purpose of the act was to reform the regulatory system for care services in England and Wales. Care services range from residential care homes and nursing homes, children's homes, domiciliary care agencies, fostering agencies and voluntary adoption agencies, through to private and voluntary healthcare services (including private hospitals and clinics and private primary care premises). The 2000 act set out legally required national minimum standards for care services.

Health & Social Care Act 2008

This act is intended to modernise and integrate health and social care services, recognising that individuals are often in need of both types of provision, especially where they have long-term conditions or complex needs. The act aims to protect the people who use services by reforming professional regulation as part of the government's response to the Shipman Inquiry. Harold Shipman was a GP who, over the course of his career, murdered over 200 people, mostly women, by injecting them with lethal doses of morphine.

The act has also set up the **Care Quality Commission** (CQC) as the new regulatory body for both health care and social care in England, replacing the previous regulatory arrangements. Wales and Northern Ireland have different regulatory and inspection bodies, although the overall purpose remains that of protecting the public.

For an overview of care provision in England, read the 'State of Care' publication available on the CQC website (www.cqc.org.uk).

Activity 7   P5   M3   D2

Using the CQC website (www.cqc.org.uk), find an inspection report for a residential or nursing home near where you live. Identify how well they are meeting the equality requirements. How is the home promoting anti-discriminatory practice?

Look at the checklist of statutory requirements towards the end of the report.

What, if any, are issues for equality? Do wheelchair users have access to all public areas? Are people given a choice of food? Are they encouraged to be independent? What difficulties might arise when implementing anti-discriminatory practice and how might you overcome them?

The Employment Equality (Age) Regulations 2006

Since 1st October 2006, there has been legal protection against age discrimination. The new regulations make it illegal to discriminate for jobs and training on the grounds of age. They apply to all employers, private and public sector, vocational training providers, trade unions, professional organisations, employer organisations, trustees and managers of occupational pension schemes. The regulations cover employees of any age, and other workers, office holders, partners of firms and others. Areas covered include recruitment, terms and conditions, promotions, transfers, dismissals and training. The regulations do not cover provision of goods and services.

Codes of practice and charters

Codes and charters are guidelines recommending what should happen. Unlike the laws, conventions and regulations already mentioned, they are not legally binding.

Social workers must be registered with the General Social Care Council (GSCC) and nurses, midwives and health visitors with the Nursing and Midwifery Council (NMC). The respective councils produce codes of practice for registered practitioners and employers. In Wales, the Care Council for Wales fills a similar function and, in Northern Ireland, it is the Northern Ireland Social Care Council.

Nurses, midwives and specialist community public health nurses have to abide by the NMC code of professional conduct: standards for conduct, performance and ethics published by the Nursing and Midwifery Council.

A summary of this code can be found on the following weblink: www.nmc-uk.org

Patient Advice and Liaison Services (PALS)

The 1991 Patient's Charter was abolished in 1997 and replaced by PALS, which is intended to involve the public and patients in the NHS. It does not set out rights but rather provides:

- confidential advice and support to patients, families and their carers
- information on the NHS and health-related matters
- confidential assistance in resolving problems and concerns quickly
- information on and explanations of NHS complaints procedures and how to get in touch with someone who can help
- a focal point for feedback from patients to inform service developments
- an early warning system for NHS trusts,

primary care trusts and patient and public involvement forums by monitoring trends and gaps in services and reporting these to the trust management for action.

Organisational policies and procedures

The purpose of organisational policies and procedures is to ensure that the organisation and its employees comply with the law. Each health or social care provider should have the following policies in place:

- recruitment
- health and safety
- confidentiality and record-keeping
- service user involvement
- complaints procedures
- staff development and training.

Employers should ensure that they use fair and ethical methods of interviewing and hiring staff and that equal opportunities are monitored and reviewed as necessary. Induction of new staff should ensure that the relevant induction standards are used and that training covers the practical implications of confidentiality, such as how to record, report, store and share information. Staff should understand their role in relation to the policies and procedures of each workplace.

4 Know how anti-discriminatory practice is promoted in health and social care settings

Active promotion of anti-discriminatory practice

Anti-discriminatory practice is promoted through the actions of individuals and organisations following the law, aiming for best practice, delivering care that is person-centred and ethically based, and challenging others where there are breaches in best practice. This means that organisations need mechanisms so that staff can legitimately report poor practice and possible abuses without fear of reprisals. This is called 'whistle-blowing' and it is monitored by the CQC, forming part of their inspection process.

The government has made provision for individuals who need care services to receive payment directly so that they can arrange for and purchase their own care, instead of having care services provided by local authority providers. Look at the case study below and identify the ways in which anti-discriminatory practice is being promoted.

Activity 8   P4   M2

Compare and contrast the induction standards for social care workers, childcare workers and foster carers. These can be found at www.skillsforcare.org.uk and www.cwdcouncil.org.uk.

How do these induction standards help to promote equality? What legislation are they linked to? What legislation is not covered by these standards?

Activity 9   P5

How does the CQC involve service users and experts by experience in inspections? Examine some inspection reports involving service users and experts by experience and identify their contribution. How might this help to promote anti-discriminatory practice?

Case Study

James lives on his own in a semi-detached bungalow in an ordinary residential close in a suburban area. He bought the house through a shared ownership scheme with Advance Housing and uses income support to pay the mortgage. The bungalow and garden are adapted for James' wheelchair, and there is space for the equipment he needs (e.g. a ceiling hoist from his en-suite bathroom through to his bedroom, a special bed, lots of storage space for supplies). There is also a bedroom for a personal assistant to sleep overnight, as James needs 24/7 support. James also has a Motability car in which he can be driven in his wheelchair.

James has an individual budget, funded 50/50 by the local authority and the health service. He also receives Independent Living Fund monies and other benefits. This pays for 1:1 support in the morning, afternoon and evening and at weekends. Support is provided by a local service agency and James' parents play a central role in selecting, training and working with staff to ensure James gets the support he needs. During the day he attends a nearby day centre provided by social services.

Source: Raising Our Sights: Services for Adults with profound intellectual and multiple disabilities. Report by Professor Jim Mansell for Department of Health, March 2010.

Personal beliefs and value systems

We are all human beings and have been influenced by our culture, beliefs and life events. Sometimes we accept the beliefs and values of our parents, but as we go through life and have different experiences, we might examine them and find we cannot agree with them. Each person is entitled to their own beliefs and values, but a health and social care professional must not let their beliefs influence the care they give.

In the Case Study overleaf, Paula changed from being prejudiced to seeing people as individuals. Not everyone changes their beliefs, but professionals in health and social care must be self-aware, tolerant of differences and non-judgemental in their practice. Legal, ethical and policy guidelines say what professionals should do, but unless they are really committed to the care value base, they will not be anti-discriminatory.

Case Study – changing minds

Paula was brought up in a working-class family. People expressed their views openly. Her dad lost his job when the local factory closed down and resented the fact that the Sikh family next door always seemed to have plenty of money. He assumed they were all scroungers on benefits and said so to his mates down the pub.

When Paula was 18, she got a job as a care assistant at the local care home and was surprised to see the woman from next door working there. They got chatting and Paula learned that Mr Singh worked as a bus driver and left for work at 4am. He also had a part-time job as a porter at the local hospital. That explained why they always seemed to have a new car and nice things. Mr Singh told his wife they were always looking for staff.

Paula mentioned this to her dad and suggested he might try for a job at the hospital. He got angry and said he wasn't a porter. He was a skilled craftsman and wasn't going to turn his hand to such work. Jobseeker's allowance was enough for him.

Next time he went on about the scroungers next door, Paula was quiet. She knew how hard Mr Singh worked. She loved her dad, but she could see that he was wrong about Mr Singh.

A few months later, Paula's dad fell over on his way home from the pub and broke his leg. He found it difficult to use his crutches and was stuck in the house. Paula told Mrs Singh at work and the next day Mr Singh came round to ask whether he could do anything to help. Mrs Singh came too and brought them some homemade vegetable soup. At first, Paula's dad didn't want to let them in, but Paula asked them in. Next day, Mr Singh offered to take Paula's dad to the hospital for his check-up.

Paula's dad never really accepted his neighbours, but Paula began to see them as people. When she started her nursing course, she had a good understanding of some of the Sikh customs and even knew that Mr Singh's wife was called Kaur, not Singh.

Summary

This unit is about understanding that everyone has fundamental rights to fair and equitable treatment, which are enshrined in law. Health and social care practitioners must be sure to uphold and respect these rights, whilst being aware that sometimes an individual's rights will conflict with those of the wider group or community.

It is important for health and social care practitioners to understand that our views, beliefs and values are formed as a result of our experiences, both within our families and in wider society. The more experiences and differences you are exposed to, the more broad-minded and tolerant you are likely to be.

Britain is a diverse multi-ethnic and multi-cultural society, known for being generally tolerant and accepting. Health and social care practitioners appreciate this diversity and the value it adds to society as a whole. Effective practice for health and social care practitioners means that they do not discriminate and are able to uphold and promote the rights of the individuals in their care.

Assessment and grading criteria

In order to pass this unit, the evidence that the learner presents for assessment needs to demonstrate that they can meet all the learning outcomes for the unit. The assessment criteria for a pass grade describe the level of achievement required to pass this unit.

To achieve a pass grade the evidence must show that the learner is able to:	To achieve a merit grade the evidence must show that, in addition to the pass criteria, the learner is able to:	To achieve a distinction grade the evidence must show that, in addition to the pass and merit criteria, the learner is able to:
P1 explain the concepts of equality, diversity and rights in relation to health and social care		
P2 describe discriminatory practice in health and social care	**M1** assess the effects on those using the service of three different discriminatory practices in health and social care settings	
P3 describe the potential effects of discriminatory practice on those who use health or social care services		

To achieve a pass grade the evidence must show that the learner is able to:	To achieve a merit grade the evidence must show that, in addition to the pass criteria, the learner is able to:	To achieve a distinction grade the evidence must show that, in addition to the pass and merit criteria, the learner is able to:
P4 explain how national initiatives promote anti-discriminatory practice	**M2** assess the influence of a recent national policy initiative promoting anti-discriminatory practice	**D1** evaluate the success of a recent initiative in promoting anti-discriminatory practice
P5 describe how anti-discriminatory practice is promoted in health and social care settings.	**M3** discuss difficulties that may arise when implementing anti-discriminatory practice in health and social care settings.	**D2** justify ways of overcoming difficulties that may arise when implementing anti-discriminatory practices in health and social care settings.

Weblinks

www.adviceguide.org.uk:
Advice Guide from Citizens Advice
www.equalityhumanrights.com:
Equality and Human Rights Commission
www.equalities.gov.uk:
Government Equalities Office
www.ico.gov.uk:
Information Commissioner's Office

www.doh.gov.uk:
Department of Health
www.cwdcouncil.org.uk:
Children's Workforce Development Council
www.skillsforcareanddevelopment.org.uk:
Skills for Care and Development
www.nmc-uk.org:
Nursing and Midwifery Council

3: Health, Safety and Security in Health and Social Care

Introduction

This unit looks at how to promote health, safety and security in health and social care settings. Health and social care settings frequently present potential hazards, which can pose a threat to the health and well-being of service users, staff, visitors and others.

In this unit, you will learn how to identify hazards and also how to avoid them. It is important to have a safe environment for our service users, both indoors and outdoors. Legislation provides a framework to which we can adhere, so we can keep our service users safe. You will investigate and understand the need for legislation and risk assessment and be able to carry out a risk assessment in a care setting.

When dealing with an incident or accident, it is important to be aware of your role and responsibility to ensure your own safety and the safety of your service users. This unit will allow you to understand what your priorities are when dealing with an emergency.

Learning outcomes:

On completion of this unit, you should:

1 Understand potential hazards in health and social care

2 Know how legislation, policies and procedures promote health, safety and security in health and social care settings

3 Be able to implement a risk assessment

4 Understand priorities and responses in dealing with incidents and emergencies.

1 Understand potential hazards in health and social care

Key terms

Hazard – something that can cause harm.
Risk – the effect of a hazard and the probability of a hazard occurring.

Hazards

There are many possible hazards within health and social care environments. Hazards that may occur within a health and social care setting can have numerous causes. They may be the result of the working environment, such as poor working conditions, including bad lighting, equipment that is not properly maintained or substances that you might have to use (such as bleach), or from incidents, such as challenging behaviour from service users.

Physical environment

Hazards in the physical environment may be indoors or outdoors.

Outdoor hazards can be made worse by weather conditions. For example, an uneven driveway is a hazard in itself, but it will become even worse if wet, slippery or icy. Outdoor hazards may consist of any of the following:

- Poor lighting
- Unsecure entrances
- Poor access arrangements, e.g. high steps, no handrail, narrow doorways, poor parking arrangements, especially if passengers are unable to reach the setting's entrance
- Pollution, which includes air, noise, chemicals and water.

Indoor hazards can cause many accidents and can be easily identified and remedied with a consistent and careful eye. Think of your work setting – how many hazards do you identify and rectify without thinking about it? How many do you miss?

!

REMEMBER

Your working environment might not be just your health and social care setting; it can also be out in the community, in service users' homes or in the premises of another organisation. You will not have as much control over hazards in these environments.

Activity 1

Look at the picture on the following page.

1 What hazards can you spot?

2 What could be the consequences of these hazards?

3 What could you do to reduce the risk?

Remember, hazards may be a risk for elderly service users but not for children, so consider who you are caring for.

Activity 2

Follow this weblink and try the 'Slips, trips and falls quiz':

www.teched101.com/pdf/sliptripfalls.pdf.

The indoor physical environment will also include the following:

- lighting
- heating
- ventilation.

Equipment

Hazards that are associated with equipment are as follows:

- Incorrect storage
- Irregular maintenance checks

- Faulty equipment not reported
- Incorrect positioning of equipment
- Equipment used without training
- Equipment used without supervision.

Within settings, equipment should be labelled, stored and checked routinely by a nominated person. This reduces the hazards and, therefore, the risks to service users and staff.

Infections

When assessing the risk of infection, a number of questions should be asked:

- What is the source of the pathogen?
- How does it spread?
- Are there additional risk factors?
- What is the general mental and physical condition of the patient?
- Are other patients or staff at risk?

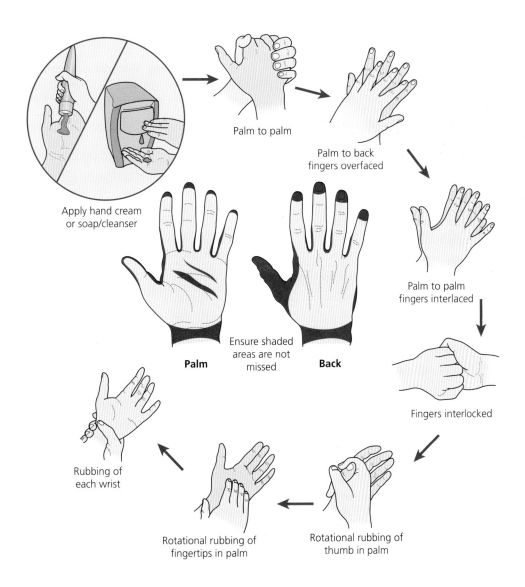

Apply hand cream or soap/cleanser

Palm to palm

Palm to back fingers overfaced

Palm to palm fingers interlaced

Fingers interlocked

Ensure shaded areas are not missed

Palm   **Back**

Rotational rubbing of thumb in palm

Rotational rubbing of fingertips in palm

Rubbing of each wrist

Hand-washing procedures

- What staffing facilities are available?
- What could be contaminated?

Key term

Pathogens – micro-organisms that are capable of causing disease.

Service users may be more at risk of acquiring infections if they are very young, elderly or ill. Therefore, it is important that we do not spread infections or, in other words, we practise infection control by avoiding cross-infection. Effective hand-washing is the key here. Investigate your work setting – what is their hand-washing policy? Is it effective?

Substances

Substances that are not stored or used appropriately are a hazard.

Activity 3

What hazards come to mind in the following situations?

- Paint and glue left out after creative activities in nursery.

- Bucket of soapy water left in corridor.

- Medication given by unqualified staff members.

- Cleaning fluids left by side of toilets in a school.

Working conditions

Hazards may arise within the working environment. Poor staff training or the environment itself could lead to risks to service users, staff and property. Low pay and poor working conditions may lead to unqualified staff being employed, putting service users at risk. This may occur through lack of knowledge and inadequate staff ratios.

Activity 4

Find out what the service user/staff ratios are in your setting. Do they differ from setting to setting? Are they different for different age groups?

Working practices

These are activities that you carry out every day within your working life. During these practices, you may come across some things that can present hazards, including day-to-day activities, for example craft activities or cooking, or not using equipment properly. Moving and handling policies ensure staff and service users' safety; to disregard them would be extremely hazardous.

Security systems

Security systems vary depending on the setting and the service users being cared for. Some settings have strict entry requirements for staff, with a swipe card, identification badge or an entry code to open the door. Others have a signing in and out book for staff and visitors, with a manned reception area to gain access. Some care settings have a more relaxed approach, particularly if the service users are able to come and go freely. Security systems are in place to protect service users, staff and visitors from intruders and bogus or nuisance callers.

In the service user's own home, these procedures are difficult to put in place so, when caring for service users in their own home, you should advise them to check callers' identification, have a telephone at hand and make appointments for people to call. You could also advise them to have a door chain fitted, which they can open when they know who the caller is. This also discourages doorstep sales.

Intruders in any care setting can cause harm and damage, and they could potentially steal valuables and personal effects.

Harm and abuse

Abuse

When working in health and social care, it is important for the well-being of service users to be aware of signs and symptoms of abuse and to know what to do if you have suspicions. Vulnerable people are especially prone to abuse. This includes children, older people and those with physical and learning disabilities. Abuse can take many forms, including physical, emotional, sexual, mental and social abuse.

The NSPCC defines physical abuse as hitting, shaking, kicking, punching, scalding, suffocating and other ways of inflicting pain or injury to a child or other individual; emotional abuse is when a parent or carer behaves in a way that is likely to seriously affect their child's emotional development; sexual abuse as forcing or tricking a child or other individual into taking part in any kind of sexual activity (source: www.nspcc.org.uk).

Abuse can also be financial, and can include using a person's money without their knowledge or understanding, or theft of an individual's money and possessions.

Abuse can also take the form of neglect, which means depriving a vulnerable person of what they need, such as food, warmth, medication and activities.

Abuse can also be termed as institutional, where a setting's routines and work patterns override the care needs of the service users, so meal times and rest times are controlled, all service users are treated the same, and independence and choice are removed.

There are different reasons as to why abuse occurs. It may be due to someone trying to take power and control, so it is intentional abuse, or it could be unintentional abuse, such as work-related issues, exhaustion or stress because of the way in which an organisation is run. People may be unaware of the effect they are having on someone else.

Signs and symptoms of abuse are discussed in depth in Unit 10.

Injury

If vulnerable service users are left unsupervised, then major or minor injuries are a possibility. Injuries from hazards are dependent also on the service user group. For example, a child who falls over a trailing wire may sustain a minor superficial graze, whereas an older service user may fracture a bone and require hospitalisation.

We should remember that injuries may be due to poor work practices and an unsafe environment, so it is imperative that members of staff are trained to survey environments for hazards and to tidy equipment, report faults, and store and use equipment appropriately. Without this, service users and work colleagues could be put at risk.

Did you know...

If you are caring for service users in their own home, you should bear the following in mind:

Slips, trips and falls are the most common accidents in the home and lead to more than a million people going to hospital annually. More than 500,000 are hurt when they strike things (such as walking into furniture) or are struck by moving objects (such as dropping something on your foot) and around 230,000 suffer cuts or tears. The top three causes of death in home accidents are falls, poisoning and the effects of fire and smoke.

About 2.7 million people go to hospital A&E departments after accidents in the home each year – about a million of them are children under 15 years old and 500,000 are under 5 years old. About 4,000 people are killed in home accidents each year – about 120 are under 15 and 1,300 over 75. The young and elderly are those most at risk in the home. Source: **www.rospa.com**

Acquired infection

Infections that vulnerable service users acquire from different sources can be from cross-infection. Basic hygiene routines reduce the risk of cross-infection (these have been discussed in the section above).

Service users who are admitted with contagious infections may require specialised care to avoid the spread of infection to others. If possible, they should be cared for in their own environment – for example, a child who arrives at nursery with impetigo, a contagious skin infection, should be taken home and given medication until the symptoms clear up.

However, some infections make the service user ill so care in a hospital may be necessary. Some people may need to be cared for in isolation, so extreme care should be taken with hand-washing, wearing protective clothing and disposal of waste.

Appropriate disposal of needles and sharp objects is vital as, if not dealt with correctly, they could cause injury to you or your service user. Infections, such as Hepatitis B, Hepatitis C or HIV, could be transmitted.

A sharps bin should be used for disposing of used needles and sharp objects

There are three ways that we acquire pathogens (micro-organisms that are capable of causing disease):

1 Contact – this the most common way to spread infections. Contact can be direct from touch and handling, or indirect from food or water. Diseases that can occur are salmonella, E.coli and listeria.
2 Airborne – from coughing, sneezing and dust particles. Diseases that can occur are clostridium difficile, staphylococcus aureus, methicillin-resistant staphylococcus aureus (MRSA, which can also be contracted by contact).
3 Arthropods – these are fleas, flies, mites, midges and mosquitoes and can cause diseases such as scabies and malaria.

Psychological distress

Service users who have any psychological disorders may not have the ability to think clearly or logically so may pose a potential risk to themselves as well as others. Service users in this situation should be supervised and carers should anticipate hazards in their environment. For example, prescribed medication should be clearly labelled and stored if the service user is unaware of their medication regime or dosage.

Inappropriate care planning

As carers, we should plan, deliver and review the care we give to all our service users, regardless of their age or ability.

An older person who always uses a walking frame to move around may deteriorate and require further mobility assistance, so it is up to us as carers to observe our service users and plan accordingly.

A seven-month-old baby in a nursery may progress quickly to crawling from sitting so safety equipment will need to be changed in the environment to avoid accidents and injuries.

Exposure to danger

An environment that has not been appropriately risk assessed and does not have adequate policies, procedures and guidelines for care staff to follow and to deliver care will expose service users to unnecessary dangers, which will inevitably lead to accidents and incidents, causing harm to service users, staff and visitors.

Stress

Increased stress levels in care settings can lead to potential hazards in our environment. A staff member who is stressed or preoccupied by other problems will not be thinking about the service users in his/her care so they may be at risk.

Stress levels caused by a poor working environment – for example, reduced staffing levels or broken or inadequate equipment – can also lead to a hazardous environment. Stressed staff may not show as many caring qualities, so service users may be exposed to mood swings and poor communication. Tired or ill staff may make more mistakes, so medication or treatment errors may occur.

Loss/damage to belongings and premises

In most settings, there is a potential risk of property being stolen, damaged or lost. The following points can minimise that risk:

● There should be strict policies in place about entrance and access to the setting to deter intruders.

Activity 5

Investigate the settings shown in the diagram below and suggest who may use those settings from the list of users provided on page 52.

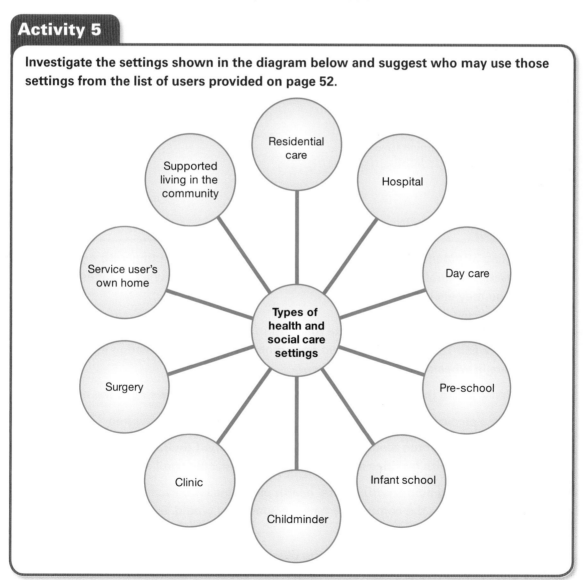

- There should be maintenance of policies for dealing with aggressive or dangerous behaviour, which may put service users, staff and property at risk.
- As the service user is admitted to the setting, list all belongings and lock away valuables or send these home with a relative if necessary.
- Follow procedures when items have been damaged, lost or stolen.

Types of settings

You may work in a variety of care settings during work experience and then be required to complete further training in care establishments with a preferred service user group.

Remember, in all settings, there are individuals who are common to each setting. For example:

- those receiving care
- care workers in the setting, who may be qualified, training or visiting
- support staff – for example, catering staff, domestic staff and administrative staff
- visitors – for example, relatives, friends or volunteers.

Users of health and social care services

These include:

- older people
- people with learning difficulties
- young people
- young children
- babies
- people with physical difficulties
- people with sensory impairments
- people with mental health problems.

REMEMBER

A potential hazard is something that may cause harm, and service users who are in unfamiliar surroundings are at greater risk.

Activity 6

After looking at potential hazards, imagine you are planning an outing with a group of service users to a public environment. Look at the scenarios below and suggest what hazards you may encounter.

- You plan a trip to a shopping centre for a group of six residents from a care home aged between 75 and 85 years – two have mobility aids, one is hearing impaired and three are in wheelchairs.

- You plan a trip to the swimming baths for a group of four babies aged ten months.

- You plan a picnic at the local public park for a class of 15 infant children.

- You take a group of ten teenagers who have just finished their GCSEs to a local sports ground, with facilities such as tennis, bowling, crazy golf and football.

- A group of young adults with mental health problems who live in supported living accommodation in the community have decided they would like a day trip to the beach.

- A 20-year-old service user with learning difficulties is going to be shown how to use the local bus service to get to and from his day care setting.

Activity 7 P1

If you have a work experience placement, then this next activity would be ideal for gathering evidence towards P1.

Design an annotated poster (a poster with written notes, highlighting points) that highlights at least six potential hazards in your environment, then explain these hazards and the potential harm that may arise. For example, substances left unattended that should be stored away may be dangerous to a child if they spill, drink or play with them. If the service user group is older people, they may be sight-impaired and mistake it for a drink it, knock it over and slip, or burn themselves if it is a chemical.

2 Know how legislation, policies and procedures promote health, safety and security in health and social care settings

Legislation and guidelines

Legislation, policies and procedures exist to promote a safer working environment and reduce the potential for risks occurring. They should be tailored to the needs of each setting, known and understood by employers and employees and reviewed on a regular basis.

Health and Safety at Work Act 1974

This is the main piece of British health and safety law and has led to the development of many other pieces of health and safety legislation. It sets out the general duties that employers have to their workers and to any members of the public that might enter the premises. It also lists the responsibilities employees have to themselves and to each other.

The main part of the act requires employers to carry out risk assessments and to appoint a person responsible for health and safety in the workplace.

Employers' responsibilities include:

- so far as it is reasonably practicable, to ensure your health, safety and welfare at work
- to consult employees or their safety representative on matters relating to health and safety at work
- to carry out risk assessments or implement measures as identified in the assessment
- to report certain injuries, diseases and dangerous occurrences.

Employees' responsibilities include:

- taking reasonable care for their own health and safety and that of others
- cooperating with their employer on health and safety
- correctly using work items provided by their employers
- not interfering with or misusing anything provided for their health, safety and welfare.

Source: Health and Safety Executive (HSE)

Key term

Regulations – laws approved by Parliament.

Activity 8

Each workplace should display the health and safety law poster and appoint a person responsible for health and safety. Within your work placement, locate the poster, find out who your health and safety representative is and write down some of the responsibilities your employer and the employees have.

Health and Safety Law poster

Food Safety Act 1990

Within a health and social care setting, workers must ensure good food hygiene so that health is not at risk.

Food safety (general food hygiene regulations)

This is about managing food hygiene, identifying the risks and what could go wrong and then bringing in checks and controls to ensure that any risk is reduced. This act covers anyone who deals with food, from farmers right through to the catering and restaurant trade. The act protects the person buying the food (consumer) from poor hygiene standards and poor grades of food, and also from food that has not been labelled correctly. The act allows local authorities to enforce laws and give out penalties if the laws are broken.

Food Safety (General Food Hygiene) Regulations 1995

These regulations specify standards for the structural requirements for the premises, equipment, personal safety and wholesomeness of the food.

These regulations apply to food businesses, not to farms or abattoirs.

In care settings, the following standards apply:

● Food preparation and cooking areas should be clean and all personal hygiene should be of a high standard.
● All foods should be stored and cooked thoroughly.
● Cross-contamination should be prevented.

Manual Handling Regulations 1992

Key term

Manual handling – lifting or moving objects or people without a mechanical aid or equipment.

The Manual Handling Regulations aim to reduce the risk of injury from lifting or moving objects or people. This may include lifting, lowering, pushing, pulling or carrying.

Activity 9

Within your placement or a general health and social care setting, answer the following questions:

● Who might be injured from poor manual handling?

● For each of the people you have identified, what parts of the body would be damaged from poor manual handling?

● What would be the consequences of this? Think of the whole person (physical, intellectual, emotional and social) and the working environment.

Working with a partner, decide why correct manual handling procedures are so important.

These regulations provide information for both employers and employees. The main principle is that you should avoid any manual handling if it is at all possible. An example of this would mean using a hoist rather than carrying someone yourself.

If is not possible to avoid manual handling altogether, it is important that the risk of injury is assessed. This means looking at the whole job that is to be undertaken and deciding who might get injured, why this might occur and the impact that this potential injury would have. Generally, most manual handling injuries that occur could have been avoided. The risks that have been identified should then be reduced as much as possible (source: HSE).

Activity 10

You are working at Rose Cottage Nursing Home. Derek needs a bath, an occasion on which you would normally use a hoist. Your two colleagues say, 'Oh, I can't be bothered using that, it's in another room. Let's just lift him.'

How would you react to this situation? What could you say to ensure that he is handled appropriately? Do you envisage any difficulties in tackling this issue?

REMEMBER !

Within health and social care, a hoist can be used to move people. As well as reducing the risk of injury, it is more professional. Why do you think this is? (Think of the rights of service users.) Any equipment used should also be maintained and employers should train staff so that they know how to use the equipment safely.

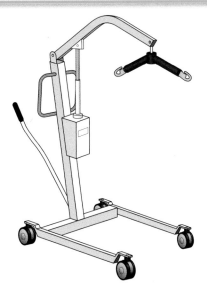

Hoist used in health and social care settings

If you do have to lift, the appropriate manual handling work should be undertaken. In a care setting, you will often be involved in helping people to move. It is important that this is done safely. Often people can present a hazard themselves. Think of the clothes they wear. For example, a service user who is wearing a long dressing gown may present a trip hazard to staff or service users.

Reporting of Injuries, Diseases and Dangerous Occurrences Regulations (RIDDOR) 1995

This legislation covers injuries, certain diseases and dangerous occurrences. These events must be recorded and may be reported to the Health and Safety Executive (HSE). In the case of serious accidents, the HSE will investigate. Incidents reportable under the regulations include the following:

● death or major injury of an employee on the premises, or if an injury that occurs within the workplace results in the employee being off work for three or more days
● diseases – certain diseases are also reportable
● dangerous occurrences –incidents that have happened but did not result in a reportable injury. An example would be an electrical short circuit or explosion.

Source: HSE

Accident book

RIDDOR requires all workplaces to keep a record of all accidents or near accidents. An accident book should include the date, time and place, who was involved, what happened, any injury and then action taken. Confidential details such as an address should be recorded separately. Under the Data Protection Act, accident books now have a detached sheet, i.e. they are not kept confidential. Accidents should be reviewed every so often to identify how they could be prevented in the future. The RIDDOR regulations require the workplace to notify the HSE of any occupation injury that occurs. This could be a death, reportable injuries such as a fracture, certain diseases or dangerous occurrences (these are incidents that happen which do not result in a reportable injury but could have done).

Once reported, an accident will be investigated and the enforcing authority can advise on further preventative measures. It is also important that accidents are recorded in case of legal implications.

Activity 11

In your work setting take a look at the accident book and how accidents are recorded. Discuss this with your class members.

Data Protection Act 1998

In health and social care settings, personal information, whether paper-based or electronic, should be held securely and used appropriately. Personal information, like address, diagnosis and medication, can be misused. Therefore, this information should be accessed by authorised people only. Service users do not always want their relatives to be aware of their diagnosis or medication and if addresses are misused unauthorised people may become aware of empty homes, which is a security issue. Imagine how you would feel if some of your personal information was left on a desk for anyone to read.

The Data Protection Act also states that medical records should not be destroyed. When a service user dies, a time limit is given before destruction of records is allowed, in case of legal complications.

Investigate your work setting and find out how personal records are kept, where they are kept and who has access to them.

The Data Protection Act also requires those who record and use personal information to follow the eight principles of good information handling (see Unit 2, page 37, for further information).

Management of Health and Safety at Work Regulations 1999

These regulations state that employers have a responsibility to train staff in health and safety. This is in relation to all the major points of the legislation, so includes preventing fire, controlling the spread of infection, and moving and handling appropriately. It also requires employers to carry out risk assessments.

Organisational policy and procedures

Each workplace has policies and procedures that state what the employer has done and what employees should do to maintain health and safety. These policies and procedures will reflect health and safety legislation.

Care Home Regulations

The Care Home Regulations form the basis of the inspections upon which the registration of a home is based, along with the national minimum standards. The Care Home Regulations are legal requirements that must be met if the setting wishes to be a registered provider. If regulations are breached then a setting can be barred from providing care.

Control of Substances Hazardous to Health (COSHH) 2002

COSHH covers the use, storage and disposal of any substances. The basis of this act is that employers should assess the risk that hazardous substances can present and then take precautions to minimise the risk. The act provides eight basic principles that should be followed (source: HSE):

- Assess the risk – who might be harmed and how severely?

- Decide what precautions are necessary – what needs to be in place as a preventative measure?
- Prevent or control exposure – this is putting the precautions into place.
- Ensure control measures are used – check regularly that the workplace is using the measures in place.
- Monitor exposure – ensure workplaces are not being subjected to high levels of harmful substances.
- Carry out health surveillance.
- Plan to deal with emergencies – provide guidance on what to do in the event of an emergency.
- Train and inform employees – train new employees and update staff as necessary.

Under the act, substances should be stored correctly (for example, not placing them in an area where children may be able to gain access), labelled properly (for example, not putting bleach in a lemonade bottle) and disposed of appropriately.

There are many hazardous substances that you may use in a health and social care setting. As well as the obvious medical ones, everyday items such as bleach, washing-up liquid and soup are covered. Your health and social care setting should have COSHH information for all of these substances. Workers then have a responsibility to follow these risk assessments. COSHH regulations also inform workers of any protective equipment that they may need to use.

Hazard signs

Some products display hazard signs, such as those below. These provide additional warnings for these chemicals.

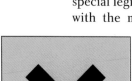

Activity 12

Your work placement should have a COSHH file, which contains risk assessments on using hazardous products. Ask whether your workplace has one and make a list of any of the substances mentioned in it.

Civil Contingencies Act 2004

The Civil Contingencies Act delivers a single framework for civil protection in the United Kingdom, capable of meeting the challenges of the twenty-first century. It followed major incidents like the foot-and-mouth outbreak in 2001 and severe flooding in 2000. The act is separated into two parts: local arrangements for civil protection (Part 1) and emergency powers (Part 2).

Part 1: Local arrangements for civil protection

Part 1 of the act establishes a clear set of roles and responsibilities for those involved in emergency preparation and response at the local level. This helps to deliver greater consistency of civil protection activity at the local level, facilitate more systematic cooperation between responders and lay the foundation for robust performance management. It requires local and regional authorities to design and deploy plans for dealing with major incidents and emergencies.

Part 2: Emergency powers

Part 2 of the act allows for the making of temporary special legislation (emergency regulations) to deal with the most serious of emergencies. The use

Extremely or Highly Flammable

Harmful or Irritant

Corrosive

of emergency powers is a last-resort option and planning arrangements at the local level should not assume that emergency powers will be made available. Their use is subject to a robust set of safeguards – they can only be deployed in exceptional circumstances.

Care establishments, therefore, have a duty to assess risks and put in place plans to deal with major incidents.

The following weblink gives advice about how to prepare for emergencies, what to do in an emergency and useful information about specific emergencies: www.direct.gov.uk/en/Government citizensandrights/Dealingwithemergencies/Preparingforemergencies/index.htm.

National Minimum Standards

The National Minimum Standards were last revised in 2003 and consist of 38 standards. They are set out under the Care Standards Act 2000 by the Secretary of State for Health, along with the Care Home Regulations. These are minimum expectations the state sets for English and Welsh care providers.

The National Minimum Standards are not legally enforceable but are guidelines for providers, commissioners and users to judge the quality of the service.

Services covered by the National Minimum Standards are:

- care homes for people aged over 65 years
- care homes for people aged 18 years to 64 years
- domiciliary care
- adult placement schemes
- nurses' agencies.

The Commission for Social Care Inspection (CSCI) performs inspections in care establishments against these standards and then publishes reports and findings.

Safeguarding

Independent Safeguarding Authority

The Independent Safeguarding Authority (ISA) was created as part of the government's Vetting and Barring Scheme (VBS) to help prevent unsuitable people from working with children and vulnerable adults. It is a non-departmental public body, sponsored by the Home Office.

This authority works in partnership with the Criminal Records Bureau (CRB) to help ensure that there is 'no known reason' why individuals who work or wish to work or volunteer with children or vulnerable adults shouldn't do so

The ISA's role within the VBS is to make independent barring decisions and place or remove individuals on either the ISA's Children's Barred List or the ISA's Vulnerable Adult's Barred List, or both.

Increased safeguards were introduced under the Vetting and Barring Scheme from 12th October 2009:

- It is a criminal offence for individuals barred by the ISA to work or apply to work with children or vulnerable adults in a wide range of posts, including most jobs in the NHS, the prison service, education and childcare. Employers also face criminal sanctions for knowingly employing a barred individual across a wider range of work.
- The three former barred lists – POCA (Protection of Children Act), POVA (Protection of Vulnerable Adults) and List 99 – are being replaced by two new ISA-barred lists.

Employers, local authorities, professional regulators and other bodies have a duty to refer to the ISA regarding information about individuals working with children or vulnerable adults where they consider them to have caused harm or pose a risk of harm.

ISA registration for the Vetting and Barring Scheme started for new workers and those moving jobs from July 2010, but ISA registration does not become mandatory for these workers until November 2010. All other staff will be phased into the scheme from 2011.

At the time of writing, all staff are required by law to have been checked by the Criminal Records Bureau. This is either an enhanced check, which provides full details of any criminal convictions or cautions, or a POVA check, which is a shorter check and looks at the employee's name against the Protection of Vulnerable Adults list, to ensure employees, whether trained, training, volunteers or students, have not previously harmed or put at risk a vulnerable adult.

Safeguarding of Vulnerable Adults Scheme 2004

In 2003, Ian Huntley was convicted of the murder of Holly Wells and Jessica Chapman. This trial highlighted gaps in the police checking system. Ian Huntley was a school caretaker and his criminal record did not show the previous allegations against him of sexual abuse. Because of this, the government developed a vetting scheme, which is set out in the Safeguarding Adults Group Act 2006. This updates employers with new or changed information about an employee.

In 2005, *Safeguarding Adults* was published by the Department of Health (with the Commission for Social Care Inspection), which sets standards for good practice in adult protection; this covers procedures from reporting concerns to contributing at a case conference.

Policies and procedures

Policies and procedures vary according to care settings and the service user group. They cover all aspects of relevant legislation and are reviewed on a regular basis.

Activity 13

Look at the diagram on page 60 of possible policies and procedures. Investigate policies and procedures in your care setting and discuss the differences as a class. (Gain consent/ permission from the supervisor or setting first.)

What similarities do they have? What differences do they have?

Influences

Table 3.1 How legislation, policies and procedures influence care settings and their service delivery in health, safety and security

Influences	Effects of these influences
Staff	<ul><li>Recruitment of suitable staff</li><li>Provide training regarding policies and procedures</li><li>Oversee health and safety regulations</li><li>Provide security in employment</li><li>Maintain appropriate staff ratios</li><li>Job descriptions allow staff to know their boundaries</li></ul>
Premises	<ul><li>Safe working environments</li><li>Safe environments for service users</li><li>Give relatives and friends confidence in appropriate care given</li><li>Appropriate locations</li><li>Adequate adaptations and access to meet all needs</li></ul>
Practices	<ul><li>Policies and procedures regularly reviewed and updated</li><li>Regular evacuation and emergency procedures carried out</li><li>Safety equipment and protective clothing supplied</li><li>Concise, clear record-keeping</li></ul>

Possible policies and procedures in care settings

Key terms

Policy – a plan of action that has been adopted by the setting.
Procedure – a set of actions or steps that meets the requirements of the policy or strategy.

Roles and responsibilities

The HSE, employers and employees have responsibilities to help maintain a healthy workforce.

The HSE is responsible for enforcing health and safety laws. HSE inspectors visit the workplace to make sure that the legislation is being followed. Although they do have a role in investigating accidents and complaints, they generally help workplaces to interpret and put into action health and safety legislation. The HSE does have powers to enforce legislation not being followed, however.

Employers have the responsibility to keep employees informed about health and safety. This involves providing training and necessary equipment and informing employees of their roles and responsibilities.

Employees have the responsibilities of following procedures and notifying their employer of any extra measures that need to be in place or if something is not working. If employees are aware of a problem, they have a responsibility to discuss it with the employer, or in the cases of some larger organisations, to discuss it with a health and safety representative.

Activity 14

During one day at placement, make a list of anything that you or other people do that helps maintain a healthy and safe workplace. You may come up with some of the following:

- Dealt with spilling of hazardous or non-hazardous substances.
- Followed correct manual handling procedures.
- Reported health and safety issues to the appropriate people.
- Checked the identity of people entering the building.
- Disposed of waste immediately and safely.
- Identified a potential health, safety or security risk and reported accordingly.
- Completed a health and safety record.

Table 3.2 Examples of responsibilities

Responsibilities	Employer role	Employee role
Risk assessment (examination of what may cause harm to people)	To examine the workplace and identify what may cause harm, to whom and how to minimise the risk. To inform employees of risk assessment.	To follow risk assessment procedures in place and to notify employer of any changes.
Monitoring of working practices	To put measures in place to monitor workplace and practices.	To follow working practices and inform employers of any changes.
Storing equipment	To provide guidance on how to store equipment and materials and the means to carry this out.	To follow policy and procedure and store equipment and materials appropriately.
Dealing with hazardous and non-hazardous materials	To provide risk assessments, policies and procedures on how to use these substances. Train workers to use them.	To follow policies and procedures. To clear up spillages according to risk assessments.
Manual handling	To assess the risks and reduce the need for manual handling. To train workers in manual handling.	To follow manual handling procedures and report any faults with equipment.
Reporting health and safety issues	To report major accidents to the HSE.	To report any issues to your employer or representative.
Completing health and safety and security records	To keep all records, such as risk assessments, up to date.	To keep all records up to date and confidential. These may include accident books.

As health and safety are protected by law, some of the responsibilities are determined by law. Each organisation will have policies that should also be followed.

There are other responsibilities to do with health and safety, including checking rights of entry. This will assist service users to feel safe within their homes. Employers should have procedures on how to do this, which employees should follow. Employees should be aware of the security measures within their workplace. For example, some workplaces have swipe card entry or provide identity cards, which employees should wear. Workers should not allow people they do not know or who have not provided sufficient identification onto the premises.

It is important that an employee operates only within the limits of their role and does not undertake an activity that they do not feel confident in doing. You should follow these procedures, take care not to misuse anything, ensure your health and safety, and tell your employer about anything that might impact upon people's health and safety.

REMEMBER

If you have been given training and you do not follow it, you will be responsible for any consequences.

Activity 15 P2   M1

Case Study

The Rainbow Centre is a day care centre for adults with learning difficulties. It is in a small town centre and is a purpose-built setting. Adults are transported to and from this setting at various times from other areas. The adults who attend this setting range from 19 to 55 years old. There are a range of activities provided for the service users, some on-site and some off-site. Some service users are taught independence skills, for which one-to-one care is needed – for example, learning how to use public transport. Staff ratios are adequate and the opening hours are 8am–6pm.

Outline how legislation, policies and procedures that relate to health, safety and security would influence the Rainbow Centre (P2).

Describe how the legislation, policies and procedures you have outlined promote safety of the service users at the Rainbow Centre (M1).

3 Be able to implement a risk assessment

Risk assessment

Some service users, such as children, older people or those in residential care, may go out of their environment and enter another one. This can pose an additional health, safety and security risk as you have less control over this environment. Possible trips include going to a park, playground or cinema, going shopping or going swimming.

Before taking a service user into the environment, you should undertake a risk assessment and survey the area. This will ensure that you know the layout of the area and where the toilets are, etc. It also means you can be prepared for taking vulnerable people out into the community itself. By being prepared, you can minimise the possibility of risks within the area. This may include injury or harm to service users. Service users may abscond or may not feel confident in meeting and mixing with strangers. In addition, vulnerable service users may present a risk to the public. Service users with challenging behaviour may, on occasion, be aggressive towards members of the public.

There are additional dangers that will present themselves outside only, such as traffic accidents and fires. While many of these you cannot account for, being familiar with an area and preparing yourself as much as you can will minimise the risk.

A risk assessment not only forms part of legislation but also is integral to minimising the possibility of accidents.

Risks which may be present when going to the park

When surveying an area, you should consider health, safety and security risks:

- Health – will the environment pose any risk to a person's health, e.g. high-pollen areas may attract bees. This should be a consideration if a person has an allergy.
- Safety – is the area safe? Is there a litter problem? If you will be using any equipment, is it in working order?
- Security – does the area pose any security risks?

Incidents

These are events that may occur within your workplace. It will not be possible to plan for these as they may include intruders or aggressive and dangerous occurrences involving service users. Other possible incidents include bomb scares or chemical spillages. However, your employer should have policies and procedures for actions in the event of these emergencies.

Fire is one example of an incident. Policies and procedures within the workplace should minimise the risk of this occurring. It is far easier to prevent a fire happening than to address the consequences.

Calculating the degree of risk

To minimise the risk of hazards to service users, you may have to take certain measures – for example, including extra staff. You may also show staff the area before taking service users into it so they know what to expect. You may like to undertake work with service users to prepare them for what they are doing.

Once the risk has been thoroughly investigated, you can make recommendations and then put these into action.

There are numerous potential risks going into the local environment. Take going to a park, for example (see diagram on page 63).

Activity 16

Think of another environment, possibly one you take service users to. List the risks within that setting.

Risk assessment process

A risk assessment is an investigation into what can cause harm to people. The reason for doing this is to ensure that no one gets hurt. It also fulfils a legal requirement. The Health and Safety Executive provides five steps to risk assessment. These steps are shown in Table 3.3, with information and an example.

Table 3.3 Five steps to risk assessment

Step and explanation	Example (walking to the shops)
1 LOOK FOR HAZARDS What can cause harm? If you are unsure, ask others or look at previous accident book records.	The following could cause harm: • crossing the road • slips, trips and falls • being in the community.
2 DECIDE WHO MIGHT BE HARMED AND HOW Don't forget that some groups or individuals may be more at risk of harm than others.	The service user could be involved in a road traffic incident or damage property. Those with particular illnesses may be at risk due to their illness (e.g. someone with epilepsy may have a fit). The service user is at risk of absconding and is vulnerable from other members of the public.

Step and explanation	Example (walking to the shops)
3 EVALUATE THE RISK AND DECIDE WHETHER EXISTING PRECAUTIONS ARE ADEQUATE OR WHETHER MORE SHOULD BE DONE Here you are looking at how you can minimise the risk.	Many of the precautions are already in place, such as taking medication for service users with specific conditions, or ensuring vehicles are roadworthy to minimise risk of road traffic incidents.
4 RECORD YOUR FINDINGS	You could carry out risk assessments with the service user (or advocate). This gives them control over their own lives and independence. Risk assessments should be dated and should demonstrate where checks have been made and how hazards have been addressed.
5 REVIEW ASSESSMENT	Hazards and risks may change, so it is good practice to review and change if necessary.

An example of a risk assessment is shown in Table 3.4. This risk assessment should then be dated and reviewed to see where improvements can be made.

Table 3.4 Example of a risk assessment

Activity	Hazard	Hazard rating	Control measures in place	Likelihood	Hazard → likelihood	Assessed by	Review date
Walking to the park	Road traffic accidents	3	1:1 supervision. Only one road to cross. Staff and service users to follow highway code.	1	3		6 mths
	Slips, trips and falls	2	Do not go if icy. Wear sensible footwear.	1	2		6 mths
	Service user absconding	3	Adequate supervision. Carry mobile phone and contact numbers.	1	3		6 mths

Generally, hazards are rated on a scale of 1–3 depending on the severity. Likelihood is also on a 1–3 scale (1 = unlikely). The chances of the hazard occurring are the two multiplied together. If the risk is 3 or less than 3, then the activity is safe to carry out. Any more, then further action to reduce the risks would be necessary.

Activity 17

Using your work experience setting, carry out a risk assessment. Use Tables 3.3 and 3.4 to help you. Remember to inform your setting and gain permission first (P3).

With this information, assess the hazards you have identified in a findings report (M2).

To conclude your report, make recommendations to minimise the risks to your service users from the hazards you have identified (D1).

4 Understand priorities and responses in dealing with incidents and emergencies

As we have discussed throughout this unit, it is important for care workers to have knowledge of health and safety laws and regulations, and be aware of their effect on practice and the care setting.

It is important to recognise the signs and symptoms of an incident, accident or emergency and deal with it appropriately. As care workers, we should always reflect on our practice, so when an incident has occurred and been dealt with, you should reflect on the process in order to change, adapt or improve practice.

Activity 18

Look at Table 3.5, which shows a range of incidents and emergencies with appropriate responses. Discuss in your class how responses may be changed to meet the needs of your care setting and service user group.

Table 3.5 Incidents, emergencies and responses

Incidents and emergencies	Responses
Suspected /actual abuse	**What to do:** any suspicion or disclosure of abuse must be taken seriously and be properly looked into. You must report any allegation of abuse to your line manager as soon as possible. You have a legal responsibility to report it. You should also record in writing exactly what the conversation was, rather than rely on your memory. You should not discuss the disclosure with the person who is alleged to be the abuser or with other members of the staff team. You should avoid saying that you 'won't tell anyone' if the person disclosing it asks you. Even though they may be seeking this reassurance from you, withholding the allegation may result in more harm. **Writing the report:** when writing your report of the allegation, you should ensure that the information is exactly what the person said to you rather than your interpretation of it. It must be an accurate account and it should also record the time and place of the conversation and any other relevant details. **What happens once an allegation has been made?** Each workplace will have its own policies and procedures on addressing allegations of abuse and it is these that will be followed in the event of a disclosure. The allegation should always be taken seriously and investigated thoroughly. Support will be offered to the individual making the allegation and all those involved within the investigation. All of these factors may have implications in the short term, medium term or long term.

Accidents	First aid procedures: first aid should protect you, the first aider and the casualty. The principles of first aid are:
	● to preserve life
	● to limit the effect of the condition
	● to promote recovery.
	
	When dealing with a first aid situation, whether minor or severe, certain qualities and skills are very valuable and will help you to deal with these situations.
	
	Life-saving procedures: the following information complies with the Resuscitation Council guidelines (2005) (source: www.redcross.org.uk).
	1 Injured person unconscious and breathing – recovery position.
	  If an adult is unconscious but breathing, place them on their side in the recovery position.
	
	  Place arm nearest you at a right angle, with palm facing up.
	  Move other arm, palm upwards, against the person's cheek. Then get hold of the knee furthest from you and pull up until foot is flat on the floor.
	  Pull the knee towards you, keeping the person's hand pressed against their cheek, and position the leg at a right angle.
	  Make sure the airway remains open by tilting the head back and lifting the chin. Check breathing.
	  Monitor the casualty's condition until help arrives.

Incidents and emergencies	Responses

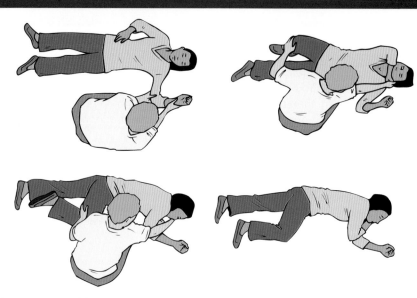

Recovery position

2 Injured person (adult) unconscious and not breathing.
  If the person is not breathing normally, you should call an ambulance and then start cardio pulmonary resuscitation (CPR), which is a combination of chest compressions and rescue breaths.
  Place your hands on the centre of the chest and, with the heel of your hand, press down (4–5 cm). After every 30 chest compressions, give two rescue breaths.

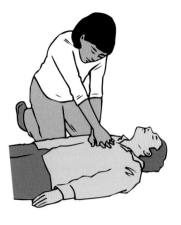

CPR

Open the airway – place one hand on the forehead and gently tilt the head back and lift the chin. Pinch the person's nose. Place your mouth over their mouth and, by blowing steadily, give two rescue breaths, each over one second.

Incidents and emergencies	Responses
	Continue with cycles of 30 chest compressions and two rescue breaths until emergency help arrives or the person begins to breathe normally. If you are unable or unwilling to give rescue breaths, just give chest compressions – this is better than doing nothing at all.
	Once you have dealt with an accident, particularly if it is a major accident, it is important for you to discuss your emotions with someone. You may feel very upset by the incident and may wonder if your actions were correct or adequate. These are normal feelings and it is very important that someone reassures you.
Exposure to infections	**Plan management** aims to reduce the risk of transmission of infection. This can be achieved by the implementation of standard infection control precautions. These are designed to protect both service user and carer. Standard precautions should be used for all service users at all times and in all care settings, thus minimising risks from unknown sources and protecting service user confidentiality. Additional precautions might be required for specific infections where additional risks of transmission exist, as in infectious diarrhoea and pulmonary (open) tuberculosis. Local policies should be followed and guidance sought from local infection control nurses in such circumstances.

Hand-washing is an infection control practice with a clearly demonstrated efficacy. See page 47 for correct procedures.

Personal protective equipment (PPE): protective clothing should be worn whenever contamination or splashing with blood or body fluids is anticipated.

Preventing and managing sharps injuries: contaminated sharps such as hollow bore needles and scalpel blades are hazardous – they pose a risk of causing infection with blood-borne viruses. Use risk reduction procedures:
- Dispose of sharps into appropriate containers immediately after use.
- Never overfill sharps containers. Close lids securely, label with source and dispose of by incineration.
- Discard disposable syringes and needles as a single unit, whenever possible.
- Remove needles from syringes only when essential.

Employers should also ensure that there is a written policy for correct disposal of sharps and that staff are aware of it.

Clinical waste: this includes waste contaminated with potentially infectious substances, including body fluids and human tissue. Clinical waste must be contained in a yellow plastic bag, tied at the neck and labelled with the source prior to incineration.

In healthcare settings outside hospital, generally the same rules apply for segregation, handling and disposal. However, local environment agencies might allow a risk assessment to be carried out and less infectious waste might be disposed of as household waste. |

Incidents and emergencies	Responses
	Clinical waste from the home should have a special collection arranged with a licensed waste contractor or the local authority.
	Household waste: household waste includes packaging, paper towels, dead flowers, and other waste not contaminated with potentially infectious substances. Household waste must be contained in a black plastic bag, tied at the neck and labelled with the source before going for landfill.
Exposure to chemicals and spillages	All chemicals are labelled and should be stored according to COSHH regulations.
	When using chemicals or working in an environment where you may be exposed to spillages, you should wear protective clothing. Types of protective equipment include:
	● disposable gloves – these must be of an appropriate material
	● plastic aprons
	● eye protection, including safety spectacles, goggles and visors
	● mouth/nose protection, including face masks
	● foot protection, such as wellington boots, often worn in operating theatres
	● fluid repellent gowns (disposable and reusable).
	Disposable items are designated for either single or multiple use and must be changed appropriately.
	If a spillage occurs, check the container for a hazard symbol. This will be listed in the COSHH file about how to clean up or what to do if chemicals come into contact with the skin.
	Any spillage is classed as a risk and should be cleared up immediately; wet or slippery floors should be identified ('wet floor' sign) to make others aware of the hazard.
Intruders	All staff should be confident in challenging someone who enters the premises who they do not recognise. Callers should always produce identification and have an appointment time. Any unannounced callers may have bogus identities so it is always better to check with the manager to see if the person is expected. Efficient security systems will protect the setting and the service user's home. For example:
	● swipe cards
	● locks, chains and keys
	● identification cards
	● alarm systems
	● panic buttons
	● methods of contact with local emergency services
	● policies and procedures for intruders and security in the setting
	● communicating with service users about personal protection.

Incidents and emergencies	Responses
Aggressive and dangerous encounters	When faced with aggressive or dangerous behaviours, try to remain calm and consider what triggered the behaviour. Try to diffuse the situation – do not approach violence or aggression with the same behaviour as the situation may get worse. If the setting has a panic button, press it or call security or other co-workers to assist. It may be necessary to call the police. As a care worker, you should always be made aware of any service users who have violent or aggressive tendencies – you should never be alone with them. It is useful to understand what may trigger aggressive or violent behaviour in service users. For example: ● a service user in pain ● a service user who is confused or frightened ● a service user who is frustrated at losing independence ● a person with a different language ● a person with mental illness. This knowledge will help us to protect ourselves, others and the service user themselves.
Fire	All care settings will have their own fire procedures but basic steps will always be followed to comply with the Fire Precautions (Workplace) Regulations 1997. Some settings are split into zones and separated by fire doors. This allows service users to be moved to a place of safety in the event of a fire and saves evacuating the whole building. ● As soon as you discover a fire, raise the alarm. Either break the glass in the fire alarm or ring emergency services – 999. ● Ask for the fire service and give your address and where the fire is situated. ● Remain calm – do not rush. ● Prevent the fire's spread by closing windows and fire doors. ● Move the people who are able to walk to safety via a fire exit or fire escape. ● Those people who you are unable to move should be moved when the fire service arrives, unless you have the manpower and equipment to do so. If people are in beds with wheels, keep them there and move the bed. Use wheelchairs also. Move service users to a safe zone if possible. ● Reach the assembly point and check you have accounted for everyone. ● Do not re-enter the building until the fire service gives you the all clear. ● Replace all emergency equipment that has been used. ● Write a detailed account of the event.
Major disasters	The Civil Contingencies Act 2004 requires the setting to have a plan in place for major disasters. The term 'disaster' or 'major emergencies' should be defined according to the setting, and then actions should be listed and staff should be made aware of their duties in the case of major disasters.

Other critical incidents

Incidents may include terrorist attacks, outbreaks of diseases, earthquakes or 'acts of God'. Think how the volcano eruption in Iceland in April 2010 caused disruption to working lives.

Priorities

When dealing with any incident or emergency, there are steps that have to be followed in order to deal with it appropriately, safely and professionally. These can be applied to all incidents and accidents. Look at the diagram below.

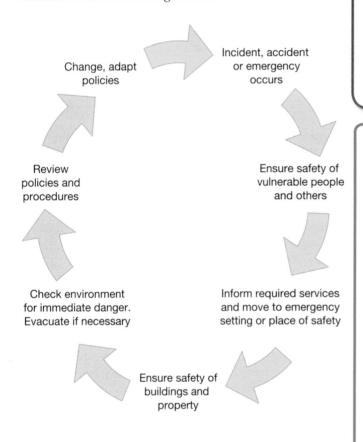

Activity 19

Choose two incidents or emergencies you may come across in a care setting and explain the priorities and responses to both of these cases. Remember you may have been involved in a fire evacuation, bomb scare or accident, so use this previous knowledge to help you (P4).

Using one of these particular cases, discuss what health, safety or security concerns arose (M3).

Justify (explain why) those responses where necessary (D2).

Summary

There are many potential hazards within health and social care environments. Minimising the risks reduces the possibility of harm to service users, staff, visitors and property.

A number of laws exist to promote health, safety and security in the workplace. Enforcing bodies include the local authority and the Health and Safety Executive. Each workplace will use the laws in making policies and procedures, which employees should follow. Employers and employees have responsibilities to promote and maintain a healthy workplace.

There are many hazards that may occur within local environments. A thorough risk assessment will highlight these and putting appropriate measures in place will reduce the risk. Occasionally extra measures will have to be put in place to minimise the risk of harm.

Assessment and grading criteria

In order to pass this unit, the evidence that the learner presents for assessment needs to demonstrate that they can meet all the learning outcomes for the unit. The assessment criteria for a pass grade describe the level of achievement required to pass this unit.

To achieve a pass grade the evidence must show that the learner is able to:	To achieve a merit grade the evidence must show that, in addition to the pass criteria, the learner is able to:	To achieve a distinction grade the evidence must show that, in addition to the pass and merit criteria, the learner is able to:
P1 explain potential hazards and the harm that may arise from each in a health or social care setting		
P2 outline how legislation, policies and procedures relating to health, safety and security influence health and social care settings	**M1** describe how health and safety legislation, policies and procedures promote the safety of individuals in a health or social care setting	
P3 carry out a risk assessment in a health or social care setting	**M2** assess the hazards identified in the health or social care setting	**D1** make recommendations in relation to identified hazards to minimise the risks to the service user group
P4 explain possible priorities and responses when dealing with two particular incidents or emergencies in a health or social care setting.	**M3** discuss health, safety or security concerns arising from a specific incident or emergency in a health or social care setting.	**D2** justify responses to a particular incident or emergency in a health or social care setting.

Resources

Department of Health (2003) *Care Homes for Older People: National Minimum Standards – Care Home Regulations, 3rd ed.*, London: Stationery Office Books.

Mandelstam, M. (2008) *Safeguarding Vulnerable Adults and the Law*, London: Jessica Kingsley Publishers.

Morris, C. (2008) *Knowledge Set for Safeguarding Vulnerable People*, Oxford: Heinemann.

Weblinks

www.dh.gov.uk:
Department of Health
www.hse.gov.uk:
Health and Safety Executive

www.rospa.com:
Royal Society for the Prevention of Accidents
www.foodstandards.gov.uk:
Food Standards Agency

4: Development Through the Life Stages

Introduction

This unit spans the whole of life, from birth to the end of life. It is essential for anyone working with people as it explores the changing needs of individuals as they grow, mature and decline.

This unit will investigate normal patterns of individual development and factors that can affect that development, including external factors, lifestyle factors and genetic factors. This will highlight areas where development may be delayed or altered. This unit will also explain how nature and nurture are responsible for the development of individuals.

As we age, changes take place physically and psychologically. This unit will investigate those processes and explain why body systems decline. It will give reasons for changes which take place during the normal ageing process. You will investigate particular disorders which relate to body systems and how that system is affected by the ageing process.

Learning outcomes:

On completion of this unit, you should:

1 Know stages of growth and development through the human lifespan

2 Understand potential effects of life factors and events on the development of the individual

3 Understand physical and psychological changes of ageing.

1 Know stages of growth and development through the human lifespan

Activity 1

Make a list of people you know who are different ages. Try to choose examples from a wide range of ages. Compare this with a partner.

Do you know someone you think of as really old?

Do you know anyone a lot younger than you?

Compare people from two different age groups. What can they do physically, intellectually, socially and emotionally?

● Physically – can they dress/wash/feed themselves?

● Intellectually – can they communicate with those around them? Are they learning new skills?

● Emotionally – do they express their feelings? Do they understand when others are upset or happy?

● Socially – do they interact with others? Do they have friends?

Life stages and definitions

Conception – the beginning of life

Sperm fertilises the ovum and a new life begins. About two weeks after conception the hormone human chorionic gonadotrophin (hCG) can be found in the woman's urine and a pregnancy test will be positive. Follow this weblink to investigate more about the process of conception: www.babyworld.co.uk/information/trying/secretsofconception.asp.

Pregnancy

Pregnancy lasts for approximately 40 weeks but this varies depending on the individual. A pregnant woman may feel nauseous, have a metallic taste in the mouth and experience breast tenderness. Physical growth is rapid at this stage.

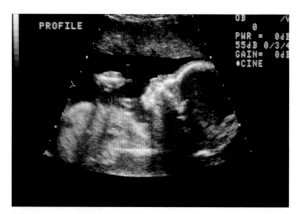

Ultrasound scan of a foetus at 23 weeks

Key term

Growth – an increase in physical size. Most babies grow bigger.

Visit the following weblink, which shows in detail the weekly development of the unborn child: www. ivillage.co.uk/pregnancyandbaby/pregnancy/ weekly/articles/0,,166200_168991,00.html.

An unborn baby is called an embryo from conception until the end of the eighth week, when it is called a foetus. Sometimes the embryo does not develop and the pregnancy ends in a miscarriage. Occasionally, a pregnancy is unwanted. The pregnancy may be ended by doctors with a medical or surgical abortion up to 23 weeks and 5 days. After that, an abortion is illegal and only allowed in exceptional circumstances. One of the problems with late abortions is that we now realise that the unborn baby can do more than we previously thought.

Did you know...

Using a 4D scanner, Professor Stuart Campbell has shown that babies start making finger movements at 15 weeks, yawning at 18 weeks and smiling, blinking and crying at 26 weeks. To read more, go to http://news.bbc. co.uk/1/hi/health/3105580.stm.

Birth and infancy – 0–3 years

In the last few weeks of pregnancy, the baby settles into the birth position, which is usually head down. Sometimes a baby settles bottom or feet first. This is a breech position.

When the baby is ready to be born, labour starts. The body has been preparing for this event with Braxton-Hicks contractions, where the uterus contracts in practise for birth. Labour is different because the contractions are regular and get stronger. Sometimes there is a show of mucus as the protective mucus plug in the cervix loosens, ready for the baby to come out. Sometimes the waters break, leaking fluid from the amniotic sac, which holds the baby. The baby can then move further down the birth canal, as the cervix widens. Labour is usually longer for the first pregnancy.

Once the baby is born, the midwife checks the Apgar score at one minute, five minutes and, if necessary, again at ten minutes after birth. The five criteria of the Apgar score are shown in Table 4.1.

From birth to 18 months is a period of rapid physical and emotional development. The newborn baby can see and hear. Reflex actions that occur without thought are already present in a baby's nervous system. They have reflexes such as the startle or Moro reflex. This means they throw out their arms and legs if startled or falling.

Another important reflex is the suckling and rooting reflex. If a baby is touched gently at the side of the mouth, it will automatically turn to that side and try to suck. A third reflex is the grasp reflex. If you place your finger in a baby's hand, it will grasp your finger.

Child of Our Time is a long study, planned to be over 20 years, following a group of children born in 2000. The study examines physical, social and emotional development. It looks at whether the position in the family has an impact on development, what makes children happy and the development of a sense of right and wrong. Log on to the *Child of Our Time* website (www.bbc.co.uk/ programmes/b0072bk8) and read about whether brothers and sisters (siblings) matter.

Table 4.1 Criteria of the Apgar score

	Score of 0	Score of 1	Score of 2	Acronym
Skin colour	blue all over	blue at extremities	normal	**A**ppearance
Heart rate	absent	<100	>100	**P**ulse
Reflex irritability	no response to stimulation	grimace/feeble cry when stimulated	sneeze/cough/ pulls away when stimulated	**G**rimace
Muscle tone	none	some flexion	active movement	**A**ctivity
Respiration	absent	weak or irregular	strong	**R**espiration

Activity 2

Watch a video clip of the Moro reflex on http://video.google.com/videoplay?docid=-2508818082092298520&q=moro+reflex.

Key terms

Development – an increase in skills. Babies learn to talk and to smile. Teenagers learn to use MP3 players. An older person may learn a new language before going on holiday abroad.

Growth – is not the same as development. Some people grow but do not develop. Sometimes babies are born with brain damage and do not develop the skills of walking and talking. A pregnant woman who gets German measles (rubella) may feel unwell. If she is in the early stages of pregnancy, the virus can cause severe damage to the unborn baby. For more on this, see www.medinfo.co.uk/conditions/rubella.html.

Developmental norms – there are stages of development which people pass through in a certain order. So a baby starts to coo and babble before forming words. Some people think babies should reach developmental milestones at certain ages, or there is something wrong. In fact this is a complex subject. Each child is unique. It is rumoured that Einstein did not talk until he was nearly four years old and some people thought he had learning difficulties. He went on to become one of the most famous mathematicians of all time.

Psychological – thinking skills.

Psychological development – developing mentally, learning new ways to think and feel.

Some people develop but do not grow because of genetic problems. One example of this is people with achondroplasia. Many people with achondroplasia lead full and active lives. Dr Tom Shakespeare is Director of Outreach for the Policy, Ethics and Life Sciences Research Institute. He is also achondroplasic. See his website for more links about restricted growth (www.bbc.co.uk/ouch/writers/tomshakespeare.shtml). According to www.achondroplasia.co.uk, achondroplasia includes short stature. Legs and arms are short compared with the trunk (body); this shortness is more noticeable in the upper arms and legs (proximal).

Babies vary in their physical, social and psychological development. By three years old, many variations occur. Some children are talking. Those who hear more than one language may be able to speak more than one language. Children whose parents speak different languages may at times appear to be slow in developing speech, but they are learning two languages at once!

Those children who are isolated or hear only baby talk may have a limited vocabulary. Children who are read to regularly will be familiar with books and stories and some can read at this age. Children who hear music and see adults playing instruments may learn to play a musical instrument early. Children who are used to having people around may be able to cope socially. An only child with limited social contact may be shy.

Emotionally, a child who feels secure and loved will gain confidence. A child who has no main carer or who has been moved from foster carer to foster carer may be less secure and less able to relate to others. (See www.bbc.co.uk/parenting/your_kids/babies_devstagesintro.shtml.)

There are many accounts of children living with animals; some are quite recent. Some are just hearsay, but the account in the case study on page 79 was proved and is one of the earliest.

Did you know...

A child who is isolated from human company may not learn to speak.

◯ Case Study – Victor, The Wild Child of Aveyron

Victor was discovered in woods in Saint Sernin sur Rance, southern France at the end of the eighteenth century. Thought to be about 12 years old, Victor was human in appearance alone. When he was found, he could not speak and behaved like a wild animal. He enjoyed eating rotten food and was unable to distinguish hot from cold. Scientist Dr Jean-Marc-Gaspard Itard dedicated himself to educating the boy, with the aim of teaching him to speak and to show emotion, but Victor's progress was limited. Over the years, the only words Victor learned to speak were 'lait' (milk) and 'Oh Dieu' (my God). His sense of touch was particularly strong and far more valuable to him than his sense of sight. Throughout his life, he was unable to distinguish right from wrong and was indifferent to sex. Victor did make progress, however, in some menial tasks such as setting a table. Victor lived in Paris with Jean-Marc-Gaspard Itard and his housekeeper Madame Guerin until he died, in 1828, aged 40.

To find out more, go to www.feralchildren.com.

Childhood – 4–9 years

Table 4.2 Development chart for four-year-olds

Motor development
Sits on chair with knees crossed
Stands, walks and runs on tiptoe
Can bend from the waist keeping legs straight to pick up objects from the floor
Climbs trees and ladders
While running, can turn sharp corners
Can walk and run upstairs and downstairs, placing one foot on each step
Can kick, catch, throw and bounce a ball
Hops on favoured foot and balances upon it for 3–5 seconds

Hand and eye development
Names and matches colours
Can pick up crumbs or small objects with one eye covered
Can thread beads but still cannot thread a needle
Builds a ten-cube tower
When shown how, can arrange six cubes into three steps
Copies letters H O T V
Draws a man showing head, legs and maybe arms

Hearing and voice
Talks intelligibly, using correct grammar
Knows and will give own name, age and address in full
Asks what different words mean
Loves hearing and telling long stories
Mixes up fact and fantasy
Counts to 20 and counts actual objects up to 5
Likes jokes
Accurately sings and says a few nursery rhymes

Play and social development

Uses fork and spoon well

Cleans teeth

Washes and dries hands

Will dress and undress himself but needs help with difficult fastenings

Independent (may answer back)

Enjoys dressing up

Less tidy than at age three

Argues with other children but needs their companionship

Learns to take turns

Sympathetic towards siblings and playmates

Understands past, present and future

Source: Nottingham University Hospital – Queen's Medical Centre

Children develop at different rates from 4–9 years. This is a period of rapid physical growth if the child is well nourished. There are several possible causes of delayed development. It may be due to genetic disorders such as chromosomal abnormalities. Down's syndrome is one example of this.

Biological issues such as rhesus factor may cause a newborn baby to be jaundiced. If this is not treated, the baby may develop complications, such as deafness, blindness, and possible learning difficulties.

Environmental factors, such as exposure to harmful organisms, may damage a baby. The German measles (rubella) virus may damage an unborn baby, causing deafness and visual impairment. This may delay speech and social interaction as the baby who cannot see does not respond to a smile. A baby may fail to develop properly in the uterus. Physical problems, such as a cleft palate, may delay speech.

Socio-economic factors may delay development. Mothers who smoke during pregnancy have lower birth weight babies. According to the National Statistics database,

> 'women from the manual social classes remain more likely to smoke than those in the non-manual groups. In 2000, 4 per cent of women in the "professional class" reported smoking while pregnant, compared with 26 per cent in the "unskilled" group.'
>
> Source: www.ons.gov.uk

Activity 3

Look at the development chart for four-year-olds.

What reasons can you think of for a four-year-old not reaching some of these milestones? Hint – think about genetic, biological, environmental, socio-economic and lifestyle factors. Environmental differences could include things such as living in a high-rise flat versus living in a house with a garden. Socio-economic factors could influence how much time adults spend talking or playing with a child. Affluent parents may be able to spend more time with their children.

Ask permission to observe a three-year-old. Can the three-year-old do any of these activities?

Activity 4

In small groups, find out more about Down's syndrome, rhesus factor, German measles, cleft palate and low birth weight. Prepare a presentation for the rest of your class.

Adolescence: 10–18 years

Adolescence is generally marked by the onset of puberty. It is the transition stage between childhood and adulthood. In some Western cultures, adolescence may be marked by emotional turmoil. In other cultures, there is less emotional upheaval.

Puberty is the physical transition from child to adolescent and varies with eating habits, social and psychological factors. Undernourished

Key term

Puberty – the first phase of adolescence, the time when sexual maturity becomes evident. A large increase in hormones – oestrogen in girls and testosterone in boys – leads to a range of physical and emotional changes that are completely natural but sometimes hard to deal with. Source: http://hcd2.bupa.co.uk/fact_sheets/html/puberty.html.

Activity 5

Find out more about the changes that happen in puberty by going to the BBC Science website: www.bbc.co.uk/science/humanbody/body/index.shtml?lifecycle. Here you can watch an interactive demonstration of the changes that occur in puberty.

If you want to find out more about sexual changes, look at the link site, www.bbc.co.uk/science/humanbody/body/articles/lifecycle/teenagers/sexual_changes.shtml.

children may start puberty later. In 1890, girls generally started their periods at about 15, but now it is around 13. Some even start as young as 8. Boys reach puberty at anything between 9 and 14. Better nutrition in the developed countries has been a factor in this.

Physical maturation may vary with age, culture and nutrition and with what part of the body is maturing. The brain takes longer to mature. We are born with all our brain cells. We cannot grow more if we damage them, but we can develop the nerve pathways between the cells. These are called neural pathways.

Did you know...

Scientists have discovered that the brain's centre of reasoning is among the last areas to mature. The finding, by a team at the US National Institute of Mental Health, may help to explain why teenagers often seem to be so unreasonable. To read more, go to **http://news.bbc.co.uk/1/hi/health/3724615.stm.**

Adolescence is not clearly defined. Legally in England, the age of consent for sex is 16 years old, but the age for legal drinking is 18 years. In America, you have to be 21 to drink alcohol.

Adulthood: 19–65 years

Key terms

Maturation or **maturity** – this is a holistic process. It includes physical, social and emotional aspects. Emotional maturation comes with thinking about experiences. Some young people who have had a lot of responsibility may be very mature in their outlook. Adults are expected to be experienced and wise, but this is not always the case. An older person who has never had any responsibility may lack experience and be immature, even though they are physically old.

Ageing – the process of growing older. We are all ageing from the minute we are born!

The age at which one becomes adult varies between countries and has varied in the same country according to the period of history. In Europe in the Middle Ages, people were considered adult at seven years old. In some Jewish cultures today, people are considered adult at 12 or 13 years old. In Yemen, girls are expected to be adult enough for marriage at nine years old (source: Human Rights Watch, www.hrw.org/wr2k1/mideast/yemen.html). Adults are expected to be responsible, serious, emotionally controlled and able to manage their behaviour.

Activity 6

Think of two adults you know. Are they responsible, serious, emotionally controlled and able to manage their behaviour? Why do you think they meet (or fail to meet) these criteria?

Adulthood is the age when people usually are economically productive, contributing to the economy by working and earning. Socially, they are able to make their own decisions about when and whether to marry, whether to have children and whether to care for older relatives. Emotionally, adulthood can be a time to build relationships and also a time to leave relationships.

Older adulthood: 65+ years

According to the government website, 16 per cent of the UK population are aged 65 or over (source: www.ons.gov.uk).

Key term

Life expectancy – how long a person is expected to live. This varies depending on the individual.

Life expectancy

Life expectancy for both men and women has continued to rise. In 2002, life expectancy at birth for females born in the UK was 81 years, compared with 76 years for males. This contrasts with 49 and 45 years respectively in 1901.

In recent years, the increase in life expectancy among older adults has been dramatic, particularly for men. Between 1981 and 2002, life expectancy at age 50 increased by four-and-a-half years for men and three years for women. For those aged 65 and over, the extra years of life were three years and two years respectively. By 2002, women who were aged 65 could expect to live to the age of 84, while men could expect to live to the age of 81.

Projections suggest that life expectancies at these older ages will increase by a further three years

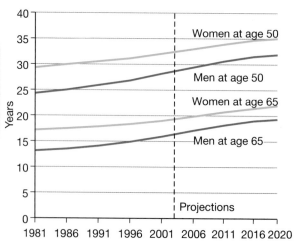

Expected further years of life at ages 50 and 65, UK

Source: www.statistics.gov.uk/CCI/nugget.asp?ID=168&Pos=1&ColRank=1&Rank=374

Activity 7

Look at the information on page 82 and answer the questions.

1 What has happened to life expectancy – has it got longer or shorter?

2 In 2006, what was the life expectancy for women?

3 In 2006, what was the life expectancy for men?

4 What were these figures in 1901?

5 Are there more people over 70 now or fewer?

Now look at causes of death in Table 4.3 below.

Table 4.3 Major cause of death: by sex and age, 2002

	Men (%)			Women (%)		
	50–64	65–84	85+	50–64	65–84	85+
Cancers	39	32	18	53	29	12
Circulatory system	36	42	42	22	40	44
Digestive system	7	4	3	6	5	4
Respiratory system	7	13	19	8	13	17
Injury and poisoning	4	1	2	3	1	2
Nervous system	2	3	3	3	3	3
Mental and behavioural	1	1	3	–	2	6
Other	4	5	9	5	7	14
All deaths (=100%) (thousands)	35.6	144.6	53.6	23.0	129.6	116.3

Sources: Government Actuary's Department for expectation of life data; Office for National Statistics for mortality data

1 What is the most common cause of death for those aged 50–64 years?

2 What is the most common cause of death for those over 65 years?

or so by 2020. The expectation of life for people at 70 and 80 has also gone up. At present, there are more older people aged 70 and 80 than ever before.

Over the last 30 years, death rates for men have fallen faster than those for women, but men still have higher rates than women at all ages. Death rates increase with age, from 8 per 1,000 men aged 50–64 to 188 per 1,000 men aged 85 and over in England and Wales in 2002. The equivalent rates for women were 5 and 160.

The most common cause of death for people aged 50–64 was cancers. Overall, 39 per cent of male and 53 per cent of female deaths in this age group were due to cancers. Lung cancer was the most common cause of cancer death for men in this age group. Breast cancer was the most common cause for women.

For those over the age of 65, circulatory diseases are the most common cause of death. Within this age group, heart disease as a cause of death decreases with age and strokes increase.

Pneumonia as a cause of death also increases with age to account for one in ten deaths among those aged 85 and over. (Sources: Government Actuary's Department for expectation of life data; Office for National Statistics for mortality data.)

Note: the expectation of life at a given age is defined as the average number of years that a person could be expected to live if their rate of mortality at each age was that experienced in that calendar year. Projections are 2002 based.

The final stages of life

As people get older, they may find it difficult to live alone. Their health may deteriorate, eyesight may fail, and heart problems may limit what they can do. If they have smoked, they may have lung problems. According to National Statistics Online (www.statistics.gov.uk), 'In 2001, 4.5 per cent of people aged 65 and over were resident in communal establishments in Great Britain. This proportion was greatest among people aged 90 and over.' According to National Statistics Online, 3 in 5 women over 75 live alone.

Activity 8

If 4.5 per cent of people aged 65 and over live in residential care, how many do not live in residential care?

Answer: 100% – 4.5% = 95.5 per cent do not live in residential care.

Activity 9

What kind of care do planners need to think about when they see these statistics?

Would they need to provide more home care or more residential care if people wish to stay in their own homes?

Key term

Life course – the events in a person's life. Sometimes it can be described as a river, starting in the hills as a small stream, running fast, then broadening and slowing as it gets bigger. As it matures and approaches the sea, it slows down. It may be deep and powerful but calm on the surface. Eventually it joins the sea, which is the end of the journey, and for humans, the end of life. Some people have an easy life, with no real problems. Other people have a rough journey, facing obstacles along the way.

Activity 10

Draw your own river, as described in the 'Key term' box above, and include the key events in your life so far. Choose things you remember and that have affected you. A young person will be able to draw only the young river because no one knows the future. An older person may be able to draw a longer river and include more events.

Development

Holistic development

One theory brings together all the life stages. Erik Erikson (1902–1994) was a German developmental psychologist and psychoanalyst known for his theory on social development of human beings. He developed a theory of eight life stages or crises that we all pass through. He looked at holistic development – seeing the person as a whole, not just a collection of physical systems. This theory is detailed in Unit 8 Psychological perspectives page 197.

Erikson looked at the continuum of life, where change is social, emotional and intellectual. You can read more about this on www.business balls.com/erik_erikson_psychosocial_theory. htm#erikson_psychosocial_theory_summary.

2 Understand potential effects of life factors and events on the development of the individual

The nature–nurture debate

This debate is a well-discussed topic between theorists and argues whether genetics (nature) or our environment (nurture) is responsible for our behaviour and development. Early theorists believed that our personality, intellect, behaviour and gender role were determined by our genes and therefore could not be changed. This meant we would have no free will or control over our actions.

The key principles that are under discussion are outlined below.

Biological programming

This area of the debate looks at genetics. Genetics are a blueprint or set of instructions for our development and are unique to each individual. Genes contain the code to guide the construction of our body and are carried on chromosomes, which are arranged in 23 pairs, half from each parent, so we can see parental likeness in ourselves. For example, you may inherit height from one parent and hair colour from the other. The big question is, do we inherit intellect, behaviour or diseases through our genes? This is the nature side of the debate

Experiences and environment

This side of the debate sees the mind as a 'blank slate' at birth, so behaviour, knowledge and skills are all a result of learning through social experiences. For example, aggression and violence are learned by observation and imitation, so children brought up against a violent and aggressive family background will learn that violence is normal and will have a violent and aggressive temperament. Nurture theorist B.F. Skinner argued that language is learned from others.

Maturation theory

Maturation theory was developed by a theorist in child development called Arnold Gesell in the 1940s. He explained that child development was a result of body changes as a result of the aging process (or maturation). This means that the genetic make-up of the child is responsible for development from conception onwards; their

Activity 11

Look at the table below and list people you know who fit into the categories.

Category	People
Strong personality	
Intelligent	
Aggressive	
Prone to ill health	

Do you think that the above traits are inherited (nature) or socially acquired (nurture)? Discuss your ideas in a group and try to explain your answers.

environment is there to nurture this development but genes are the main drive behind it. The maturation theory states that the child is unique and will develop at their own rate, regardless of environmental factors.

Environment versus genetics

As we try to separate the two sides of this long-discussed debate, we realise that a combination of the two sides may be responsible for our development. For example, the genetic disorder PKU (phenylketonuria) is inherited but can now be avoided, since it has been found that diet will help to avoid the serious brain effects associated with the condition.

Life factors

Genetic

Each living cell in our body contains a set of 23 pairs of chromosomes (apart from sex cells, ova and sperm, which have 23 single chromosomes). These contain genes, which are a set of instructions responsible for making us who we are. Half of these are from our mother and half from our father.

Because of our genetic make-up, it is said that we are predisposed to certain disorders, so we are more likely to suffer a disease, condition or portray behaviours because of the way our genes are. Others argue that it is environmental and social forces that allow these traits to occur – for example, do you think anorexia nervosa is in our genetic make-up?

During the replication of genes in the development process, there can be mistakes or mutations, which result in abnormalities, such as phenylketonuria, cystic fibrosis and Down's syndrome. Some of these have been discussed earlier in this unit.

Biological

As the foetus develops over the 40-week period, it is exposed to many factors that could cause long-term harm or irreversible damage. The most critical period is during the first 16 weeks, when major systems are developing.

It is a well-known fact that smoking and drinking alcohol can damage the unborn child, so antenatal

---

Activity 12   P1   M1   D1

Produce a case study/fact file about a chosen individual; this could be a friend, family member, person from work experience or a TV character. An older individual will give you more information for your assignment. (Remember to ask permission.) Include pictures and diagrams.

1 Interview your chosen person and produce a description of their physical, intellectual, emotional and social development at each of their life stages (P1).

2 Discuss the nature/nurture debate in relation to your case study (M1).

3 Choose two of your individual's life stages and evaluate how the nature/nurture debate may have affected their development (D1).

For example, as a teenager, your chosen individual may have done very well at school and gone into higher education. Is this because of their upbringing or because their parents went into higher education?

---

care is important for educating parents-to-be and for passing on advice. Because some pregnancies are unplanned, the harm may already have been started, so early diagnosis of pregnancy and a change of habits will benefit the unborn child.

Environmental
Water and sanitation

Lack of clean water and appropriate sanitation will lead to the spread of water-borne disease, which may result in severe diarrhoea and possible death. Water may also be polluted with toxic or radio-active chemicals. The World Health Organisation (WHO) is responsible for improving access to safe drinking water. Follow this weblink to discover the

Activity 13

Look at the diagram below and investigate how these agents may affect the unborn child.

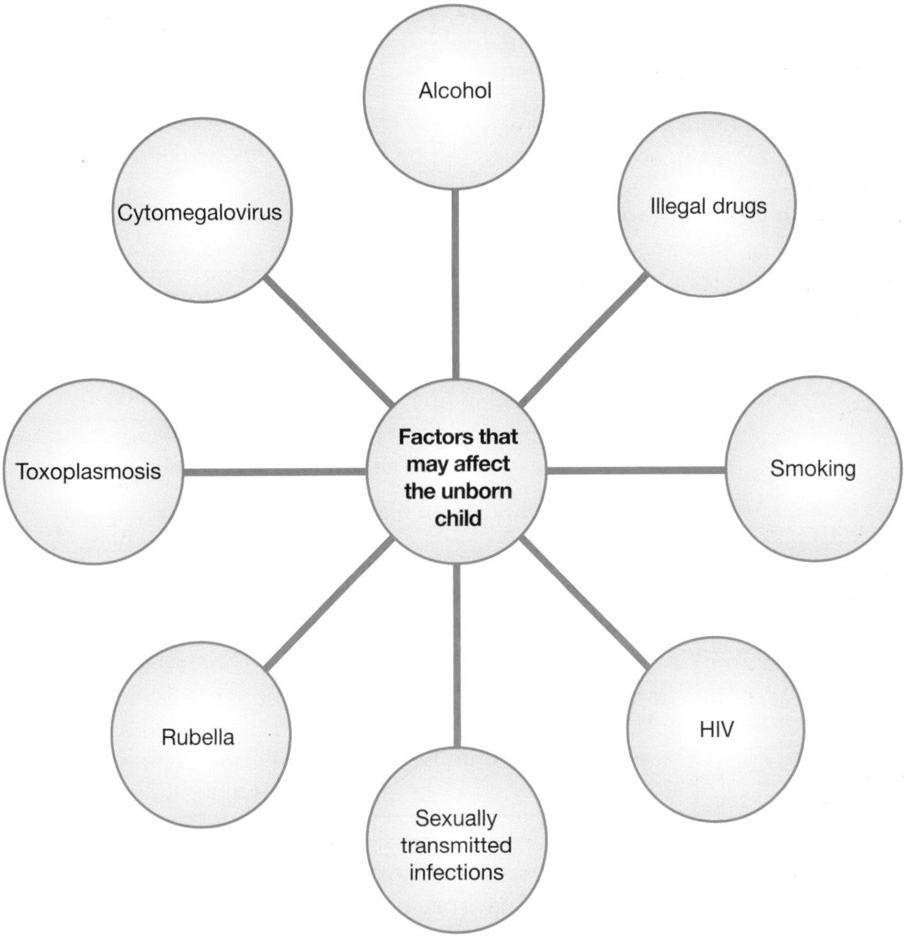

work of the WHO in other areas of health and well-being around the world: www.who.int/en.

Pollution

There are many areas of pollution that can impact on our health needs. Pollution may be in the form of air, light, water or noise. These kinds of pollution can have a number of effects on the health and needs of service users. For example, air pollution has been linked to breathing and allergy problems, which may cause or make asthma worse. Noise pollution can impact upon people socially and also can be so extreme it can affect sleep patterns and cause anxiety and depression.

Take a look in your local newspapers. Are there any environmental issues that have been highlighted recently?

Socio-economic

In 1980, the Black report was carried out, which revealed that there were links between social class and health. The report found that the lower the social class, the more likely you were to suffer ill health. This may be because lower social classes are in lower-paid employment so may not have an adequate diet or living conditions, which all affect the health of the family. Those in higher social classes have a higher income and so may be able to afford a wider variety of foods from specialised shops and also may be able to afford membership to gyms or clubs, which will improve their health. The Acheson report continued this research and revealed similar findings that, nearly 20 years later, health is still affected by income and ill-health and is more prevalent in lower socio-economic groups. These reports are investigated further in Unit 20 (available online, see inside front cover for details).

Look at Table 4.4, which defines your occupation with your social class.

Table 4.4 SOC 2000 major groups

1	Managers and senior officials
2	Professional occupations
3	Associate professional and technical occupations
4	Administrative and secretarial occupations
5	Skilled trades occupations
6	Personal service occupations
7	Sales and customer service occupations
8	Process, plant and machine operatives
9	Elementary occupation

Source: Standard Occupational Classification 2000, Office for National Statistics

Table 4.5 Socio-economic factors and the effects on health

Socio-economic factors	Effects on health
Income and expenditure	A low income can cause poor dietary choices and so ill health and lower life expectancy. Housing choices may be limited and may be in polluted areas where there are high crime rates, overcrowding and a stressed environment. People more likely to be on a low income are lone parents, the sick or disabled, unemployed and older people.
Education	Schools in depressed areas are more likely to suffer problems as they may have short-term members of staff that do not stay in the area for long. They may encounter problems, such as children who are undernourished, depressed or do not speak English as their first language, so only low levels of education are achieved. In more affluent areas, success in education is more likely and children are more likely to move onto further or higher education, thus accessing a better quality of employment.
Values and attitudes	Values and attitudes arise from primary and secondary socialisation and form the basis of our culture. Negative anti-social behaviour can affect life chances. Positive parenting, schooling and formation of sound attitudes that embrace society and culture will ultimately lead to a healthy view of society. This will provide emotional and social well-being.
Peer groups	Positive and negative attitudes in our health choices can come from our peer groups, which include friends, family, school and the media. Violent and anti-social behaviour may be linked with exposure to violence on TV from an early age and exposure to a violent environment. Read this newspaper article, which claims that violence in the media can lead to aggressive behaviour: www.guardian.co.uk/technology/blog/2007/nov/29/mediaviolenceisalmostasba.

Socio-economic factors	Effects on health
Employment status	Employment provides a financial income so necessities can be acquired. If employment is not fulfilling or is in a dangerous environment, it can cause unnecessary stress, anxiety and depression.

Lifestyle

We have investigated how the unborn child may be affected by the lifestyle choices of the mother; we now look at the choices we make as we grow and develop.

Nutrition and dietary choices

Healthy dietary choices come from education, so knowing what constitutes a healthy diet and following government recommendations (for example, 5-a day – see Unit 21) is critical when choosing healthy foods. Income also plays a major role in dietary choices. The Acheson report (1998) highlighted that those on a low income have poor nutrition, which in turn can lead to ill health. Families on a low income may find it difficult to travel to supermarkets, and the storage of items on offer may also be a problem, so those on a lower income may have to buy convenience foods or higher priced products at local stores. See the following weblink for further information on the Acheson report: www.archive.official-documents. co.uk/document/doh/ih/contents.htm.

Activity 14

As excessive alcohol intake is becoming an increasing problem in our society, discuss with your class what advertisements you have seen recently that educate the public about safe limits of alcohol. Do you feel they are working? How might you approach the topic differently?

Alcohol intake

The government recommends safe limits of alcohol intake for men and women. These are recommended guidelines to avoid the harmful effects of alcohol. Visit the following weblink and read about these safe limits and what constitutes 'binge' drinking: www.patient.co.uk/health/ Alcohol-and-Sensible-Drinking.htm.

Misuse of substances

There is a wide range of drugs – some are legal and some are illegal. We can all think of legal drugs – for example, paracetamol and ibuprofen can be bought in a shop or pharmacy. Used in small quantities, they should not cause harm. However, using illegal drugs can have serious implications – not only can they impact on an individual's health and well-being but their use can lead to prosecution.

Drugs can be divided into different categories: stimulants and depressants. Stimulants increase activity in the brain. Some examples of stimulants are tobacco or ecstasy. Depressants, meanwhile, decrease activity in the brain. Alcohol is in this category. Drugs may also be hallucinogens – these alter the way a person sees or hears things. Hallucinogenic drugs include cannabis, magic mushrooms and LSD. Drugs that have a painkilling effect are known as analgesics – such as heroin. Some drugs, such as cocaine, may have a stimulant effect at first, then cause depression later. For some people, alcohol also has this effect. As you can see, people respond to drugs in different ways.

Follow this weblink to find out more about drug misuse: www.talktofrank.com.

Illegal drugs are categorised according to their level of penalty and are as shown in Table 4.6.

Table 4.6 Categorisation of drugs

		Possession:	Dealing:
Class A	Ecstasy, LSD, heroin, cocaine, crack, magic mushrooms, amphetamines (if prepared for injection)	Up to seven years in prison or an unlimited fine, or both	Up to life in prison or an unlimited fine, or both
Class B	Amphetamines, cannabis, methylphenidate (Ritalin), pholcodine	Up to five years in prison or an unlimited fine, or both	Up to 14 years in prison or an unlimited fine, or both
Class C	Tranquilisers, some painkillers, gamma hydroxybutyrate (GHB), ketamine	Up to two years in prison or an unlimited fine, or both	Up to 14 years in prison or an unlimited fine, or both

Source: www.homeoffice.gov.uk/drugs/drugs-law/

Activity 15 P2

Continuing with the case study/fact file that you began for Activity 15, explain the potential effects of five different life factors on your chosen individual's development.

Major life events

If you reflect on the information earlier in this unit about life course, and the information you gathered when you completed Activity 13 on the life river, you will appreciate that, along life's way, may different events occur, which can be either predictable or unpredictable. These events can have both positive and negative effects on our life stages and development.

Key terms

Predictable event – a planned or chosen change.
Unpredictable event – a sudden and unexpected change.

Activity 16

Study the lists below and discuss the positive and negative influences that each event may have on a person's life.

Predictable life events:

● Starting school or nursery

● Moving house

● Employment

● Leaving home; leaving care; leaving prison

● Marriage

● Parenthood

● Retirement.

Unpredictable life events:

● Birth of a sibling

● Redundancy

● Serious injury or illness

● Divorce

● Bereavement.

Activity 17   P3

Adding to your fact file/case study, explain two predictable and two unpredictable major life events that have occurred in the lifetime of your chosen individual and explain how they have influenced their development.

For example, have they experienced marriage, divorce, employment, retirement or redundancy? Have these events had positive or negative effects on their development?

3 Understand physical and psychological changes of ageing

Physical changes

The ageing process happens to all adults at varying rates, depending on lifestyle, and socio-economic, environmental and genetic factors. Physical changes affect all body systems, but we should remember that there are also positive aspects of ageing – for example, maturity, wisdom, life experiences and development of self-concept.

Male
- Prostate changes
- Reduced fertility.

Both
- May need glasses
- May need hearing aid
- Loss/thinning of hair
- Poor memory
- Slower reactions
- Cardiovascular changes
- Respiratory changes
- Musculo skeletal changes
- Deterioration of sense of smell/taste
- Skin less elastic
- Decline in mobility.

Female
- Osteoporosis
- Menopause.

Hormones

Puberty is when male and female hormones activate the secondary sex characteristics in males and females. The menopause is also controlled by the female hormone oestrogen and causes the eventual cessation of menstruation and production of eggs from the ovaries. This means that women are no longer able to conceive. During the female menopause, women can experience some very uncomfortable symptoms. Follow this link to find out more: www.netdoctor.co.uk/diseases/facts/menopause.htm.

The male menopause is also caused by a decline in hormone production, but the ability to produce sperm declines very gradually and men are able to father children quite late in life.

Activity 18

Read the following news article about one of the oldest fathers in Britain: www.independent.co.uk/news/uk/this-britain/man-76-claims-britains-oldest-father-title-1934366.html.

Discuss in your class the benefits and drawbacks of older fathers.

Cardiovascular system
Atherosclerosis

This condition is a build-up of fatty deposits within the walls of the coronary arteries. The fatty deposits are called atheroma, which are made up of cholesterol and waste materials from cells. As the atheroma builds, it forms raised areas in the arteries called plaques. These areas cause a reduction/slowing of oxygen-rich blood flow to the cardiac muscle and so in turn make the cardiac muscle (heart) less efficient. (For further information about atherosclerosis and its effects, visit www.bhf.org.uk/living_with_a_heart_condition/understanding_heart_conditions/types_of_heart_conditions/cardiovascular_disease.aspx.)

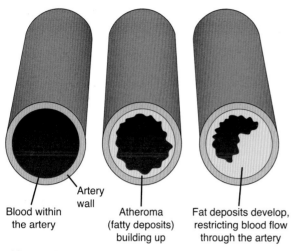

How atheroma builds up in the arteries

Blood within the artery — Artery wall — Atheroma (fatty deposits) building up — Fat deposits develop, restricting blood flow through the artery

Coronary heart disease

All arteries have different names depending on which area of the body they supply. The arteries that supply the heart and cardiac muscle are called coronary arteries, so when they are affected the result is coronary heart disease (CHD).

The heart requires oxygenated blood to function properly and this is supplied via the coronary arteries. If these are restricted by atherosclerosis or blocked by a clot (thrombosis), then angina or heart attack (acute myocardial infarction) can result.

Factors that increase the risk of CHD are high cholesterol, smoking, high blood pressure, physical inactivity, obesity, diabetes and family history.

Respiratory changes
Chronic Obstructive Pulmonary Disease (COPD)

This is a collective respiratory disorder which includes the conditions chronic bronchitis, emphysema and chronic asthma. It affects the respiratory systems, making breathing difficult.

As it is a 'chronic', or long-term, disease, it usually affects people over the age of 40. It is responsible for over 30,000 deaths a year in England and Wales.

COPD is usually caused by smoking. Other causes can be occupational exposure to dusts, indoor pollutants, air pollutants or inherited causes – for example, some people have an inherited form of

emphysema where a lack of protein alpha-1-antit-rypsin results in emphysema.

Emphysema

This is also caused by lung damage caused by infection (chronic), smoke or pollutants and it damages the elastic structure supporting the air sacs (alveoli) in the lungs. Alveoli are grape-like structures where gaseous exchange takes place. This is reduced to a sac structure in emphysema; the result is reduced surface area, therefore reduced carbon dioxide exchange, so breathlessness occurs.

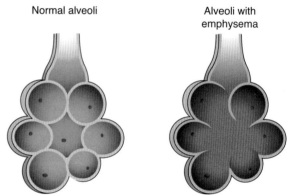

Normal alveoli   Alveoli with emphysema

Alveoli with and without emphysema

Nervous system changes
Cognitive changes

Cognitive changes are very general changes in the nervous system, which are expected and are a normal part of the ageing process.

With age, nerve cells do not transmit messages as efficiently as they used to because of general wear and tear. Sight, hearing and mobility can be affected, and occasional memory lapses are considered normal.

Motor Neurone Disease (MND)

This is a rare condition, which is caused by the breakdown of the nerve cells in the brain. Research is under way to understand the causes and develop a cure. MND usually begins between the ages of 50 and 70 and affects around two people in 100,000 in the UK.

MND affects the muscles used to move (voluntary muscles), but not the nerves dealing with sensation, so there is no numbness or pins and needles. The parts of the brain dealing with intelligence and awareness also remain unaffected.

Degeneration of the sense organs

Our sensory organs receive information from our environment and, within the central nervous system, the information is taken to motor neurones or effector glands and organs. This information allows our bodies to respond accordingly.

As we age, particularly after 45, our sight deteriorates and detailed vision and focusing is more difficult, particularly when reading, driving or watching television.

Cataracts are changes in the lens of the eye, which make vision cloudy. Cataracts can occur in one or both eyes. Diabetes can also contribute to the development of cataracts.

As we age, hearing can become more difficult, particularly for high-pitched sounds. Sometimes hearing can be affected by chronic infections, build-up of wax or from injury or illness.

Degeneration of the nervous tissue

Degeneration of nerve tissue may lead to conditions like multiple sclerosis. This is damage to the protective myelin sheath that insulates the nerves and allows electrical messages to be sent all over the body. If this sheath is worn or damaged then nerve impulses are delayed or unable to travel at all.

Musculo-skeletal changes

Muscle wasting

As we age, our appetite reduces and so low or poor nutrition may lead to muscle wasting. Poor nutrition may occur as a result of disorders, such as Crohn's disease or ulcerative colitis. Older people, if living alone, may not eat adequate diets if they do not feel inclined to cook for one.

Arthritis

Arthritis is a painful condition of the joints. There are different types of the disease, many inflammatory and some degenerative. All age groups can develop arthritis, even children, but arthritis is three times more likely to occur in women than men.

Rheumatoid arthritis

This is an inflammatory disease, mainly affecting joints and tendons. An inflamed joint looks swollen and red and appears warm to the touch. The disease usually starts in the wrists, hands or feet, and can spread to other joints and parts of the body. Usually, inflammation is the body's way of healing. In rheumatoid arthritis, the immune system starts to attack the body instead of defending it.

Osteoarthritis

This is a degenerative joint disease, which is a gradual breakdown of cartilage in the joints. This chronic condition can cause pain and impair movement, especially in the elderly population. Many people consider osteoarthritis a natural part of ageing. It usually occurs in the knees, hips, back, hands and feet. It may be limited to one joint, but can affect several joints throughout the body. Around 20 per cent of people over 60 have osteoarthritis.

For further information about physical changes in the ageing process, visit www.nhsdirect.nhs.uk or www.ageconcern.org.uk.

Skin changes

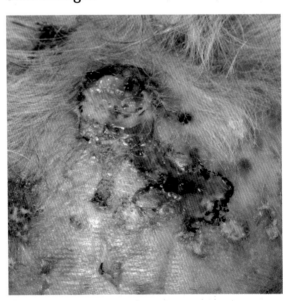

Skin damage caused by the sun

Some obvious signs of ageing are the lines and wrinkles that appear on the skin. Young people's skin is supple and is able to return to its original shape when stretched. However, tissue in the skin loses its elasticity with age, causing the skin to wrinkle rather than bounce back into place. The skin's properties can be destroyed more rapidly with excessive exposure to the sun's harmful rays, from excessive use of sun beds or from smoking.

In a similar way, loss of elasticity in lung tissue means that elderly people are more prone to respiratory problems and diseases like pneumonia. Even eyesight is affected by loss of elasticity – the eye lens becomes less supple with age and is unable to focus as well.

Common illnesses of ageing

Illnesses related to age include some types of dementia, like Alzheimer's disease, as well as sensory disorders that affect sight and hearing. Read this article on how scientists are discovering how we can live longer and avoid age-related illnesses: www.guardian.co.uk/society/2006/mar/08/health.longtermcare.

Psychological changes

Effects on confidence and self-esteem

The life events that we experience up until old age can reduce or improve our confidence and self-esteem. For example, retirement can give people the freedom to travel, to relax or to be released from the ties of regular work. However, retirement can also take people away from social contact and financial security, so can be a worrying time and can have an impact on confidence and self-esteem.

The loss of a partner may mean having to learn new skills, such as cooking, gardening or managing finances. These new challenges may be embraced or it could be a time when confidence is low.

Ill health may also reduce self-confidence because it may cause isolation. Therefore, support from family and health and social services is paramount.

Effects of ageism

Older people can often be stereotyped as being 'past their best' and not able to contribute to society any longer. This may result in the older person believing this to be true and so conforming to society's expectation of them. Because faculties like hearing, sight and mobility have diminished, they may feel that they are not functioning well, or be seen not to be.

Ageism can lead to abuse in care establishments. Vulnerable older service users may be abused emotionally, physically and financially.

We should always try to learn from older service users. It can be easy to overlook the fact that they may once have had important careers, have taken part in war actions or have brought up a family.

Ageism is a form of discrimination and brings with it all the effects of discrimination that you will have studied in Unit 2.

Theories of ageing

Activity theory

This theory states that if people keep actively involved with others in a social network, they will be more satisfied with their life. Being an active member of society maintains mental and physical health. According to Havighurst (1963), 'In its latest projections the Office of National Statistics indicates that nearly a third of the labour force will be over 50 by 2020. Businesses increasingly need to recognise the benefits of age diversity in the workplace.' (Source: www.dti.gov.uk/files/file29239.pdf)

Criticisms of activity theory

Some individuals prefer to live alone and be independent. Not everyone wants to be active. Not everyone is able to participate in a social network. Those with dementia or Alzheimer's disease may have difficulty in maintaining social contacts. People with limited mobility may not be able to go out of the house and those on limited income may not be able to afford to take part in activities.

Disengagement theory

In the early 1960s, Cumming and Henry described disengagement theory. They said that social structures encourage older people to withdraw from society so that younger people may take their place. An example is the decline in family size and the break-up of families, which leads to more isolation,

Activity 19

Interview an older person about their social network. Remember to maintain confidentiality when presenting your findings. Change names and any details that might identify them. You need to obtain their consent to use the anonymous information.

You should be sensitive about asking questions. A good way to interview someone is to start with 'Tell me about …'. Ask open questions such as, 'How has that affected you?'.

The following interview schedule may be helpful, or you may prefer to make your own.

- Who is part of their social network?
- Do they go out to visit friends or do people come to visit them?
- Do they have a pet to talk to if they live alone?
- Do they live with family or friends, or do they live alone?
- What physical changes have they noticed about getting older?
- How have any of these physical changes affected how they live their lives?
- When do they meet people? Is it every day or not so often?
- How do they keep in touch with people? Do they telephone, email or write letters?

Compare your findings with others in your group. Are there any similarities? Are there any differences?

Table 4.7 Two theories of ageing

Activity theory	Disengagement theory
Maintains independence	Encourages dependency
Gives choice	Little choice
Values individuals	Devalues individuality and treats everyone the same

especially for older people, who may lose contact with grandchildren after a divorce or separation.

According to this theory, ageing is seen as a negative withdrawal from society. For many, this happens when they stop work. In the 1960s, many women did not work. At that time, according to this theory, their role in society finished when their husband died.

Criticisms of disengagement theory

Society and the nature of work have changed. Many retired older people play an active part in their community and may continue to work in a part-time job. Some stores have a good reputation as employers of older people. The old heavy industrial jobs where people, mostly men, were frequently injured no longer exist. Most people work in safe and clean environments, so that when they retire they are not 'worn out'.

The theory denies that individuals have a choice. Not every older person wants to stay at home and watch television. It also devalues older people. It does not acknowledge the wisdom some have. A company director who manages a company on Monday, then retires on Tuesday still has the same skills.

Demographic changes mean that there are fewer young people to take the place of those who retire. If everyone retired early, there would be increased cost to the government for benefits and pensions. People are living longer and staying healthy for longer. Those who retire at 60 may live until they are 80 and are not economically productive.

Since 1st October 2006, it has been illegal to discriminate on the grounds of age, so this theory, based on age discrimination, is technically illegal! Read more on the government website: www.dti.gov.uk/files/file29239.pdf.

Find more theories on ageing on the Geriatric Medicine website: www.gerimed.co.uk/sites/Gerimed/downloads/2004aug11.doc.

Activity 20

Which of the two theories described here fits your interviewee best? Are they active or disengaged?

Read the case study opposite and decide which theory best applies: activity or disengagement theory.

The UK Inquiry into Mental Health and Well-Being in Later Life reported in June 2006. You can download the executive summary from www.mhilli.org/documents/InquiryreportPromotingmentalhealthandwell-beinginlaterlife-ExecutiveSummary-andRecommendation.pdf. Table 4.8 outlines its recommendations.

Case Study

Mary is 82 years old. For the past 20 years, she has made weekly visits to her local bingo hall, where she meets up with friends. As well as the socialising benefits, she enjoys the game because, as she says, it 'keeps her brain ticking over'. Her friend of 50 years, Sue, recently celebrated a £300 win. She claims her success is down to her quick reflexes and the ability to play several bingo cards at once.

Did you know...

Bingo is good for you! Older people who go to bingo keep mentally active.

Activity 21

Which theory is reflected in the recommendations in Table 4.8 – older people should be active *or* older people should disengage?

What advice can you give an older person to help them become active in society?

Activity 22   P4   M2   D2

As part of your fact file/case study explain two theories of ageing (P4).

Discuss and link these theories with your chosen individual (M2).

Look at current health and social care provision and evaluate how well they meet the needs of these two contrasting theories (D2).

Table 4.8 Recommendations of the UK Inquiry into Mental Health and Well-Being in Later Life

who	no.	what
Local authorities	1	Establish 'Healthy Ageing' programmes, involving all relevant local authority departments, in partnership with other agencies.
	2	Identify funding for and support community-based projects that involve older people and benefit their mental health and well-being.
Government	3	Introduce a duty on public bodies to promote age equality by 2009.
	4	Ensure that the Commission for Equality and Human Rights tackles age discrimination as an early priority in its work programme.
	5	Ensure that the 2007 Comprehensive Spending Review takes into account the findings of this inquiry, and commit to setting a target date for ending pensioner poverty. Government should publish, by 2009, a timetable for achieving this and report on progress against milestones.
	6	Work to achieve consensus, both within government and with external stakeholders, on long-term pension arrangements.
Health departments	7	Ensure that active ageing programmes promote mental as well as physical health and well-being in their design, delivery and evaluation.
	8	Ensure that mental health promotion programmes include and provide for older people.
Education departments	9	Ensure that school programmes promote attitudes and behaviour that will lead to good mental health and well-being and healthy ageing.
Public bodies	10	Encourage work practices that support a healthy work–life balance for employees, as a contribution to long-term mental health and well-being.
	11	Abolish mandatory retirement ages and enable flexible retirement for older employees.
	12	Provide pre-retirement information and support for all employees.
Public bodies and businesses	13	Educate and train all staff who have direct contact with the public to value and respect older people.
Age Concern and the Mental Health Foundation	14	Work with other organisations, including the media, to improve public attitudes towards older people and promote a better understanding of mental health issues.
Voluntary organisations and local authorities	15	Encourage and support older people to take advantage of opportunities for meaningful activity, social interaction and physical activity, and provide information, advice and support to enable people to claim the benefits to which they are entitled.

Activity 23 P5 M3

As a conclusion to your fact file/case study, explain what physical and psychological changes may be associated with your chosen individual's ageing process (P5).

Discuss how these changes affect the self-esteem and self-confidence of your chosen individual (M3).

Summary

After working through this unit you should be able to describe physical, intellectual, emotional and social development through the life stages. You should also be able to describe the potential influences of five life factors on the development of individuals and describe the influences of two predictable and two unpredictable major life events on the development of the individual. You should understand and be able to describe two theories of ageing and describe physical and psychological changes due to the ageing process.

Assessment and grading criteria

In order to pass this unit, the evidence that the learner presents for assessment needs to demonstrate that they can meet all the learning outcomes for the unit. The assessment criteria for a pass grade describe the level of achievement required to pass this unit.

To achieve a pass grade the evidence must show that the learner is able to:	To achieve a merit grade the evidence must show that, in addition to the pass criteria, the learner is able to:	To achieve a distinction grade the evidence must show that, in addition to the pass and merit criteria, the learner is able to:
P1 describe physical, intellectual, emotional and social development for each of the life stages of an individual	**M1** discuss the nature–nurture debate in relation to the development of an individual	**D1** evaluate how nature and nurture may affect the physical, intellectual, emotional and social development of two stages of the development of an individual

To achieve a pass grade the evidence must show that the learner is able to:	To achieve a merit grade the evidence must show that, in addition to the pass criteria, the learner is able to:	To achieve a distinction grade the evidence must show that, in addition to the pass and merit criteria, the learner is able to:
P2 explain the potential effects of five different life factors on the development of an individual		
P3 explain the influences of two predictable and two unpredictable major life events on the development of an individual		
P4 explain two theories of ageing	**M2** discuss two major theories of ageing in relation to the development of the individual	**D2** evaluate the influence of two major theories of ageing on health and social care provision.
P5 explain the physical and psychological changes which may be associated with ageing.	**M3** discuss the effects on self-esteem and self-confidence of the physical changes associated with ageing.	

Resources

Beckett, C. (2002) *Human Growth and Development*, London: Sage Publications.

Havighurst, R.J. (1963) 'Successful ageing', in *Process of Ageing* (Williams, R.H., Tibbits,

C. and Donahue, W., eds), New York: Atherton, pp.299–320.

Meggitt, C. (2006) *Child Development: An Illustrated Guide*, Oxford: Heinemann.

Weblinks

www.communitycare.co.uk:
Community Care magazine

www.dh.gov.uk:
Department of Health

Introduction

This unit provides an understanding of the anatomy and physiology of human body systems. It begins with cellular structure and function and builds to a more detailed knowledge of the body systems involved in energy metabolism. It provides knowledge of homeostatic mechanisms involved in regulating bodily systems to maintain health. This unit will also teach you how to take vital measurements of health and how to recognise variations from the normal.

Anatomy is the structure or make-up of our body, and physiology is the function of our body. The human body is made up of various levels of structures. This unit will start with the low-level structure (i.e. cells), then progress towards the complex workings of body systems.

Learning outcomes:

On completion of this unit, you should:

1   Know the organisation of the human body

2   Understand the functioning of the body systems associated with energy metabolism

3   Understand how homeostatic mechanisms operate in the maintenance of an internal environment

4   Be able to interpret data obtained from monitoring routine activities with reference to the functioning of healthy body systems.

1 Know the organisation of the human body

The human body is made up of several different levels, starting from a very simple form, cells, and building to a much more complex arrangement of systems. These systems work together to maintain a homeostatic environment.

Key terms

Anatomy – the study of the body's structure and how each part relates to others.
Physiology – the study of how the body works and functions within the organs and alongside other structures.

Cells

Key term

Cytology – the study of cells.

All cells develop, change and function together as a specialised tissue. Whatever the specialisation, all cells have the same basic structure and general features. Cells are too small to be seen by the naked eye. Our bodies are made up of many different types of cells carrying out specialised functions. Examples are shown in the diagram below.

Cells that function together are called tissues; for example, the cells lining your digestive tract or your respiratory tract all work together and form tissue.

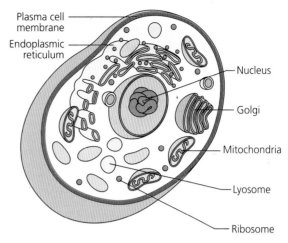

Plasma cell membrane
Endoplasmic reticulum
Nucleus
Golgi
Mitochondria
Lyosome
Ribosome

A basic human cell

Activity 1   P1

Draw and label a diagram of a basic human cell, showing the main functions of its structures in the key.

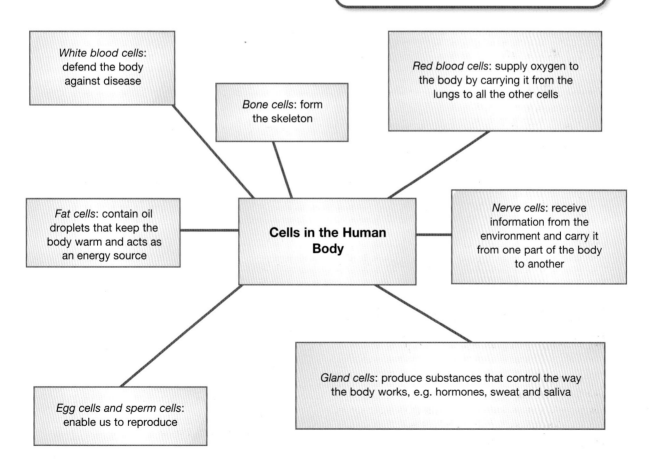

White blood cells: defend the body against disease

Bone cells: form the skeleton

Red blood cells: supply oxygen to the body by carrying it from the lungs to all the other cells

Fat cells: contain oil droplets that keep the body warm and acts as an energy source

Cells in the Human Body

Nerve cells: receive information from the environment and carry it from one part of the body to another

Egg cells and sperm cells: enable us to reproduce

Gland cells: produce substances that control the way the body works, e.g. hormones, sweat and saliva

Table 5.1 What is in a cell?

Part of cell	Description
Cell membrane	This is the skin of the cell. It gives the cell its shape and allows the entry and exit of materials.
Nucleus	This is the control centre of the cell. It is surrounded by a porous membrane, which allows for the exchange of proteins and nucleic acid. It is usually the largest part of the cell. Apart from red blood cells, which do not have a nucleus, cells are unable to survive and reproduce without this structure.
Cytoplasm	This is a gel-like fluid that contains a complex mixture of chemicals and nutrients that are the basic living materials for the cell.
Organelles	These are various parts of the cell with particular functions and are like miniature organs.
Mitochondria	These are sausage-shaped bodies called the 'power houses' of the cell. In these structures, energy is released during cell respiration.
Endoplasmic reticulum	This is a series of membranes continuous with the cell membrane and assists with the exchange of materials inside and outside the cell.
Golgi apparatus	These are flattened sacs which package proteins and deliver them to other organelles in the cell. They also produce lysosomes.
Lysosomes	These are spherical bodies which store enzymes and then release them to destroy old or damaged organelles. They can be called the 'suicide bags'.

Tissues

> ## Key term
>
> **Histology** – the study of tissues.

There are four main tissue types found in our body, with special functions. Read about the tissue types below and then complete Activity 2 on page 104.

Epithelial tissue

Simple epithelial tissue is: cuboidal, columnar, squamous, ciliated.

Compound epithelial tissue is: simple, keratinised.

Epithelial tissue is arranged in a single or multi-layered sheet and usually covers internal and external surfaces of the body. The name tells us what shape they are.

- Cuboidal – shaped like little cubes. Found in glands and in the lining of the kidney tubules as well as in the ducts of the glands.
- Columnar – rectangular in shape. Simple columnar epithelium can be ciliated or non-ciliated. The nuclei are elongated and are usually located near the base of the cells. Ciliated tissue is found in the female reproductive tract. Non-ciliated tissue is found in the uterus and digestive tract.
- Squamous – from the side, they look like a fried egg. Simple squamous epithelium is a common site for filtration. It is found in the lungs, walls of capillaries and inside blood and lymphatic vessels. They form the lining of cavities (such as the mouth), blood vessels, heart and lungs and make up the outer layers of the skin.
- Ciliated – these are simple columnar epithelial cells, but they have fine hair-like outgrowths, cilia, on their free surfaces. These cilia wave in certain directions and are found in air passages, like the nose, and in the uterus and Fallopian tubes.

Compound or stratified epitheliums are present in body linings where they have to withstand wear and tear. The top cells are flat and scaly and they may be keratinised. Skin is an example of dry, keratinised, stratified epithelium. The lining of the mouth cavity is an example of an un-keratinised, stratified epithelium.

> ### Key term
>
> **Keratinised** – the process by which keratin is deposited in cells and the cells become hardened (as in nails and hair).

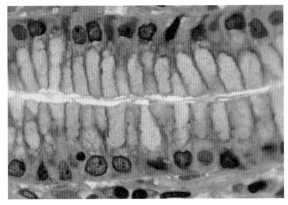

Epithelial tissue

Connective tissue

Types: blood, cartilage, bone, areolar, adipose.

Connective tissue is supporting; it contains fibres that are tough and non-elastic (e.g. cartilage, tendons, eyeball).

- Blood – blood is considered a connective tissue. It consists of cells suspended in a matrix of fluid, called plasma. It transports gasses such as oxygen and carbon dioxide and functions in clotting and immunity.
- Cartilage – cartilage is rigid and strong so it can provide support and protection. It also forms a structural model for developing bones. Cartilage has no direct blood supply so nutrients must enter by diffusion. It gives strength, toughness, flexibility and slight cushioning when depressed. Found in symphysis pubis, inter-vertebral discs and the knee.
- Bone – bone is the most rigid of connective tissues. Its hardness comes from mineral salts such as calcium phosphate and calcium carbonate. The primary cell of bone is the

osteocyte. There are two types of bone: (1) compact-hard and dense, which forms the outer layer of bone, and (2) cancellous – sponge-like structures, which are found inside most bones.

- Areolar – this is a loose, moist tissue, with irregular fibre arrangement. Found in the dermis of the skin, superficial fascia, between muscles and around organs, it provides strength, elasticity and support.
- Adipose – adipose connective tissue consists of cells containing lipid (fat) called adipocytes. The lipid is used to store energy to be used by the body if needed. Adipose tissue is also found around some organs and joints. It forms a cushion for shock absorption. Adipose tissue also insulates the body.

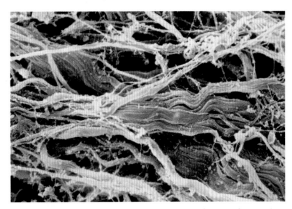

Connective tissue

Muscle tissue

Types: striated, non-striated, cardiac.

- Striated (voluntary) – under control of the brain (e.g. muscles). Skeletal muscle is striated. The striations are caused by the density of overlapping protein filaments, giving it a stripped appearance. Skeletal muscle is usually under voluntary control.
- Non-striated (involuntary): under hormone and nervous control (e.g. muscles in the gut). Smooth muscle is not striated because the protein filaments are not as dense as in cardiac and skeletal muscle. Smooth muscle is found in organs such as in the gastrointestinal system and the arteries. Smooth muscle is usually under involuntary control
- Cardiac – found in the heart. Cardiac muscle is also striated but has a unique structure

called an intercalated disk. The disks are special intercellular junctions that allow electrochemical impulses to be conveyed across the tissue.

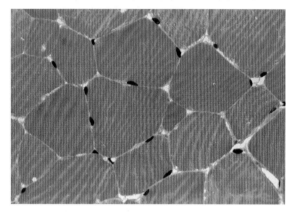

Muscle tissue

Nervous tissue

Nervous tissue consists of neurons that form the nervous system. Their function is to rapidly regulate and integrate the activities of the different parts of the body. They can be found in the brain, spinal cord and nerves.

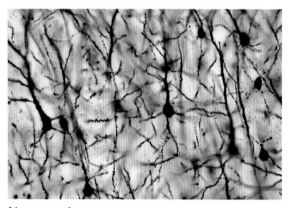

Nervous tissue

There are two kinds of cells:

- nerve cells/neurons – conducting units of the system
- neurolgia – special connecting and supporting cells.

Activity 2   P2

This activity will give you evidence to complete P2 of your assignment. You need to produce this information individually and formulate a short presentation for your colleagues. You may want to produce handouts.

When listening to your colleagues' presentations, you need to take notes about websites and books they have used to help you with your work.

Your presentation should include:

- name of tissue type
- an outline of its structure/inclusion of a picture
- an outline of where the tissue can be found
- an outline of the role of the tissue in the body.

Body organs

Tissues can be grouped together to form larger structures called organs. So a group of tissues can work together to carry out a particular function (e.g. the eye, the heart, the liver). Organs have specific functions and distinctive shapes.

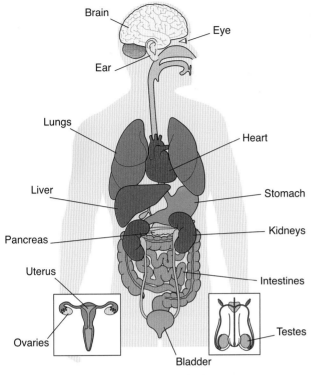

Brain
Eye
Ear
Lungs
Heart
Liver
Stomach
Pancreas
Kidneys
Uterus
Intestines
Ovaries
Testes
Bladder

The organs of the human body

Systems

Many organs in the body work together to perform a particular function. For example, the kidneys, ureters, bladder and urethra work together in the renal system to filter the blood and excrete urine.

Structure and main function of body systems

The cardiovascular system

The cardiovascular system consists of the heart, blood vessels and blood.

The main function of this system is to transport oxygen and vital nutrients to the body cells and remove carbon dioxide and waste products from the body cells by means of an intricate network of vessels, which is controlled by the major organ, the heart. (This system is discussed in depth on pages 113 and 114.)

Activity 3

As a class, divide into small groups, each taking one of the following organs:

- Heart
- Lungs
- Brain
- Stomach
- Liver
- Pancreas
- Ovaries/testes
- Duodenum
- Ileum
- Colon
- Kidney
- Bladder
- Uterus
- Skin.

Each group should draw the organ, label it and give a brief description of its function.

On a large piece of paper with a gingerbread person as an outline, place your organ and description in its correct location. Display this in your classroom to help you with this unit.

The following weblink will help with the structure and functions of human body organs: www.bbc.co.uk/science/humanbody. Follow the interactive body link and play the organs game.

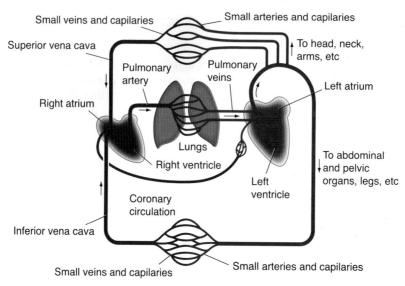

The cardiovascular system

The respiratory system

This system consists of the nose, larynx, trachea, bronchi and two lungs, which contain bronchioles and alveoli. Also included in this system are the muscles that assist with the breathing mechanism: the diaphragm, and the intercostal muscles, which are attached to the ribs.

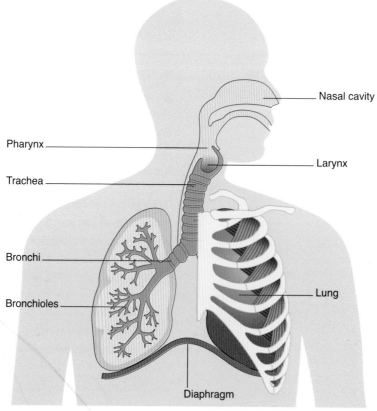

The respiratory system

The main function of the respiratory system is to supply the body with oxygen from inhaled air and remove carbon dioxide by exhaling air. (This system is discussed in depth on page 117.)

The digestive system

This system consists of the alimentary canal, which begins at the mouth and ends at the anus. The organs in the alimentary canal are the mouth, pharynx, oesophagus, small intestine (duodenum and ileum) and large intestine (colon, rectum and anus). Other organs involved in the digestive tract are teeth and tongue, salivary glands, pancreas, liver and gall bladder.

The main function of the digestive system is to physically and chemically break down large molecules of food to small, simple substances that can be absorbed and used in the body. It also removes waste products. (This system is discussed in depth on page 119.)

The renal system

The renal system, sometimes called the urinary system, consists of two kidneys, two ureters, the bladder and urethra.

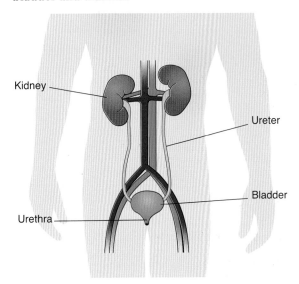

The renal system

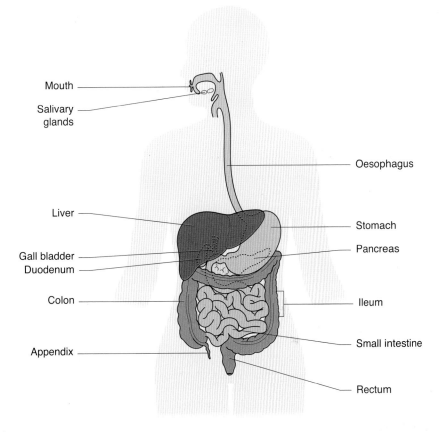

The digestive system

The main function of this system is regulation of salt and fluid balance in the body. The kidneys act as filters for the blood, ensuring important nutrients like protein and glucose remain in the bloodstream and unwanted or excess products like urea, salt and water are excreted. This is a complex and selective process and is assisted by hormones that regulate salt and water levels – depending on the body's needs, more or less urine is produced. After the blood is filtered in the kidneys, the fluid travels down the ureters to the bladder where urine is stored. It is then eliminated from the body via the urethra.

The nervous system

The nervous system consists of the peripheral nervous system and the central nervous system.

The peripheral nervous system includes sensory organs like the skin, ears, eyes nose and tongue These organs receive messages from our environment, which are then relayed to the central nervous system: the spinal cord and brain. Messages are interpreted and passed back to the peripheral nervous system where motor nerves carry information to muscles and glands to effect change within the body system.

The main function of the nervous system is to receive, interpret and make appropriate responses to the environment around us.

The endocrine system

The endocrine system consists of a collection of ductless glands scattered over the body that secrete hormones. This controls how many internal organs work. The whole system is under the control of the hypothalamus and the pituitary gland in the brain. Together, they regulate hormone levels in the blood. Some hormones act quickly, like adrenaline; other hormones produce slow responses, like growth hormones.

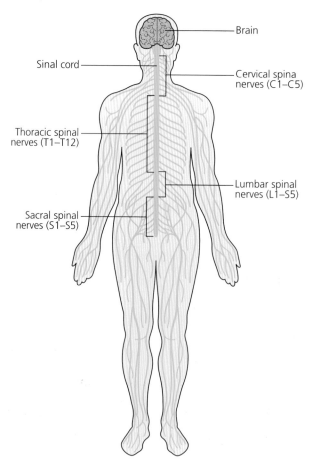

Brain

Sinal cord

Cervical spina nerves (C1–C5)

Thoracic spinal nerves (T1–T12)

Lumbar spinal nerves (L1–S5)

Sacral spinal nerves (S1–S5)

The nervous system

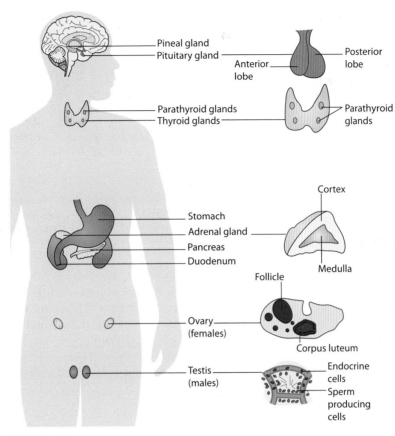

Hormones and their effects

Key term

Hormone – a chemical messenger that travels throughout the body but may affect only certain cells.

The female reproductive system

The female reproductive system consists of two ovaries, two Fallopian tubes, uterus, vagina, external genitals and two mammary glands.

An egg or ova is produced by the ovary and travels along the Fallopian tube where fertilisation can take place. Once fertilised by a sperm, the egg, now called a zygote, will embed into the wall of the uterus and be nourished for nine months. During birth, the baby will be pushed out of the uterus via the cervix and down the vagina. After birth, the mammary glands automatically

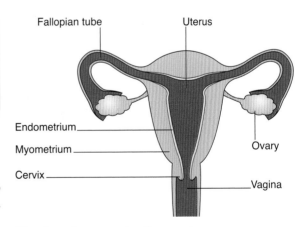

The female reproductive system

produce milk; when the baby suckles at the breast, milk is produced. If the ova is not fertilised, then the lining of the uterus is shed during menstruation.

The male reproductive system

The male reproductive system consists of two testicles, two vas deferens, prostate gland and penis.

The testes hang externally on the male body and produce the male hormone testosterone and store sperm. The penis consists of erectile tissue, which fills with blood during an erection. The sperm travels along the vas deferens past the prostate gland where it receives nourishment and fluid to form semen. It then travels down the urethra to be ejaculated during sexual intercourse.

The function of the female and male reproductive systems is to reproduce through the fertilisation of female ova by a male sperm. The female reproductive system is responsible for the nurture of the foetus and delivery and nourishment of the baby.

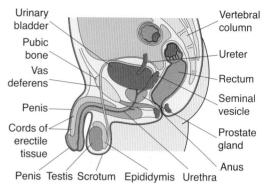

The male reproductive system

The lymphatic and immune systems

These two systems are responsible for protection of the body.

The lymphatic system consists of lymphatic nodes, ducts and lymph. There are also organs which contain lymphatic tissues and also assist in the protection of the body when it is damaged or in times of infection. These are the tonsils, adenoids, thymus gland, spleen and appendix.

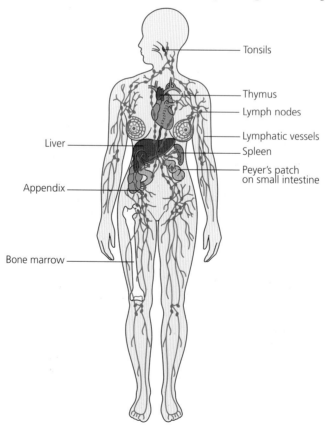

The lymphatic and immune systems

The main function of these two systems is to protect the body from infection, drain excess fluid from the tissues and transport dietary fats to the blood via lacteals. When an infection is detected in the body, an immune response takes place and lymphocytes and macrophages start to engulf and destroy the invaders, or produce antibodies to destroy the specific invader.

The musculo-skeletal system

The musculo-skeletal system consists of the bones of the skeleton, which have striated muscles attached to them in order for them to work.

The skeleton is made up of two parts: the axial skeleton (the skull and spinal column) and appendicular skeleton (the limbs and girdles, which attach to the axial skeleton). The function of the skeleton is to give protection to vital organs and provide a framework for the body. The point where two bones meet is called a joint; there are a variety of joints in our body to give different ranges of movement.

Muscles work in pairs to cause movement. They always pull in one direction so an opposite muscle is required to return the muscles to its original position. You can read more about striated muscles on page 103.

Activity 4

Design a booklet that contains an outline of all the main body systems. Include a picture for each system and a short paragraph to explain what each system contains and its main functions. Your booklet should consist of eleven systems (including the two reproductive systems).

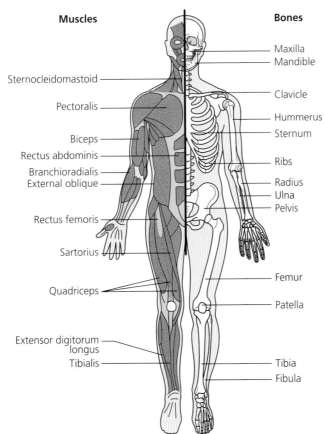

The musculo-skeletal system

Some of our body systems are inter-related – that is, they cannot function without each other. For example, during exercise, the respiratory system requires more oxygen, so the cardiovascular system works harder to supply this demand. All systems work together to make up an organism (i.e. the living human being). Recap your learning with the next activity.

Activity 5

Fill in the gaps with words from the table below to complete the passage about cells, tissues, organs and systems.

specialised	alive	impulses	blood
blood vessels	group	membrane	nerves
muscle	size	structure	shape
nucleus	bone	heart	cells

Cells

There is no such thing as a typical plant or animal cell because they vary a great deal in their _____ and _____ depending on their function. All cells have a cell _____, which is a thin wall enclosing cytoplasm; this keeps the cell _____. Most cells have a _____. This regulates chemical changes and determines what type of cell it will be. When the cells have finished dividing and growing they become _____. This means they do one particular job and have a distinctive shape.

Tissues

A tissue, such as _____, _____ or _____, is made up of hundreds of _____ of a few types. The cells of each type have similar structure and functions so the tissue then has a particular function, e.g. nerve cells conduct _____.

Organs

Organs consist of several tissues grouped together to make a _____ with a special function, e.g. the stomach is an organ that contains tissues made from epithelial cells, gland cells, muscles cells and nerve cells.

System

A system refers to a _____ of organs whose functions are closely related, e.g. the _____, _____ and _____ make up the circulatory system, while the brain, spinal cord and nerves make up the nervous system.

Answers are provided at the end of this unit.

2 Understand the functioning of the body systems associated with energy metabolism

Energy laws

Energy is required in order to perform actions. Nothing happens without energy. To enable stored energy to work, it has to be transferred or changed into a different form. This process requires work and this also involves some wastage.

Energy is never created or destroyed; it is just transferred from one form to another. This is the 'principle of conservation of energy'. For example, a car engine uses chemical energy (fuel) to make the car move – this is called kinetic energy. So if something takes energy in, it also gives energy out.

Different forms of energy include the following:

- magnetic
- kinetic (moving objects)
- electrical
- heat
- sound
- light
- gravitational
- chemical
- elastic potential
- nuclear.

The role of energy in our body

Energy is needed for our body to function. It is required for molecules to move in and out of the cells, for breaking down large molecules and also for building new molecules.

The breakdown of large, complex molecules to a simple form to release energy is called catabolism. An example is when glucose is used in a cell to release energy. The opposite reaction is called anabolism and is when energy is used to build complex structures from simple cells. For example, tissue growth and repair.

> ### Key term
>
> **Metabolism** – a continual process of chemical changes in cells which allows them to grow and function. It involves constant building of complex molecules (anabolism) and breaking them down (catabolism). These processes often release energy. The speed at which these reactions take place is called the metabolic rate.

Energy comes from sugars and fats broken down. The cardiovascular, respiratory and digestive systems are all responsible for energy transfer.

The cardiovascular system

The heart provides the power to pump the blood around the body through the blood vessels. The blood is the vehicle by which the circulatory system conveys oxygen, nutrients, hormones and other substances to the tissues, carbon dioxide to the lungs and waste products to the kidneys.

The cardiovascular system is responsible for transporting oxygenated blood around the body to the cells and collecting de-oxygenated blood ready for excretion from the cells.

The cardiovascular system consists of:

- the heart
- blood
- blood vessels.

The heart

The heart is located between the lungs, slightly to the left in the upper chest (thorax) area. The heart is the centre of the cardiovascular system and beats more than 100,000 times a day to pump blood through the vessels.

The wall of the heart is divided into:

- the epicardium – external thin layer
- the myocardium – middle layer; specialised cardiac muscle makes the heart contract
- the endocardium – inner layer; covers the valves and tendons.

The heart is divided into four chambers and is a double pump. Two upper chambers are called atriums. Two lower chambers are called ventricles.

The right and left sides of the heart are separated by the septum, a solid wall which prevents the mix of venous and arterial blood.

The flow of de-oxygenated blood from the right ventricle to the lungs and return of oxygenated blood from the lungs to the left atrium is called pulmonary circulation (it goes to the lungs and back again).

The flow of oxygenated blood from the left ventricle via the aorta to the body and return of de-oxygenated blood to the right atrium is called systemic circulation (it goes to the organs and back again).

How blood flows through the heart

Oxygenated blood from the lungs returns to the heart via the pulmonary vein and enters the left atrium. Blood passes through the bicuspid valve into the ventricle. Blood is forced out of the aorta (main artery), which carries the oxygenated blood to the rest of the body.

De-oxygenated blood returns from the body to the right atrium via the largest veins of the body, the superior and inferior vena cava. The blood is then squeezed through the tricuspid valve into the right ventricle. Blood is forced through the pulmonary artery, which carries the de-oxygenated blood to the lungs.

Follow the diagram below and use the arrows to trace the path of oxygenated blood from the lungs, ending with the return of de-oxygenated blood from the body.

The circulatory system

The following diagram illustrates arterial and venous circulation of oxygenated and de-oxygenated blood.

Arteries usually carry oxygen-rich blood away from the heart ('a' for 'arteries' = away) and veins carry de-oxygenated blood back to the heart. Which artery and which vein does this rule not apply to and why?

Vessels

There are three types of vessels in the body:

- arteries
- veins
- capillaries.

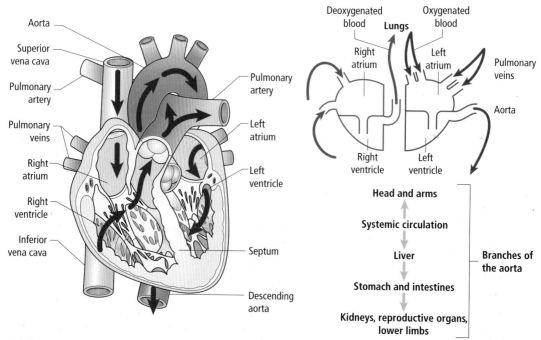

Blood flow through the heart

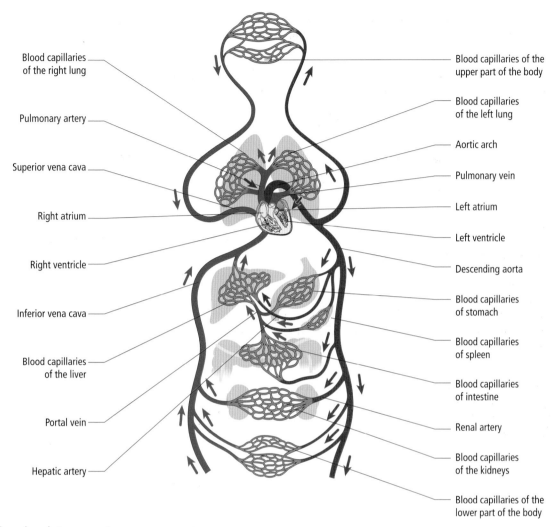

The circulatory system

Blood capillaries of the right lung

Pulmonary artery

Superior vena cava

Right atrium

Right ventricle

Inferior vena cava

Blood capillaries of the liver

Portal vein

Hepatic artery

Blood capillaries of the upper part of the body

Blood capillaries of the left lung

Aortic arch

Pulmonary vein

Left atrium

Left ventricle

Descending aorta

Blood capillaries of stomach

Blood capillaries of spleen

Blood capillaries of intestine

Renal artery

Blood capillaries of the kidneys

Blood capillaries of the lower part of the body

Arteries

Arteries have the ability to contract and must be elastic to expand under the high pressure at which blood is delivered into them from the heart. They then recoil between the beats of the heart. Arteries divide like the branches of a tree to form arterioles and then further divide into capillaries. This allows the high pressure of the blood to decrease and be delivered effectively without damage to organs, tissues and cells.

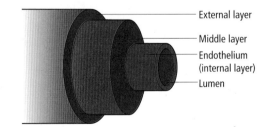

External layer

Middle layer

Endothelium (internal layer)

Lumen

Arteries carry blood away from the heart

Veins

In veins, the blood is under less pressure so the walls are much thinner. Because the blood travels more slowly and usually against gravity (uphill), veins contain valves to prevent backflow.

A collapsed valve is a varicose vein. Veins like arteries divide into smaller vessels called venules and then into capillaries.

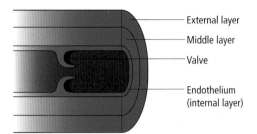

External layer

Middle layer

Valve

Endothelium (internal layer)

Veins carry blood towards the heart

Capillaries

Capillaries are thin-walled vessels which consist of a single layer of cells and are semi-permeable. This allows oxygen, vitamins, minerals and water to be exchanged into the tissues to nourish the cells. Carbon dioxide and water then pass out of the cells to be excreted. This is capillary exchange. Capillaries form a large network of blood vessels all over the body. The more metabolic activity in the tissue or organ, the greater the number of capillaries supplying it.

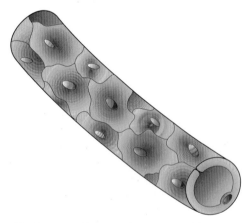

Capillaries are the smallest vessels

Table 5.2 Differences between arteries and veins

Arteries	Veins
Carry blood away from the heart	Carry blood towards the heart
Carry oxygenated blood	Carry de-oxygenated blood
Blood flows rapidly	Blood flows slowly
Blood flows under high pressure	Blood flows under low pressure
Blood flows in pulses	Blood flows by squeezing action
Walls are thick	Walls are thin
Valves absent	Valves present
Internal diameter small	Internal diameter large
Cross-section round	Cross-section oval

Function of blood

Tables 5.3 and 5.4 show what blood is composed of and how the individual components function. Blood has many important functions:

- transport of nutrients, gases, hormones and antibodies
- defence and protection from disease and infection with clotting factors and antibodies
- temperature control with the homeostatic mechanism for control of body temperature.

Table 5.3 Composition of blood

Formed Elements/Salts	
ERYTHROCYTES Red blood cells	• Carry oxygen • Made in the bone marrow • Die after 4 months
LEUCOCYTES White blood cells	• Fight infection • Made in the bone marrow • There is one white cell to every 600 red cells
PLATELETS	They help to clot the blood at wounds and so stop bleeding
Liquid Element	
PLASMA	Carries red blood cells/white blood cells/ nutrients

Oxygen	The blood transports oxygen from the lungs to the cells of the body.
Carbon dioxide	The blood transports carbon dioxide from the cells of the body to the lungs.
Waste products	The blood transports waste products from the cells to the kidneys, lungs and sweat glands.
Digested food	The blood transports nutrients from the digestive organ to the cells.
Hormones	The blood transports hormones from the endocrine glands to the cells.
Heat	The blood helps to regulate body temperature.
Clotting	The blood contains platelets to help it clot.

Table 5.4 Functions of blood

The respiratory system

The respiratory system consists of:

• mouth
• nose
• larynx (voice box)
• trachea
• bronchus (x2)
• bronchioles
• alveoli.

The functions of the respiratory system

The functions of the respiratory system are:

• to facilitate inspiration and expiration of air from the atmosphere into the lungs; this is called pulmonary ventilation

• to exchange gases between the lungs and the blood, i.e. oxygen and carbon dioxide; this is called external respiration (breathing)
• to exchange gases between blood and cells; this is called internal respiration (cell respiration or tissue respiration).

External respiration

Let us follow the path of inhaled (breathed-in) air. Air is inhaled through the nose and mouth and flows down the trachea. The trachea is a muscular tube at the top of which is the larynx or voice box. The air is warmed and particles of dust and mucus are trapped by ciliated epithelium which lines the respiratory tract.

Activity 6

Find out what happens to ciliated epithelium if you smoke. Still fancy a cigarette?

The trachea then divides into two, now called a bronchus or bronchi (plural). Then the tubes break into smaller tubes called bronchioles – this is similar to a tree trunk and its smaller branches. It is sometimes called the bronchial tree. At the end of these small tubes are grape-like structures which are one cell thick so as to allow oxygen to diffuse (cross over) into blood vessels which cover the outside of the alveoli. This is where external respiration takes place.

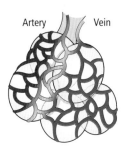

Alveoli

The lungs are different sizes. The left side is smaller to accommodate the heart. Looking at the lungs from the outside, the right side has three lobes and the left has two lobes.

The grape-like structure gives a large surface area to allow maximum exchange of gases. Oxygen diffuses into the bloodstream and then goes back to the heart to be circulated around the body. Carbon dioxide is exchanged from the blood circulation back into the alveoli and does a reverse journey through the respiratory system to be exhaled.

In the human lung, there are approximately 300 million alveoli – spaced out, this would cover a tennis court!

If you look at homeostatic control of breathing rate in this unit (page 126), you will be reminded that this process is mainly under involuntary control, with our diaphragm and intercostal muscles assisting us with inspiration (breathing in) and expiration (breathing out).

Internal respiration

This can be described as cell respiration. It is the process inside cells when glucose is used to produce energy. This requires oxygen and produces carbon dioxide as a result.

Activity 7

Label the diagram below with the correct names:

- mouth
- nose
- larynx (voice box)
- trachea
- bronchus (x2)
- bronchioles
- alveoli.

Draw the pathway of inspired and expired air.

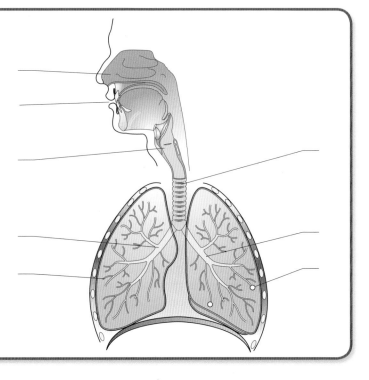

Cell respiration provides cells with energy to perform tasks, e.g. nerve cells are able to send electrical messages (impulses) and muscle cells are able to contract. Therefore, this energy is needed for the human being to live.

The energy needed for this type of respiration comes from food, mainly glucose, which is an end product of digestion from carbohydrates. Glucose is taken into the cell and, with oxygen, a metabolic process takes place whereby energy is released for the body and carbon dioxide and water are left as a waste product to be excreted into the blood system and eventually eliminated by the kidneys.

Cell or tissue respiration is different from external respiration. Cell respiration does not mean breathing.

The digestive system

The digestive system consists of the mouth, salivary glands, pharynx, oesophagus, stomach, duodenum, ileum, colon, liver and pancreas.

The process of digestion starts at the mouth and completes at the anus. This is the digestive tract or alimentary canal. Digestion is the breakdown of food to enable the body to absorb it into the bloodstream and then into the cells for energy. The breakdown of food is:

- mechanical – by teeth, tongue and gums
- chemical – by digestive enzymes.

It is only after chemical breakdown that absorption takes place.

The functions of the digestive system are:

- ingestion – taking food into the body
- digestion – breaking down the food

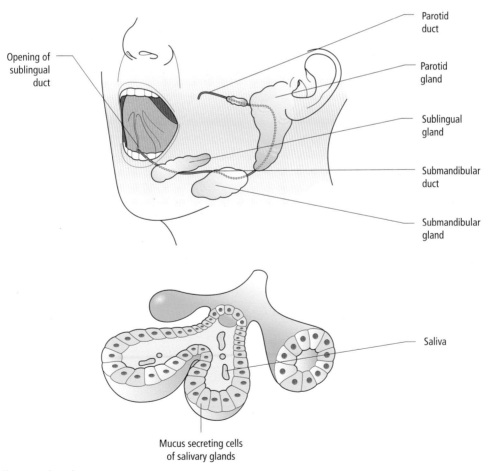

The salivary glands

Activity 8

Label the diagram of the digestive tract, giving a brief overview of the structure and function of each area. Use this link for further information: www.kidshealth.org/misc/movie/bodybasics/digestive_system.html.

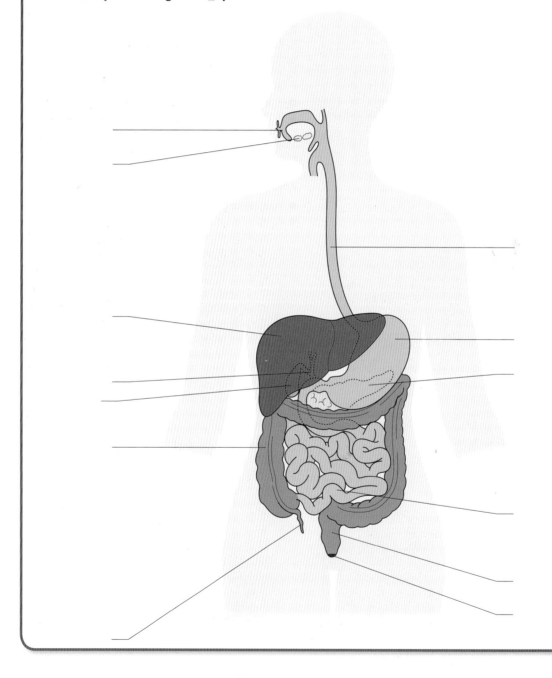

- absorption – small molecules are taken into the bloodstream
- assimilation – digested foods are used by the body
- egestion – removal of the undigested foods, waste products.

The process of digestion

Mouth

Your food starts its digestive journey in the mouth where mechanical breakdown of the food takes place. The food is chewed and broken into small pieces by the teeth and tongue. This is called mastication (chewing). The saliva causes the food to be mixed into a lump called a bolus.

The salivary glands secrete enzymes which chemically break down food. The enzyme amylase begins to chemically break down starches (in carbohydrates).

Pharynx

The food then passes through a muscular tube called the pharynx, which leads to the oesophagus. It passes down this tube by swallowing. At the same time, muscles in the larynx (see respiration) contract and a flap of skin called the epiglottis snaps shut so that food does not enter the lungs.

Oesophagus

This is a muscular tube leading to the stomach and food moves along by means of peristaltic waves.

Follow this weblink to see how peristalsis moves the food down the gut: http://health.howstuff-works.com/adam-200088.htm.

Peristalsis is explained by muscular movement like waves pushing the food. The gut muscles contract behind the bolus and relax in front of the bolus so that the food can move along the gut.

Stomach

The food then passes from the oesophagus through a muscular valve (cardiac valve) into the stomach. The stomach is the widest part of the alimentary canal and food can remain there for up to three hours. The stomach is a J-shaped organ and can be described as a strong muscular sac with many folds inside the lining called rugae. It

is here where the food is churned around by large muscles and digestive enzymes are secreted from gastric glands. The food is now in a semi-liquid form called chyme. The enzymes here are called protease (pepsin) and hydrochloric acid. The high acidity level kills most bacteria. The content of the food depends on how long it stays in the stomach:

- Fats – approximately six hours.
- Protein – approximately four hours.
- Carbohydrates – approximately two hours.
- Water – approximately 15 minutes.

Alcohol is absorbed immediately into the bloodstream from the stomach so its effects are immediate. The chyme then leaves the stomach via the pyloric valve into the small intestine.

Duodenum

This is the first part of the small intestine. It is a long, convoluted tube split into two parts – the jejunum and the ileum. Two large organs help with the digestion of food here: the liver and the pancreas. The liver connects to the duodenum with the bile duct. One of the liver's jobs is to make bile, which mainly digests fats. So as food containing fats enter the duodenum, bile is secreted (stored in the gall bladder under the liver) onto the food. This is the first point of fat digestion. Bile salts emulsify the fats (make them into a form where

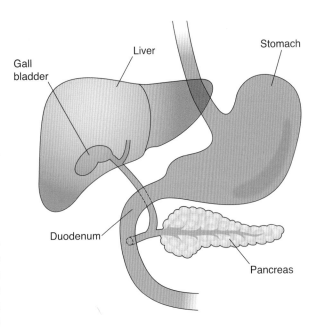

Liver, gall bladder and pancreas

they can be broken down further). They are now tiny fat globules.

The pancreas is a large, slim gland and joins the duodenum via the pancreatic duct.

The pancreas pours pancreatic juices via the pancreatic ducts into the duodenum containing the enzymes, pancreatic amylase, trypsin and lipase which further break down proteins and fats. The pancreas is also responsible for the control of blood sugar with the hormone insulin (explained in homeostasis). This hormone is secreted directly into the bloodstream, *not* the digestive tract.

As the chyme moves through the small intestine, many molecules are absorbed into the bloodstream. The small intestine has a very efficient method to assist this process. It is in the small intestine that most of the absorption takes place. The small intestine has an excellent blood supply. The inside of the small intestine has finger-like projections called villi, which increase the surface area of the gut. Inside each villi are lacteals which are connected to the lymphatic system and they are responsible for the absorption of fats. Eventually the digested fats pass back into the general blood circulation. The small intestine then leads to the large intestine through the ileocaecal valve.

The large intestine

The large intestine consists of the caecum, ascending colon, transverse colon, descending colon, sigmoid colon, rectum, anal canal and anus. It is wider than the small intestine and is approximately 1.5 metres long. It does not contain villi. The appendix is also contained in the large intestine but has no function in digestion.

The chyme continues into the large intestine and water absorption takes place, plus a little

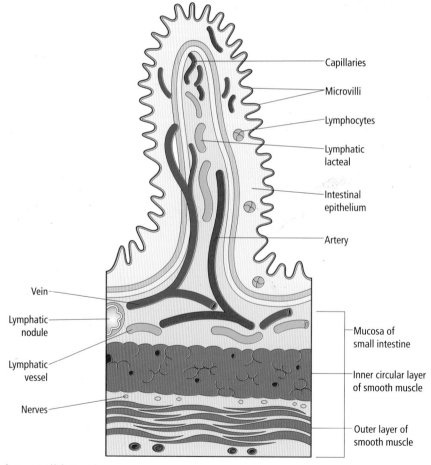

The villi of the small intestine

more absorption of nutrients. The large intestine secretes mucus that contains bacteria which ferment any remaining waste products, causing a release of gases. The waste products move through the large intestine (by peristalsis) towards the anal canal where they are expelled through the anus. This is under voluntary control in most adults.

Activity 9

Watch the digestive process following the weblink below. Click on the names of the digestive system to find out more about their workings: www. constipationadvice.co.uk/constipation/ digestive_system.html.

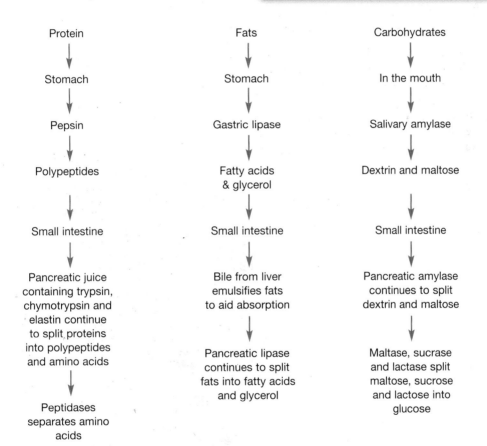

Protein → Stomach → Pepsin → Polypeptides → Small intestine → Pancreatic juice containing trypsin, chymotrypsin and elastin continue to split proteins into polypeptides and amino acids → Peptidases separates amino acids

Fats → Stomach → Gastric lipase → Fatty acids & glycerol → Small intestine → Bile from liver emulsifies fats to aid absorption → Pancreatic lipase continues to split fats into fatty acids and glycerol

Carbohydrates → In the mouth → Salivary amylase → Dextrin and maltose → Small intestine → Pancreatic amylase continues to split dextrin and maltose → Maltase, sucrase and lactase split maltose, sucrose and lactose into glucose

Major products of digestion

Activity 10 P4 M1 D1

In a written report, explain how two body system work together to metabolise energy in the body. For example, explain how the digestive system digests, absorbs and assimilates nutrients for use in cells and how the cardiovascular system transports these nutrients around the body, or how inspired oxygen is transported through the respiratory system and into the bloodstream and so transported around the body by the cardiovascular system (P4).

In your written report, discuss how energy is used in the body (M1).

To complete your report, analyse how two body systems interrelate to perform a named function – for example, analyse how gaseous exchange takes place during external respiration between the cardiovascular system and the respiratory system (D1).

3 Understand how homeostatic mechanisms operate in the maintenance of an internal environment

Homeostasis

Homeostasis is the mechanism in our bodies which regulates and maintains a stable and constant environment. The word homeostasis is taken from the Greek meaning homoios (same, like) and stasis (to stand still).

To help us understand homeostasis, imagine your body is your home and your homeostatic mechanism is your central heating system. Within the system is a thermostat, which regulates the

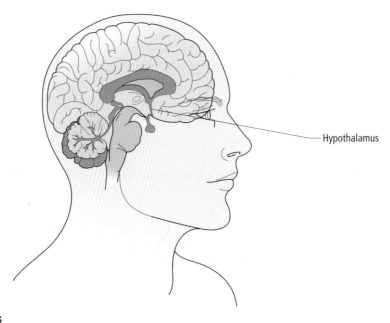

Hypothalamus

Hypothalamus

heating system, similar to the hypothalamus in our brain, which regulates our internal environment. This is the control centre.

Our bodies are continuously making adjustments to regulate normal body functions; fortunately these adjustments are done automatically, otherwise we would be very busy people, regulating our internal environment frequently. Homeostasis is controlled by the nervous system (autonomic) and the endocrine system (hormones).

Homeostasis is described as a 'negative feedback system'. This simply means that the system is able to take corrective action to maintain a constant environment. This is further explained in the diagram below.

Homeostasis is responsible for maintaining the constant level of many body functions. For example:

● heart rate
● breathing rate
● body temperature
● blood sugar levels.

Heart rate

Heart rate is under the control of the autonomic nervous system. However, it is also affected by hormones, so is under the control of the endocrine system. The system follows the principles of the negative feedback system. We do not need to tell our heart rate to increase or slow down. Exercise, fear and excitement all make our heart rate change.

The pacemaker in the heart is situated in the right atrium and is called the sino atrial node; this sends nerve impulses across the heart muscle to other nerves, which in turn stimulate other areas of the heart to beat rhythmically. The other nerve centres are called the atrioventricular node and the Bundle of His.

Go to www.youtube.com/watch?v=rguztY8aqpk and observe the animated picture of how nerve impulses stimulate the heart to beat. This is called the cardiac cycle. The cardiovascular centre in the brain (medulla) modifies the heartbeat according to the messages it is sent via the sympathetic and parasympathetic nervous system. The heart rate normally stays around 70 beats per minute.

If the heart rate needs to speed up, messages are sent along the sympathetic nervous system and the heart rate increases. If the heart rate then needs to slow down, messages are sent along the parasympathetic nervous system and a decrease is made. Detectors which send these messages back and forth are chemical receptors in the heart, blood and brain and constantly measure the acidity of the blood and the level of carbon

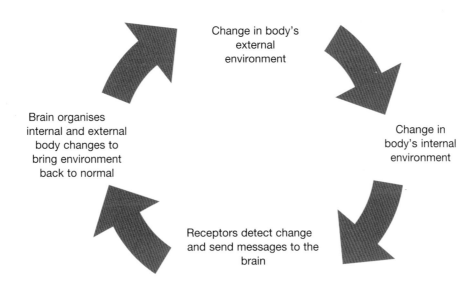

Negative feedback system

dioxide and oxygen. Adjustments are made to correct to the normal rate.

The hormone adrenaline is secreted from the adrenal glands on top of the kidneys in times of stress and exercise; this increases the heart rate and prepares our bodies for actions (i.e. fright, flight, fight).

Breathing rate

Respiration or breathing rate is controlled by nerve impulses from the respiratory centre in the brain (the medulla). It controls:

- the rhythm of breathing
- the depth of breathing
- the rate of breathing.

This centre also follows the principle of negative feedback and stimulates a change in respirations when chemo-receptors in the blood sense a decrease or increase in the amount of circulating carbon dioxide. For example, during exercise, when the receptors detect a high level of carbon dioxide in the bloodstream they send messages to the brain to increase and deepen the breathing rate in order to expel carbon dioxide and replenish oxygen. It does this by sending nerve impulses to the diaphragm (a layer of muscle below the abdominal cavity), which causes them to contract (reduce in size). The diaphragm then flattens and goes lower, thus increasing the space for the lungs to inflate so air is drawn into the lungs (inspiration). The nerve impulses also affect the intercostal muscles (between the ribs). These muscles contract and they lift the ribs up and out, again to allow air into the lungs. This is inhalation – breathing in.

Did you know...

Breathing rate is also under voluntary control – we can alter our breathing rate or hold our breath if we wish.

Activity 12

Place your hands on your ribs and take a deep breath in. Can you feel your ribs moving up and out? This can also be done automatically during exercise – you don't have to think to breathe faster when running! Explain what is happening to your diaphragm and your ribs.

Body temperature

Monitoring of body temperature is called thermoregulation. The body's core temperature is held close to 37 °C. Temperature detectors in the skin and internal organs monitor this and send messages to the hypothalamus in the brain to take corrective action when it rises or falls.

There are many ways in which we gain and lose heat. For example:

- radiation
- convection
- conduction
- evaporation.

Activity 11

Investigate the breathing mechanism which is controlled by homeostasis and draw a flowchart to explain what happens during exercise.

Activity 13

Visit the following website and discover descriptions and examples for the above: www.ergonomics4schools. com.

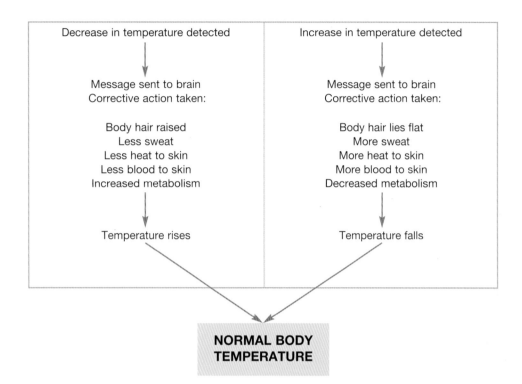

Decrease in temperature detected

↓

Message sent to brain
Corrective action taken:

Body hair raised
Less sweat
Less heat to skin
Less blood to skin
Increased metabolism

↓

Temperature rises

Increase in temperature detected

↓

Message sent to brain
Corrective action taken:

Body hair lies flat
More sweat
More heat to skin
More blood to skin
Decreased metabolism

↓

Temperature falls

NORMAL BODY TEMPERATURE

Homeostasis cannot take place without detectors and correctors. Look at the diagram above and the corrective action the body takes to maintain a constant body temperature.

There are also behavioural actions that we take in response to a rise or fall in body temperature. For example:

- have warm or cold drinks
- put on or take off clothing
- take exercise
- switch on a fan.

Activity 14

In pairs, consider the corrective action the body has taken to get the temperature back to normal and, with homeostasis in mind, explain why the corrective action has been taken. You may wish to put it in a table like the examples in Table 5.5.

Table 5.5 Reasons for corrective action

Corrective action (raised temperature)	Why?
Hair raised	To trap a layer of warm air to insulate the body
Corrective action (decrease in temperature)	**Why?**
Shivering	Small muscle movements generate heat

Facts to consider

Babies lose heat rapidly because they have a large body surface area in relation to the amount of circulating fluid. Their temperature control centre in the brain (hypothalamus) is immature so unable to work efficiently; therefore, adults assist in their temperature control with sufficient clothing and bedding. Babies also are unable to shiver and do not have sufficient fat layers to insulate them properly. Elderly people also find temperature control difficult. This could be due to being less mobile, eating less food and losing nerve sensations so that detectors and receptors work less efficiently.

When the body has an infection, the core temperature can be raised abnormally, thus upsetting the homeostatic control temporarily. In this case, the detectors now respond to 37 °C being a low temperature, so corrective action such as shivering begins and the body temperature is raised. This condition is known as a rigor.

Blood sugar levels

The control of blood sugar levels follows the same principle, the negative feedback loop. The control centre here is in the pancreas, where receptors monitor the concentration of glucose in the bloodstream and hormones control the correct balance. The hormones are responsible for the control of:

- insulin – lowers blood sugar levels
- glucagons – raises blood sugar levels.

Normal blood sugar level, if measured, is around 4–8 mmol/l (millimoles per litre). Study Table 5.6 to understand the body response:

- after a meal, i.e. high blood sugar level
- when hungry, i.e. low blood sugar level.

Table 5.6 Body response after a meal and when hungry

Eating	Hungry
Carbohydrates in food digested and changed to glucose	Low blood sugar level
Glucose high in blood	Pancreas produces the hormone glucagon
Pancreas produces insulin	Changes glycogen from the liver into glucose so it can be used in the body
Some glucose stored in liver as glycogen; some used by cells	Blood glucose level rises to normal
Blood sugar level decreases to normal	Pancreas stops producing glucagon

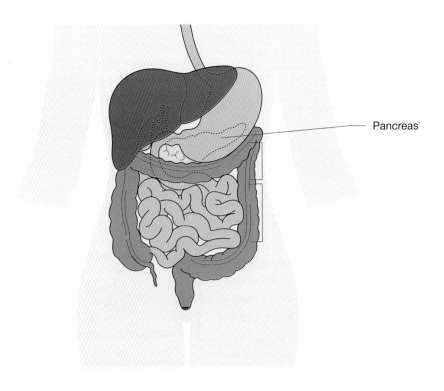

Pancreas

Pancreas

Activity 15

Case Study

After a 30-minute workout at the gym, Christopher is displaying the following signs:

- heavy breathing
- sweating
- thirst
- red, warm-looking skin
- raised heart rate.

With homeostatic mechanisms in mind, jot down why you think Christopher is showing these signs. Are they all normal?

4 Be able to interpret data obtained from monitoring routine activities with reference to the functioning of healthy body systems

Measurements

As a professional in a health and social care setting, it may be necessary for you to measure and record how the main body systems are functioning. To do this, you need to know:

- how to measure the system accurately
- what equipment to use and how to use it safely
- what the normal measurements are for that system
- how to record the measurement accurately.

Activity 16

Using flowcharts, explain the following homeostatic responses (P5):

- **control of heart rate**
- **control of breathing rate**
- **control of body temperature**
- **control of blood glucose levels.**

With these responses in mind, discuss in a piece of writing how the body's internal environment will change in response to exercise (M2).

To complete your piece of writing, evaluate the importance of homeostasis in the body. You could include what may happen if homeostasis is not achieved – for example, in diabetes, blood glucose levels are not controlled and the body requires help to manage the situation (D2).

Activity 17

In small groups, prepare an information leaflet for a care worker, giving them instructions on how to measure:

- **pulse rate**
- **breathing rate**
- **temperature.**

Include the following information with diagrams:

- **how to position the individual**
- **how to measure the system**
- **what the normal range is for an adult**
- **what equipment you may need.**

Pulse rate

The pulse is the rhythmical beat from the heart as the arteries expand and contract. It gives an idea of how well the cardiovascular system is working. A pulse can be felt anywhere in the body where an artery travels over a bone. The most common places for feeling a pulse are the wrist (radial pulse) and neck (carotid pulse).

The pulse is recorded in beats per minute (bpm). When taking a pulse rate, the beats should always be counted for a full minute. It is important to assess if the beat you are feeling is regular. Some medical conditions can affect the rhythm of the heartbeat. It is also important to note whether the beat is strong or weak. Abnormalities should always be noted and reported. In an adult, normal pulse rate is 60–80 bpm.

Breathing rate

Breathing is the process by which the body gains oxygen and expels carbon dioxide. Breathing rate is measured by watching the movement of the chest – one breath in (inspiration) and one breath out (expiration) are counted as one respiration. When measuring breathing rate, it should be counted for a full minute. Occasionally respirations may be shallow, so it may be necessary (with permission) to rest your hand lightly on the person's chest. Again, it is important to note and report the strength and rhythm of the individual's breathing rate. The normal respiration rate for an adult is 16–20 respirations per minute.

Temperature

The temperature of the body needs to be kept fairly stable as dramatic changes can seriously affect the body's systems. Body temperature monitors how effectively the homeostatic mechanisms are controlled in your body. Temperature is measured in °C.

There are different ways to measure a temperature, as well as different places on the body where temperature can be taken:

- tympanic thermometers – in the ear
- liquid crystal display (LCD) strip thermometers – on the forehead
- digital thermometers – in the mouth or under the arm.

Normal temperature for an adult is 36–37.2 °C.

There are many factors that may affect the reliability and validity of your measurements, as follows:

- age of service user
- faulty equipment
- misreading of temperature gauge
- lifestyle of service user
- miscounting of pulse/respirations
- carer not trained to use equipment properly
- anxiety of service user
- illness of service user
- recorded on the chart incorrectly
- cool/hot environment.

Equipment in care settings should be checked regularly and used according to instructions by people who have been trained.

Activity 18

In pairs, using the Harvard step test (see http://perennialperformance. com/selfassment/harvard.htm), measure heart rate, breathing rate and temperature at the following intervals (P6):

- before exercise
- one minute after exercise
- three minutes after exercise.

Record and present your findings and then comment on what factors may have affected your findings with reference to validity (M3).

Follow this weblink to download a suitable recording chart: www. trainingmasters.co.uk/media/gbu0/ prodlg/TPRchart.png.

Summary

After working through this unit, you should be able to describe the functions of the main cell components; the structure of the main tissues of the body and their roles in the functioning of two named body organs and describe the gross structure and main functions of all major body systems. You should also be able to describe the role of energy in the body and the physiology of three named body systems in relation to energy metabolism and describe the concept of homeostasis and the homeostatic mechanisms that regulate heart rate, breathing rate, body temperature and blood glucose levels.

Assessment and grading criteria

In order to pass this unit, the evidence that the learner presents for assessment needs to demonstrate that they can meet all the learning outcomes for the unit. The assessment criteria for a pass grade describe the level of achievement required to pass this unit.

To achieve a pass grade the evidence must show that the learner is able to:	To achieve a merit grade the evidence must show that, in addition to the pass criteria, the learner is able to:	To achieve a distinction grade the evidence must show that, in addition to the pass and merit criteria, the learner is able to:
P1 outline the functions of the main cell components		
P2 outline the structure of the main tissues of the body		
P3 outline the gross structure of all the main body systems		
P4 explain the physiology of two named body systems in relation to energy metabolism in the body	**M1** discuss the role of energy in the body	**D1** analyse how two body systems interrelate to perform a named function/functions

To achieve a pass grade the evidence must show that the learner is able to:	To achieve a merit grade the evidence must show that, in addition to the pass criteria, the learner is able to:	To achieve a distinction grade the evidence must show that, in addition to the pass and merit criteria, the learner is able to:
P5 explain the concept of homeostasis	M2 discuss the probable homeostatic responses to changes in the internal environment during exercise	**D2** evaluate the importance of homeostasis in maintaining the healthy functioning of the body.
P6 follow guidelines to interpret collected data for heart rate, breathing rate and temperature before and after a standard period of exercise.	**M3** present data collected before and after a standard period of exercise with reference to validity.	

Resources

Jenkins, M. (2000) *Human Physiology and Health*, London: Hodder and Stoughton.

Mader, S. (2004) *Understanding Human Anatomy and Physiology*, Blacklick, Ohio: McGraw Hill.

Minett, P., Wayne, D. and Rubenstein, D. (1989) *Human Form and Function*, London: Hyman.

Ward, J., Clarke, R.W. and Linden, R. (2005) *Physiology at a Glance*, Ames, IA: Wiley-Blackwell.

Weblinks

www.bbc.co.uk/science/humanbody:
BBC's human body and mind page
www.biologyguide.net:
Biology Guide

www.getbodysmart.com:
Get Body Smart
www.s-cool.co.uk/alevel/biology.html:
S-Cool Biology A-level revision

Activity 5 answer sheet

Cells

There is no such thing as a typical plant or animal cell because they vary a great deal in their **size** and **shape** depending on their function. All cells have a cell **membrane**, which is a thin wall enclosing cytoplasm; this keeps the cell **alive**. Most cells have a **nucleus**. This regulates chemical changes and determines what type of cell it will be.

When the cells have finished dividing and growing they become **specialised**. This means they do one particular job and have a distinctive shape.

Tissues

A tissue, such as bone, nerves or muscle, is made up of hundreds of cells of a few types. The cells of each type have similar structure and functions so the tissue then has a particular function, e.g. nerve cells conduct impulses.

Organs

Organs consist of several tissues grouped together to make a structure with a special function, e.g. the stomach is an organ that contains tissues made from epithelial cells, gland cells, muscle cells and nerve cells.

System

A system refers to a group of organs whose functions are closely related, e.g. the heart, blood vessels and blood make up the circulatory system, while the brain, spinal cord and nerves make up the nervous system.

6: Personal and Professional Development in Health and Social Care
48: Exploring Personal and Professional Development in Health and Social Care

Introduction

Units 6 and 48 bring together learning from other parts of the course. The focus of these units is on developing yourself as a person and developing your professional practice.

Unit 6 is the most important unit of the Level 3 BTEC Diploma or Extended Diploma in Health and Social Care because it is where you learn what it means to be professional. A minimum of 100 hours of work experience divided between at least three different placements is required for this unit.

This chapter also covers Unit 48 (Exploring Personal and Professional Development in Health and Social Care) as part of the Level 3 BTEC Certificate or the BTEC Subsidiary Diploma in Health and Social Care. For this unit, you are required to complete a minimum of 50 hours' work experience between two placements. You also have a little less to do, as you complete only three learning outcomes.

The first part of this chapter deals with both units, and then it will be clearly signposted where Unit 6 continues and where Unit 48 ends. It may sound complicated, but look at the learning outcomes over the page and it should become clearer.

This chapter also contains useful information for Unit 44 (Vocational Experience for Health and Social Care), Unit 17 (Working in the Social Care Sector) and Unit 18 (Working in the Health Care Sector). In each unit, you can also work towards Functional Skills ICT and English at Level 2, and personal, learning and thinking skills.

Learning outcomes:

If you are studying Unit 6, by the end of this unit, you will:

1 Understand the learning process

2 Be able to plan for and monitor own professional development

3 Be able to reflect on own development over time

4 Know service provision in the health or social care sectors.

If you are studying Unit 48, by the end of this unit, you will:

1 Understand the learning process

2 Be able to plan for and monitor own professional development

3 Be able to reflect on own development over time.

1 Understand the learning process

Key term

Learning – means more than just accumulating facts; it means acquiring information and gaining new skills that change your behaviour.

In order to survive, we have to learn. A newborn baby quickly learns how to breathe, cry and suck. Soon the baby learns to recognise the mother's face. A lot of learning happens before the child goes to school.

Theories of learning

Theories of learning explain how we learn and these theories are used in education. In this section, we examine Kolb's theory and a later theory developed by Honey and Mumford, but there are many more. If you are interested in how

we learn, find out more on websites such as the following:

- www.learningandteaching.info/learning
- www.psychology.org
- http://tip.psychology.org/styles.html

Kolb's experiential learning theory

Key term

Experiential learning – is learning by experience, not just learning from a book.

David Kolb's theory builds on three major theories of learning – those of Jung, Piaget and Rogers.

Kolb's theory focuses on learning by experience. He suggests we learn in the following stages:

- Concrete experience (CE) – we experience an event, such as getting sunburn.
- Reflective observation (RO) – we then reflect on the experience and consider why we got burned.

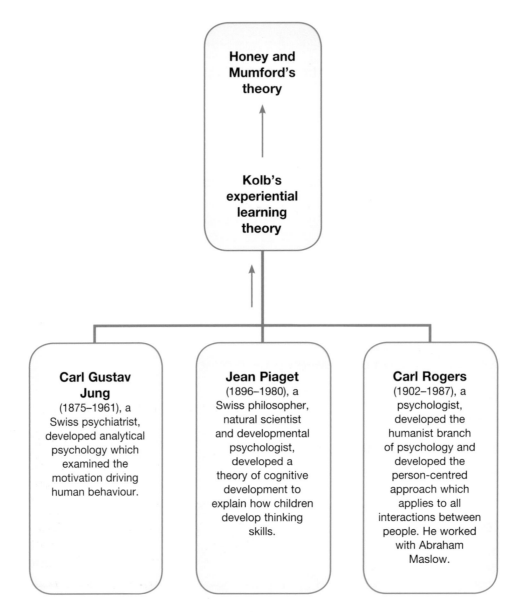

- Abstract conceptualisation (AC) – as a result of reflecting, we might develop the general idea that going in the sun without sun block is a bad idea.

- Active experimentation (AE) – next time we go in the sun, we use sun block to see whether that stops sunburn.

Kolb suggests that this is a spiral, so that when we have completed Stage 4 (active experimentation), we apply that to a new concrete experience. Thus, when we go on holiday to a hot country, we may take sun block and a hat. We can apply this learning spiral to anything.

Think of your work placement. Perhaps on the first day you had difficulty remembering people's names. You reflect on this and find a way of remembering, and then apply it next time you go to placement. When you next start a new placement, your memory of how you learned people's names last time will help you learn names quicker this time.

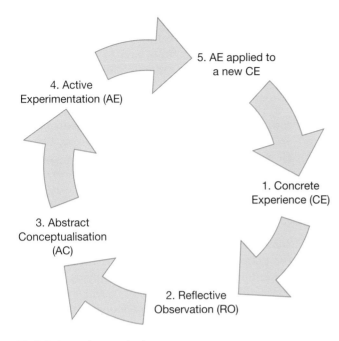

5. AE applied to a new CE

4. Active Experimentation (AE)

1. Concrete Experience (CE)

3. Abstract Conceptualisation (AC)

2. Reflective Observation (RO)

Kolb's learning spiral

Active experimentation at work

Key term

Learning styles – the preferred way or ways that people learn.

 Did you know...

The learning spiral describes preferred learning styles, but some people use more than one learning style.

Kolb used the idea of a learning spiral to explain learning styles. He suggested that:

● CE is involved with feeling

● AE is involved with doing

● AC is involved with thinking

● RO is involved with watching.

People are usually either watchers or doers. They either think logically or feel intuitively.

Table 6.1 shows Kolb's four learning styles.

Table 6.1 Kolb's four learning styles

	Doing (AE)	**Watching (RO)**
Feeling (CE)	Accommodating (CE/AE)	Diverging (CE/RO)
Thinking (AC)	Converging (AC/AE)	Assimilating (AC/RO)

You can tell a person's preferred learning style by watching how they deal with a situation. Assembling flat-pack furniture can be extremely stressful for some couples because they have different learning styles. *Diverging* learners prefer to watch rather than do. They learn by feeling then reflecting, using a diverging learning style (CE/RO). They would get a 'gut feeling' or 'intuition' for putting together a flat-pack wardrobe, take a long time to get started, and then reflect on why it did or did not work.

Assimilating learners prefer a concise, logical approach. They are thinkers rather than doers. They use the assimilating learning style (AC/RO). An assimilating learner would logically work out what the finished wardrobe should look like, think where each piece should go and think about what might happen if a piece went in the wrong way. They may spend time watching others before doing anything themselves.

Convergent thinkers are 'doers'. They use abstract conceptualisation and active experimentation (AC/AE). A convergent thinker might think what the wardrobe should look like, then try placing a few pieces together, moving them round until they fit.

Those with *accommodating* learning styles are 'hands on' and use 'gut instinct'. They use concrete experience and active experimentation (CE/AE). They might get a feel for it, put pieces together and then have to take them apart when they don't fit.

Honey and Mumford

Peter Honey and Alan Mumford developed Kolb's model further in the 1970s.

They described four learning styles:

- Activists – those who act rather than think.

- Reflectors – those who stand back and gather evidence.

- Theorists – people who like to think things through logically.

- Pragmatists – practical people, who like to get on with a job and make decisions quickly.

Activity 1   P1

In small groups, research theories of learning, and produce and present a poster to explain one learning theory.

Influences on learning

Whether you are a 'good learner' or a 'poor learner' is influenced by many factors. Previous learning and experiences shape our attitude to learning. If you are praised for something, you are more likely to try it again. If you try riding a bike, fall off and everyone laughs, you may never learn to ride a bike. However, if you fall off and someone gives you a few tips and encouragement, you are much more likely to get back on and try again. That way you learn. Next time you have to learn an active skill, you may think back to your success at a different skill – for example, riding a bike – and tackle the new skill with confidence.

The same thing happens when we learn to write assignments. If we are given helpful feedback, we are more likely to try again and improve. We are all different. Some people are naturally good at reading and writing. Some people have to work hard to learn how to spell and struggle to write assignments, but with encouragement everyone can get there.

Sometimes people have specific learning needs. For example, Dave is dyslexic. He often mixes up the letters 'b' and 'd' and finds copying from the board difficult. At school, he could explain his ideas but could never get them down on paper.

Colleges offer support for students with dyslexia. If you are not in college, you can get advice from Dyslexia Action (www.dyslexiaaction.org.uk) or the British Dyslexia Association (www.bdadyslexia.org.uk).

Some people struggle with reading and writing

Did you know...

One in ten people have dyslexia. Many people with dyslexia are of above-average intelligence. Famous people with dyslexia include Richard Branson and Bill Gates.

Specific learning needs might arise if someone is learning English. For example, Amina speaks Urdu as her first language. She speaks English only when outside the home. Her written English is weak, but her spoken English is not a problem. She may need extra support for English.

Formal learning or informal learning?

We never stop learning. From before we are born until we die, our brains are working. Have you ever been stuck with a problem, given up and gone to bed, and then the next morning the solution has just come to you? This is because our brain is programmed to think even when we are not consciously working on a problem.

Babies learn to speak their first language and to walk without any formal learning. No one ever sits a baby at a desk and instructs them in English grammar, yet by the time they are four or five they have worked it out for themselves. Ten years later, that same person struggles to learn a foreign language at school using formal learning methods. Babies learn informally. A baby learning to walk may drop onto his bottom several times, but each time he gets up and tries again. In this way, he learns to walk.

As we get older, we sometimes forget this way of learning. When we make a mistake or fail at the first attempt, we may give up and never learn a particular skill. Some people think they are no good at reading or writing because they made a few mistakes at first. Remember – a person who never made a mistake never made anything! Some people learn better through informal learning.

Formal learning is what we do at school or at college. Knowledge is broken into separate lessons, which we attend. We are assessed by a test, exam or assignment. This is useful when you need to gain a qualification, but most of our learning is informal.

Did you know...

Jamie Oliver learned to cook as a youngster in his mum and dad's pub restaurant. And, at the age of 13, Noel Gallagher received six months' probation for robbing a corner shop. While on probation, he taught himself to play the guitar.

Some factors that help you learn are listed below – this is a ten-point plan for success. How many of these factors apply to you?

1. Managing your time well – knowing when work is due in and when tests are set, and having a clear plan of when you are going to study.

2. Knowing your learning style and using techniques that work for you:
   ● Visual learners use colour and diagrams.
   ● Aural learners read their notes out to themselves.
   ● Kinaesthetic learners relate learning to a practical situation.

3. Having a place to study away from distractions, where you can leave your books out ready.

4. Having resources such as a textbook, computer and printer and knowing how to use them effectively.

5. Having a positive attitude and being self-disciplined (i.e. you do not need to be told to get on with your work).

6. Having clear aspirations and motivation – knowing where you want to be in five years' time and aiming for it.

7. Prioritising what is important and what is urgent.

8. Having reasonable health – no late nights, smoking or drinking.

9. Having sensible responsibilities – not working long hours at a job while trying to study.

10. Having secure relationships – being encouraged and supported by those close to you.

Skills for learning

Studying is a skill, just like riding a bike or swimming – anyone can learn these skills. But just like riding a bike, you need to practise to get good at it. There are lots of tips to help you improve your study technique. Think about:

● how you study
● when you study
● where you study.

Having resources and a place to study away from distractions are factors that can help you learn

Activity 2

Read through the section above and answer the following questions.

1. List the key influences on your personal learning processes in general.

2. List the key influences on your personal learning so far. Explain in a few sentences how these have influenced you – for good or ill. Give examples.

3. Evaluate how personal learning and development may influence others. To what extent may it benefit the professional, the service user and the employer?

You will need to come back to this activity and update it as you work though the unit.

Did you know...

If you spend ten minutes every day looking for a pen and paper, you could waste over an hour a week.

Here is a study tip that many people find useful. When you read a chapter or an article, follow this process, known as the SQ3R method.

● **S**urvey the material. Flick through, just as you would with a magazine.

● **Q**uestion – are there any pictures or cartoons? Does the material look interesting or boring? What do you know of the subject already? Do you really need to read the chapter?

If you do need to read the chapter, move on to the 3R stage.

● **R**ead the material with a pencil in your hand. If it is your own copy of the book or your own photocopy, write in the margin. Have a code, such as a star for an interesting example or a question mark for something you do not understand.

- **R**ecall the material. Close the book, take a clean piece of paper and jot down anything you can remember about what you read. Use pictures if it helps. You will not remember everything, but you should remember something.

- **R**eview the material. Open the book and, using a different coloured pen, add any notes you missed.

Do this a few times and you will find you remember ideas better.

When do you feel most awake, at night or in the morning? If you can leap out of bed at 6am, alert and ready to study, use that time. Many people study in the evening, but that is not always the best time. Your brain does not retain information if you are tired. In fact, our brains get tired after about 20 minutes and we need to vary activities.

In 60 minutes, you can:

- sort your notes – 5 minutes

- use the SQ3R method to make notes – 20 minutes

- word-process a draft assignment – 20 minutes

- write up your placement diary – 10 minutes

- and still have time to text a friend – 5 minutes!

Literacy, numeracy, and information and communication technology

These are essential skills in health and social care. Literacy matters because written communication is an important way for professionals to share information. Just imagine what would happen if a doctor could not spell and guessed at the spelling of a person's medication. The patient might get the wrong drug!

Spelling and grammar checkers help students, but proofreading is essential. Read this poem and spot the mistakes:

Eye halve a spelling chequer
It came with my pea sea
It plane lee marques four my revue
Miss steaks aye ken knot sea
Zar, J. H. (1992) Candidate for a Pullet Surprise

Information and communication technology is important. We use email for communication. Soon most patient records will be held on computer. The internet also helps professionals keep up to date through e-journals. You can also access a lot of information from the NHS website and it is expected that professionals know the latest information.

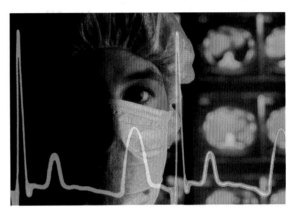

Information technology is important in the health and social care sectors

Did you know...

General practitioners already keep patient information on computer.

Numeracy matters because the ability to use numbers in a practical situation is vital in care work. For example, morphine is a strong drug used to relieve pain. The usual dose for an intra-muscular injection is 10 mg; 100 mg may kill you. Would you like to receive an injection from a nurse who could not tell the difference between 10 mg and 100 mg?

Did you know...

If you are worried about your English or mathematics skills, the following website has games and quizzes to help you learn: **www.bbc.co.uk/skillswise**.

Research skills

Anyone hoping to work in a health and social care profession must have a good understanding of research because practice is 'evidence based'. This means what you do as a professional is based on research findings.

Research skills include observation and questioning. You can read more about these skills in Unit 22 (Research Methodology for Health and Social Care).

The internet is a major research source, especially for students. However, it is important to make sure the website you use is reputable.

Did you know...

The Social Care Institute for Excellence (SCIE) website has up-to-date research articles about social care and social work: **www.scie.org.uk**.

Activity 3 P2

Find a piece of research from the SCIE website (www.scie.org.uk) and read it using the SQ3R method. Summarise the key points and explain it in your own words. Never cut and paste work from a website.

Using feedback and reflection

Feedback from service users, from colleagues and from your manager can help you improve your skills if you act on it.

Professionals in health or social care are expected to reflect on their practice. Donald Schön (1991) suggested that there are two types of reflection, as follows:

● Reflection in action – when a person is in the situation and thinks how they can improve that situation.

● Reflection on action – this is reflection after the event, when a person thinks back and says, 'If that happened again, I would do that differently'.

Both types of reflection are essential.

Support for learning

What do we mean by support? There is a Chinese saying: 'Give a man a fish and you feed him for a day. Teach a man to fish and you feed him for a lifetime.' Support is not doing the work for you; support is teaching you how to do the work.

So who can help when you are stuck and don't understand the work? I am sure you know the tutors who will take time to explain. Friends can also help. Sometimes a whole group finds a topic difficult. By talking to others in your group, your peers, you may find that no one understands referencing. If this is the case, your tutor will need to go over the topic again so you all understand.

Placement supervisors and mentors are there to help. Supervisors will explain if you do not understand what you have to do. Mentors offer a friendly ear and can suggest ideas for tackling a subject. Remember – no one can do the work for you.

Sometimes a formal meeting, such a case conference, may help you to understand a service user's background.

One of the best ways to learn is to develop self-awareness. In the case study opposite, Jenny developed self-awareness and, as a result, improved her practice. Sadly, not everyone is willing to listen to feedback. Some people say, 'I've done this job for years – you can't teach me anything!'. When you hear this, you know the person has little self-awareness. Only a person with a closed mind thinks they know it all. Not surprisingly, they never improve their practice. If you always do what you've always done, you'll always get what you've always got. Keep your ears open and make a note when you hear someone saying they know it all. You can even learn something from them – you can learn what type of thinking to avoid. Don't get stuck like they have!

How and where to access information and support on knowledge and best practice

Professionals must keep up to date. The Nursing and Midwifery Council Code of Conduct states that the nurse, midwife or specialist community public health nurse must maintain 'professional knowledge and competence' (www.nmc-uk.org).

The General Social Care Council Code of Conduct

Case Study

Jane, a staff nurse, was on duty in casualty one Saturday night. Mrs B was admitted but could not be seen for four hours because the doctor was busy with casualties from a road accident. Jane took time out to explain to Mrs B that the doctor would see her as soon as he could. She made Mrs B comfortable on the trolley and gave her an extra blanket. The doctor prescribed something for the pain. Mrs B thanked Jane.

Jane reflected on the situation and felt that she had done a good job that night. Even though she could not do any more for Mrs B, she had kept her informed of what was happening.

Contrast Jane's shift with Kylie's shift the next day:

Casualty was rather quiet. Miss C came in with severe pain in her eye. The eye was swollen, watering and very red. The receptionist told her to sit and wait her turn. Kylie, a staff nurse, was standing at the nurse station, talking to her friend about their night out the previous evening. Neither of them spoke to Miss C. Another woman arrived at casualty. She had been seen the previous day and had come for a check-up. She was laughing and chatting with her family and did not seem to be in any discomfort. She was seen by the doctor.

Two hours later, Miss C, still in pain, had not been seen. No one told her what was happening. Several people came, were seen by the doctors and left. Kylie and the receptionist were now browsing through the magazines in the waiting room and had not spoken to Miss C. After another hour, Miss C made an official complaint.

Did Kylie reflect in action? What do you think Kylie could have done differently?

Case Study

Jenny was shy and found it difficult to talk to people. At placement, she got on with the jobs but never spent time talking to service users or relatives. Jenny was horrified one day to be told that the service users and their visitors considered her to be stuck-up. As she thought about it, Jenny could see why they thought that. Whenever a relative arrived, she went to make a cup of tea for them, but never said 'Hello'. As Jenny developed self-awareness, she realised that she had to put herself in the other person's place. How would she feel if she arrived at a care home and the carer walked off without saying a word? Gradually, Jenny overcame her shyness and a year later she was voted friendliest carer by all the staff, residents and relatives.

2002 for Employers of Social Care Workers states that 'only people who have the appropriate knowledge and skills' may enter the workforce. The code of conduct for social care workers states they must 'be accountable for the quality of their work and take responsibility for maintaining and improving their knowledge and skills' (www.gscc.org.uk/Home).

Many professionals read online journals in order to keep up to date. Social workers may read *Community Care* (www.communitycare.co.uk).

Nurses may read *Nursing Standard* (http://nursing-standard.rcnpublishing.co.uk), the journal of the Royal College of Nursing or *Nursing Times* (www.nursingtimes.net).

Sector Skills represent employers and have websites such as that of the Children's Workforce Development Council (http://alltogetherbetter.cwdcouncil.org.uk/), Skills for Care (www.skillsforcare.org.uk) and Skills for Health (www.skillsforhealth.org.uk).

Did you know...

The Social Care Institute for Excellence has an excellent website and link to Social Care TV, an online channel for everyone involved in the social care and social work sector. See it at **www.scie.org.uk/socialcaretv**.

Learning opportunities

Formal versus informal

Earlier in this chapter, we looked at the differences between formal and informal learning. Now have a go at the activities below.

Learning opportunities occur everywhere. Important skills such as time management, problem solving, taking responsibility and communicating effectively can be learned just as well outside the classroom as inside.

2 Be able to plan for and monitor own professional development

At the start of the course, you may have known something of health and social care, you may have had some relevant skills and decided on a career. By the end of the course, you may still want the same career or you might have changed your mind. An occupational therapist at placement might inspire you to choose occupational therapy as a career. Speaking to a mental health nurse might lead you to consider that as a possible avenue. Part of learning is that you can change your mind.

Whether you decide to become a nurse, a social worker or opt for any of the other careers in this field, self-awareness and self-development are vital.

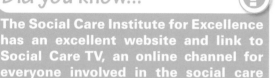

Activity 4 **M1**

List the things you learned informally before starting school. (You may have to ask a parent or an older brother or sister if you cannot remember.) Then make a separate list of the things you learned formally in class. Continue each list, adding the informal learning you acquired from friends as a teenager. Look forward and have a guess as to whether your future learning is likely to be mostly formal or informal.

What conclusions can you draw about the importance of formal versus

informal learning? You may like to use the categories given in the table below.

	Formal	Informal
Before starting school		
5–11 years		
12–19 years		
20–59 years		
60 years and above		

Activity 5 M1

Using the headings given in the table below, list three things you can learn from each situation that will help you develop as a person and as a professional worker in health and social care.

Placement	Independent studies	Life experience	Employment	Voluntary activities

Review at start of programme

In order to monitor development, it is important to look at where you started. A skills audit is a useful way of looking at where you are now. You can then decide where you want to be and plan how to get there.

If you are working on this section at the start of the course, you will be able to list your current skills and knowledge quite easily. If, however, you are partway through the course, you may have to remember what it was like when you started.

Activity 6 P2

Look at Table 6.2 on the next page, a skills review that Jay completed. Make your own blank table and fill in your details at the start of the course. Keep a copy so that you can add to it halfway through the course and then at the end to see how you have progressed.

Knowledge

What relevant formal learning have you had up to now? What informal learning? Kirsty's list is shown in the case study below.

Keep up to date with current issues. Watch the news on television. Read a newspaper, such as *The*

 Case Study

Kirsty's list
Formal learning:
First aid certificate
BTEC Level 2 Diploma in Health and Social Care
Informal learning:
Helped my gran when she came out of hospital, did her shopping.
Babysat my little sister when mum was at work.
Watched a television programme about drug addicts.
Volunteered to do a sponsored silence for Help the Heroes charity.
Read an article about a singer who was in an abusive relationship.

Guardian. You can do this online at www.guardian.co.uk. You may have to look a few words up at first, but you will soon be able to understand the issues and know what people are talking about.

Tips to develop your knowledge

- Use up-to-date journals and official websites.
- Make a list of theories, principles and concepts. Summarise each on an index card.

Table 6.2 Jay's skills review

Jay B	At the start	Halfway	At the end
Current knowledge	I've heard of the NHS but I don't know these new words like 'policy' and 'accountability'.	I've used the website www.dcsf.gov.uk/ everychildmatters to find out what the government is planning for young people. They want to get everyone aged 16–18 into education, training or employment.	People who work in health and social care must stand up for young people. I listen to the news and keep up with changes for young people in care. If I don't agree, I talk to my local MP.
Skills	My strengths are I'm friendly, I like people and I understand what it's like to get into trouble – someone in my family is on probation. My weak areas? I don't know.	My weak areas are writing assignments and getting the work in on time. My strengths are that I get good reports from placement and get on well with the rest of my group.	I've improved my time management skills and get all my assignments in on time, but I still don't enjoy writing. I really liked my last placement and I'm volunteering as a mentor for young people.
Practice	I've never done any care work.	I've learned to listen to people.	I run a weekly quiz at placement.
Values	I think everyone should be treated the same. We are all equal.	Treating everyone the same isn't being equal. Some people like to do things for themselves. Others cannot and do need help.	We should treat everyone with respect. I should ask what help they need before I make assumptions.
Beliefs	I believe asylum seekers should be sent back to their own country.	I met an asylum seeker when I went on placement. She had been raped in her own village and her father was killed trying to defend her. Perhaps not everyone should be sent back.	Every case is different and every person is different. We should not judge until we know the facts.
Career aspirations	I'm not sure what social workers do but I think I would like to be one. I've seen them on the television and it looks a good job. I don't know how to become a social worker.	I have to go to university to become a social worker. There is a code of conduct and a General Social Care Council. At my placement, I talked to a social worker about the job. I didn't realise they have to be on call at weekends.	Social work is stressful. I don't like a lot of stress. There is also a lot of paperwork, which I don't like. I can help young people if I become a youth worker. I can go to university and do that.

Table 6.2 Jay's skills review (continued)

Jay B	At the start	Halfway	At the end
Self-awareness	I know what I look like. Is that what it means?	My placement report said I was often late. I should get up earlier because I really enjoy it when I'm there.	I got a good report from placement because I took their advice and worked on my weak areas. I go to bed earlier so I can catch the early bus. They've even offered me a job when I finish my course!

Did you know...

If you are not sure what a word means, you can look it up in a dictionary or you can use the Tools, Language, Thesaurus dropdown menu in Word to find out what it means.

- Colour code them, so you have blue for principles, white for theories and yellow for concepts.

- Make mind maps so you have principles on one page, theories on another and concepts on a third page.

- Organise your file so you can find information quickly.

Where can I find out about careers?

- www.nhscareers.nhs.uk – this is a dedicated website where you can explore the range of NHS careers, such as speech and language therapy and art therapy, as well as nursing and midwifery careers.

- www.socialworkandcare.co.uk/socialwork – the Department of Health website for social work careers tells you about social work as a career.

Skills

Communication

Communication is the key skill that enables us to do our job. A healthcare worker who does not speak the language of the service user is limited in what they can do, so if you work with people with a hearing impairment, you may need to learn British Sign Language if that is their main language.

Most communication is non-verbal. People read visual clues and rely on instinct, even if you say the opposite, so if a service user asks you whether you smoke, be honest – your body language will tell the truth.

Working with others

Working with others is essential in care work. We work with service users, helping them to achieve a better quality of life. Professionals work together. A doctor prescribes medication, but relies on the nurse to give it. A care assistant may notice a side effect such as a rash and report it so the drug can be changed. Teamwork saves lives. There is no room for temper tantrums in care work.

Did you know...

Good carers get along with everyone, even people they don't like.

Technical skills

Technical skills range from using computers to craftwork. A social worker may help a child make a life storybook. A nurse sets up a heart monitor. An art therapist helps someone with depression express their feelings. Care work is varied. Be willing to learn new skills.

Research skills

Research skills are increasingly important, especially at university. You use secondary sources for your assignments, but may be less experienced with primary research and data handling. These skills develop as you study at a higher level. Computerised data-handling packages are used now at university, but you need to understand the data!

Personal skills

Personal skills are important in every job. A disorganised person may be creative but will not get very far if they miss deadlines. A professional must be organised in their work or service users suffer. A social worker who cannot find the notes for a service user's review is not doing the best for that service user. A service user who has a chaotic lifestyle will not put much faith in a social worker who is equally chaotic.

Personal skills are important in every job

Personal presentation

Personal presentation matters. A social worker dressed in a formal suit will not build up rapport with a young runaway, but might impress a panel of judges. Personal presentation should be suited to the situation, but no one respects a professional who is unkempt or uses bad language.

Practice

Care practice is based on values, sometimes called the value base of care. The aim of care practice is to empower service users, to give them choice

Did you know...

It takes about three seconds for people to make up their minds about someone, based on first impressions of appearance, dress, mannerisms and body language.

and to respect their rights and beliefs. This is done in a way that does not discriminate against people. When professionals work together, they must use these values to guide their interactions, so they must respect each other as professionals and cooperate with each other as part of a team.

A professional care worker must not impose their personal views on others, but must listen and put forward the views of service users, even if they do not share those views. A social worker who disapproves of drugs cannot discriminate against drug addicts. A nurse who does not believe in abortion cannot impose her views on a pregnant woman.

Person-centred care is at the heart of all care work. In a joint government statement, *Putting people first: a shared vision and commitment to the transformation of adult social care* (2007), the emphasis was firmly placed on empowering people and giving them 'a mainstream system focused on prevention, early intervention, enablement, and high quality personally tailored services. In the future, we want people to have maximum choice, control and power over the support services they receive.'

The standards expected of professionals are high. Case studies from the Nursing and Midwifery Council website illustrate what can go wrong when professional standards are lost. In the following cases (on page 149), both professionals had their names removed from the relevant register.

Legislation, codes of practice and policies guide what professionals do. Some legislation requires them to act, for example, in promoting equality. Some legislation requires them to maintain confidentiality. Codes of practice require them to put the individual service user or patient at the heart of what they do. All those who work in health and social care must be aware of their own responsibilities and limitations.

Case Studies

The Professional Conduct Committee considered the case of a community psychiatric nurse who faced one charge of having a sexual relationship with a patient (Ms A). The practitioner was present at the hearing and was represented by a solicitor. He admitted the charge and that it amounted to professional misconduct.

Nurse M was reported to the council for using abusive language towards vulnerable patients and for reporting for duty smelling of alcohol and in an unfit condition to work.

Career aspirations

There is a wide variety of careers in health and social care. The following websites explain some of the careers available:

- www.nhscareers.nhs.uk
- www.prospects.ac.uk
- http://bethedifference.cwdcouncil.org.uk

Plan for your own development

Action plans come in several forms. The simplest plan is a three-stage model. It asks the following questions:

- Where am I now?
- Where do I want to be?
- How do I get there?

Activity 7 | P2

What do you think? Should professionals be accountable for the care they give? What personal values are needed to support and promote good practice? Make a list.

Here are a few ideas to start you thinking:

- **Respect for others.**
- **Willingness to stand up for vulnerable people.**
- **A sense of duty towards those needing care.**

 ## Case Study

Rehan used the three-stage model to help with gaps in his current knowledge.
Here is his list:
- Where am I now? A bit lost! I don't understand these words:
  current
  contemporary
  values
  beliefs
  skills.
- Where do I want to be? I want to understand what people are talking about.
- How do I get there?

Values and beliefs

Personal values and beliefs are important in health and social care because our personal beliefs influence the way we act towards others. If someone is prejudiced, they will find it difficult to work in this sector because their values clash with the values underpinning health and social care delivery.

What suggestions can you make to help Rehan in the above case study?

Here are some ideas:

- Use a paper-based dictionary.
- Use the dictionary in Tools, Language, Thesaurus on Word.
- Ask the tutor.

● Make a list in your diary and learn a new word every day.

When Rehan looked up the meaning of 'current' and 'contemporary', he found that they mean the same thing – 'modern'. Don't be scared of words. If you see a new word, look it up, then you can use it!

This section looks at setting targets and goals, which you can develop. Targets focus on specific issues and provide a benchmark against which future development can be measured. Goals can be short term or long term. They should all be SMART (see the Did you know? box).

Did you know...

SMART stands for:
Specific
Measurable
Actionable
Relevant
Timed.

Table 6.3 Short and long-term goals.

	Unit 48	Unit 6
'Short term' means	up to three months	up to six months
'Long term' means	minimum of ten months	minimum of eighteen months

Please note the difference in meanings for Units 6 and 48.

Short-term targets are those that you can realistically achieve within three to six months. An example would be to improve your knowledge of policies and procedures within the workplace.

Goals can also be long term, which can take up to 18 months or longer. **Note:** if you are studying Unit 48 rather than Unit 6, your long-term goals will be a minimum of ten months.

An example of a long-term goal could be to develop effective communication skills with a variety of service users or learning a new skill, such as British Sign Language.

Your goals should be personal to you and relate to health and social care. These goals should be decided upon by looking at areas that you need to improve. Once you have decided your targets, consider how you are going to get there. Targets should be achievable within the time frame you have and the resources available. If your targets are too ambitious, you may become demotivated. If they are actionable and you complete them, this increases your sense of achievement. Targets should be specific – the goal should focus on a definite area, be exact and unambiguous.

You should consider the following:

● How will you know you have achieved your goals?

● Is the goal you have set relevant?

● Is it related to the area you are studying?

● Have you set yourself the right amount of time to achieve your goals? Consider whether you might need a bit more or a bit less time than you think.

Activity 8 P3

Ahmed wants to increase his knowledge of health and safety legislation. He has a work placement and also has the option of attending a health and safety one-day course. Set Ahmed some targets to achieve over three months that will meet his goal. Make sure they are SMART.

Consider personal goals

Personal goals should reflect what you need to develop.

Activity 9 P3

Look at your skills review and identify what you need to work on. Make an action plan based on what you need to achieve from your skills review. You may like to use a plan such as the one shown on page 152.

Monitor and evaluate plan in terms of own development

You need at least three goals. Once you have chosen them, monitor your progress regularly.

This ensures you are still on track and that you will achieve your targets. You could monitor your progress in a table format such as Table 6.4 on page 152.

Activity 10 P4 M2 D2

Look back at your action plan for P3 and how you have monitored the plan. Make sure you have evidence to show any progress you claim.

● How has the plan helped you develop so far?

● How far have you developed? You will need to produce evidence to support what you say.

You will need to return to your action plans and update them regularly until you have achieved your goals.

Table 6.4 Monitoring your development

Target	Date of meeting	Work done	Work still to do	Date of next meeting
1. To improve verbal communication in placement	20.09.2010	Identified weak areas. Attended first placement.	Talk to residents in lounge.	20.10.2010
	20.10.2010	Confident talking to residents on a one-to-one basis.	Speak louder so I can call the quiz questions.	20.11.2010
	20.11.2010	Confidently chat with residents on one-to-one basis and in small groups. Confidently call the quiz questions.	Get witness testimony to verify this.	16.12.2010

3 Be able to reflect on own development over time

Changes

If you regularly monitor your progress, you will meet your targets. You may even achieve targets sooner than you anticipated. However, if you find that you are getting behind, do something about it. You may need to change the targets as you reflect – you may start by thinking you need to develop verbal communication skills, but then realise you need to improve non-verbal communication too. Or you may enjoy activities and decide to learn about the role of activities coordinator at a care home. This then becomes a new goal.

Contexts

Different situations provide valuable evidence for your portfolio.

Work experience placement

Work experience placement is a compulsory element of your course. Here you put theory into practice – for example, you may know it is good practice to offer service users choice, such as what food to eat, what clothes to wear or a choice of activities. In placement, you have the chance to do this in practice. This helps you achieve your goals. Keep a record of the activities you undertake. This should be a reflective account, so you look back upon the situation and decide what your strengths and weaknesses are and where you need to develop.

Visits

Visits are part of your course. If you visit care settings, compare your own placement to the new care setting. Ask questions. Reflect on the visit and add evidence to your portfolio.

The study environment

The study environment can help you achieve. In lessons and during your own library research, make notes and re-read them. Reflect on how your study skills and time management develop over the course.

Life events

Life events can aid reflection and provide evidence in your portfolio. You might become a service user yourself and see life from a different viewpoint. This may then influence the way you interact with service users.

Other contexts, such as part-time work, give you a chance to look at working procedures, to develop team-working skills and to improve time management.

Professional development portfolio

During the course, you will assemble a wealth of evidence to include in your portfolio. Consider how you are going to present this information. It must be organised and easily accessible.

Your portfolio should include the following:

- Professional practice log book: complete a log showing attendance and reflection on your experiences.

- A clear structure: your portfolio should follow a logical order so evidence can be tracked easily.

- Indexing: this will help you and the assessor find the evidence needed.

- Authenticated records: these should include signed witness testimonies and progress reports from placement supervisors to show your developing knowledge, skills and practice over time. Include action plans to show your development and changing awareness of careers.

- Variety of contexts: reflecting on formal and informal learning in your different placements. Include reflections from your own experiences as a service user. Showing your knowledge and skills in a range of different settings provides much stronger evidence than reflecting just on one setting.

Relevant evidence

Use a variety of relevant evidence in your portfolio. An account of a holiday in Spain may not seem relevant, but if you broke your leg while on holiday, went to a Spanish hospital and then found no one spoke English, you would have a lot to reflect on about communication skills, which would be relevant.

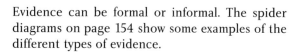

REMEMBER

Collect evidence as you go along. Don't leave it until the last month!

Evidence can be formal or informal. The spider diagrams on page 154 show some examples of the different types of evidence.

Types of formal evidence

Assessments show your understanding. If your target was to improve your knowledge of health and safety, then an assignment from the health and safety unit will show you have achieved this target.

Observations occur during classroom activities or in placement – for example, when presenting information to your class or communicating with service users in a care home.

Witness testimony evidence from the placement supervisor, a co-worker or a manager must be dated and signed. It should also say what activity you did. Service users may also give you feedback.

Placement reports may note your improved communication skills. The placement supervisor will speak to your tutor about your progress. If there is a specific goal you have set yourself, ask your tutor or placement supervisor to report on this. Feedback from tutors could relate to behaviour, such as punctuality, or to assignments.

Tutorial records provide evidence of achievement and progression towards goals. Your tutor may set you particular goals to reach, which may help you achieve your targets for this unit. Include certificates such as GCSEs, first aid, food hygiene or health and safety certificates and copies of any application forms.

Personal statements show what you have done. Keep records of the research you have carried out on what careers are available. These show evidence of research skills.

Your **curriculum vitae** displays your current skills. Include a CV at the start and end of the course to demonstrate progression.

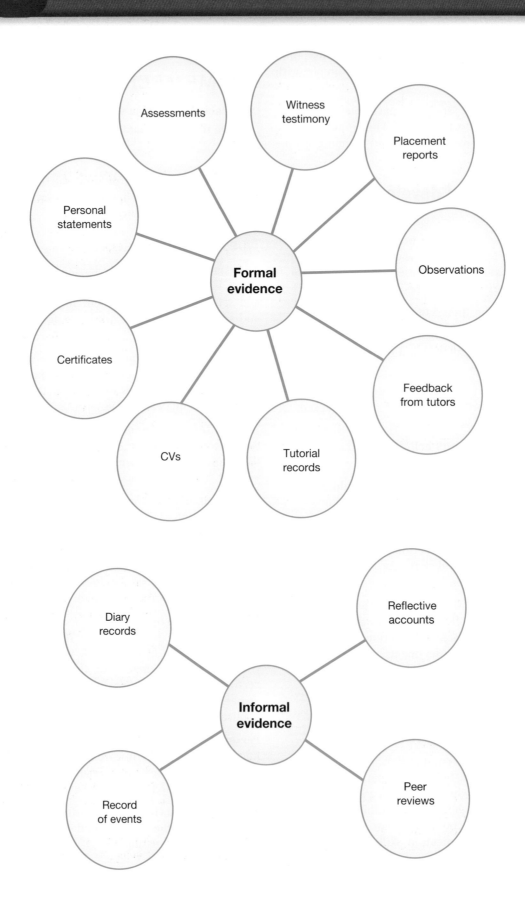

Types of informal evidence

Diary records reflect your learning in placement. Many students keep an electronic diary on the virtual learning environment used by their school or college. This is personal to the student but can be read by the tutor and used in tutorials. Relevant printouts can provide evidence for your portfolio.

Peer reviews are useful. If you present information to your group, ask them to write constructive feedback to help you develop.

Reflective accounts are particularly important and are explained in depth later in this chapter.

A record of events will give you key dates of when you carried out activities. It will then be easy to cross-reference evidence you have collected. However, a statement of what happened does not show what you learned; reflecting on the event does.

Support for development

Tutors help you develop by writing feedback on your assignments and by talking with you. Always read the feedback and ask if you are not sure what it means.

Peers provide support on an informal basis. You may not even realise you are supporting each other's development through offering advice or just listening to another student when they talk about their placement experience.

Supervisors in your workplace help develop your practice. To make the most of this, try to understand your role and the needs of the service users. You can then see how you fit in.

Mentors can help you develop skills and self-awareness.

Meetings can be useful if planned. List the issues you wish to cover with your tutor or mentor. If the meeting is to discuss your progress, ideally it should look at how you move forward as a professional.

Tutors, supervisors and mentors can all help by telling you where to get information, but they each have a different focus. A workplace supervisor or workplace mentor may tell you where you can find the health and safety policy for that workplace. A tutor might tell you where you can find information on the Health and Safety at Work Act or direct you to the Health and Safety Executive website for up-to-date information on best practice. A mentor supporting you at college may be able to tell you how to keep safe in practical situations when you are out with friends.

Reflect on own development

Reflective practice is an integral part of care practice. It is more than just 'thinking things over', as we saw earlier in this chapter. Donald Schön (1991) considered that professionals get better at their job by reflecting. In *The Reflective Practitioner*, he suggested two different times when you might use reflective practice:

- *Reflect in practice.* This is when you are involved in a situation and you reflect on it at the time. You are thinking on your feet.

- *Reflect on practice.* This occurs after the situation has taken place when you think things over at your leisure and build your knowledge or understanding.

Reflective writing is not just a description of what happened but involves actively looking back at the situation and coming to a conclusion. These conclusions then provide a guide to your own practice next time.

Reflective practice is not about making you feel bad about yourself, as this is unhelpful. Look at your practice and decide where you need to go to carry out additional development. In order to reflect effectively, it is important to 'know yourself', and understand your own values, interests and priorities. These all have an impact upon your practice and it is important to acknowledge this.

Linking theory to practice

You learn a lot of theories on this course. These theories provide models of how care practice should be undertaken. To develop as a practitioner, try out these theories in practice. In class, you learn about verbal and non-verbal communication. At placement, try out the communication skills you have learned about. This is linking theory to practice.

Reflect how well this went and what aspects you still need to develop. It might not always be successful, but making mistakes is a way of learning. Consider why something did not go according to plan and how this may be improved upon next time. However, do not forget that real and sometimes vulnerable people will be on the receiving end of any mistakes. Therefore, if you do not feel confident in undertaking an activity or carrying out something with an individual or service user, talk to your supervisor and ask them to teach you how to do it properly.

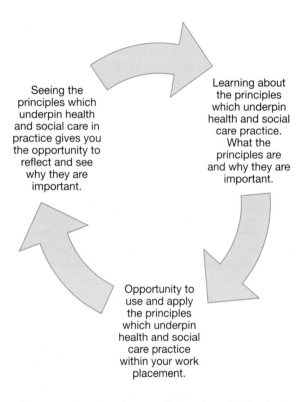

Keep a reflective diary to help identify the links between theory and practice.

Some questions when reflecting are as follows:

- What happened?

- Did you have a plan before undertaking the activity or the incident you are writing about?

- How do you feel about what happened?

- Do you need to make any adjustments?

- Have you learned any new skills?

- If you were to do this again, what would you do differently?

- What would you do the same?

- Do you need any support or to learn new skills before this occurs again?

Linking practice to theory

Sometimes an incident occurs and then we later find a theory that explains it. The case study below shows an example.

Case Study

Jake is three years old. At nursery, he is very aggressive with other children. One day, he snatches a toy car from another boy and starts hitting the other child with the toy. Sally, a student, sees the placement supervisor separate the two boys. Sally comforts the boy who has been injured, while the supervisor talks to Jake. At home time, the placement supervisor has a word with Jake's mum. Mum says that Jake has been watching his older brother play a video game that has a lot of violence. Later at college, Sally learns about Bandura's theory and the Bobo doll experiment. She can then link what happened in practice with social learning theory. Reflecting on this, she realises that this theory can explain Jake's behaviour.

The achievement of personal goals in terms of knowledge, skills, practice, values, beliefs and career aspirations

Let's look at how Sally achieves her personal goals.

Sally had set herself the following personal goals:

- Knowledge – I want to know more about why children behave as they do.

- Skills – I want to be able to intervene effectively when a child hits another child.

- Practice – I want to be able to apply my knowledge of child behaviour to stop it happening again.

- Values – I want to be able to disapprove of the behaviour, not disapprove of the child.

● Career aspirations – I want to find out about being a psychologist.

As Sally works towards these goals, her knowledge and skills develop. She learns how to manage children's behaviour. Her personal values and beliefs about 'not judging' help her to understand the world from a child's viewpoint. She also learns a bit about her own behaviour and develops a more grown-up approach to problems. Instead of giving up and saying, 'I'm stupid, I can't do that!', she learns to persevere and try again. Her tutor notices the difference and her report reflects this mature approach to problem solving. Her placement supervisor notices the difference and says that, when Sally is old enough, she can have a job at the nursery. Sally has grown up.

Activity 11 | **P5** | **M3**

Look back at your action plans.

● **How far have you developed personally and professionally since you made the plans?**

● **Give three examples of links between theory and practice from your own experience.**

At this point, if you are studying towards Unit 48, you can stop reading. Don't forget, you also need 50 hours of placement for Unit 48!

4 Know service provision in the health or social care sectors

Provision of services

The framework or way that health and social care is organised differs in different parts of Britain.

The Department of Health (DH) sets the framework for the NHS and for social services in England. The department is accountable to Parliament for the way it allocates money to health and social services. It is responsible for healthcare spending in England and for guiding local adult social services in how they spend their money. The command paper *Our Health, Our Care, Our Say*, published on 30th January 2006 by the DH, aimed to provide people with good-quality social care and NHS services in the communities where they live. Both NHS services and social care services are changing to give service users more independence, choice and control.

In health care, primary care refers to health services that are based in the local community: GPs, pharmacists, dentists and midwives. Primary care providers are usually the first point of contact for a patient. Primary care trusts (PCTs) in England receive budgets directly from the DH.

Secondary care is usually acute health care provided in hospitals. Patients are usually referred by their GP.

Tertiary care is more specialised. There is not a tertiary centre in every Strategic Health Authority (SHA) area. Specialised hospitals or departments linked to medical schools or teaching hospitals may provide tertiary care for a region. They treat patients with complex conditions, who have usually been referred by other specialists. Stoke Mandeville Hospital provides a tertiary service. It is a national spinal injuries centre and also has a regional centre for burns and plastic surgery. Patients are referred to tertiary services from local NHS hospitals.

In England, the Department of Health, headed by the Secretary of State for Health, controls the NHS.

There are ten Strategic Health Authorities (SHAs) in England. These look after local and regional services, which are organised as trusts. Health care is organised and delivered as a national service. In contrast, social care services are delivered locally by local councils, although the funding comes to local councils through the DH.

There are also National Service Frameworks (NSFs) for Health. These NSFs set standards for care, based on the latest evidence, and they also suggest ways to help organisations achieve targets. There are several NSFs, including one each for cancer, diabetes, high blood pressure, coronary heart disease, mental health and renal services. The NSFs set targets to reduce deaths from specific health problems.

The DH has direct responsibility for delivering health care, but not social care. Social care is delivered by local councils, which is why there is variation between local councils on what is available. The DH sets the overall policy for adult social care but does not interfere with local council decisions about which resources to pay for. Find out more on the Department of Health website: www.dh.gov.uk.

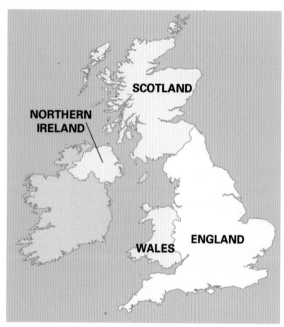

The four countries of the United Kingdom

Did you know...

Northern Ireland, Scotland and Wales organise health and social care differently from England.

Northern Ireland organises services differently from England. Health and social care work together, as a Health and Social Care Board for Northern Ireland (www.hscni.net). In Wales, the NHS combines with social care in the Department for Health and Social Services (http://wales.gov.uk). Scotland has 14 health boards. You can find out more about NHS Scotland at www.scotland.gov.uk.

Adult social care is currently undergoing a transformation. In *Putting people first: a shared vision and commitment to the transformation of adult social care* (2007), the Department of Health set out the changes needed in social services. Adult social services now must work with local PCTs to ensure a joined-up service, to offer choice and to empower service users through more direct payments. Service users who receive direct payments will then employ their own carers, ensuring they get the care they need. The personalisation of adult social services is a major reform. You can read more about it on www.dhcarenetworks.org.uk/Personalisation.

Children's social care is now partly under the direction of the Department for Children, Schools and Families (DCSF). According to *The Children's Plan* (2007), published by the DCSF, local police, schools and PCTs must work in partnership with social workers as part of the Safeguarding Agenda. Read more about this at www.safeguardingchildren.org.uk. A new workforce plan identifies specialist training for social workers working with children and young people.

Regulators

The Health and Social Care Act 2008 established the Care Quality Commission (CQC). The CQC took up its role on 1st April 2009. It brings together the roles of three previous regulators:

- Commission for Social Care Inspection
- Healthcare Commission
- Mental Health Act Commission.

The CQC regulates the quality of health and adult social care and looks after the interests of people detained under the Mental Health Act.

> 'Our aim is to make sure better care is provided for everyone, whether that's in hospital, in care homes, in people's own homes, or elsewhere.'
>
> Source: www.cqc.org.uk

Professionals in health care are regulated by their own professional bodies, but this is overseen by the Council for Healthcare Regulatory Excellence (CHRE) (www.chre.org.uk).

Professional bodies include the *General Dental Council, General Medical Council, and the Nursing and Midwifery Council*. Professions regulate themselves to ensure the service they give is up to the standard that others in the profession expect.

What do you think? Should professionals regulate themselves or should they be regulated by others?

Local health or social care service providers

 Case Study

Navdeep is studying health and social care. She wants to find out about her local health services. She chooses the local GP service and researches it using the sections shown in the table below.

Type of provision	GP service looking after patients from birth to death, also provides antenatal care.
Funding	From the PCT.
Access	People can apply to be on the GP's list if they live in the area.
Potential barriers to access	Homeless people have no address so cannot get a GP. Sometimes the GP has enough patients and does not take new patients. Sometimes GPs are reluctant to take people with expensive health needs, such as drug addicts.
Organisational policies and procedures	The number of patients is regulated by the PCT. Health and safety policies and employment policies are organised by the local PCT.
How the service fits within national framework	This is part of primary care.

Activity 12 P6

Using the same headings as shown in the case study above, complete an assessment of a local service in your area. Consider the following:

- A day centre for older people
- A residential care home.

Type of provision	
Funding	
Access	
Potential barriers to access	
Organisational policies and procedures	
How the service fits within national framework	

Did you find the following information?

Day centres for older people and residential care homes are part of social care provision. They get funding from the local authority social services. Even if they are run by a charity or by a private owner, they are paid for by the local authority.

Access is usually by referral from a social worker, although some people do pay privately for these services.

Potential barriers to access are that there may not be enough places for everyone who wants a place. An older person may not want a social worker and so may find it difficult to get to know about these services. Finally, if they are not entitled to free care, they may not be able to afford it.

Policies and procedures are organised by the local social services department. They work with care home managers to develop their own policy based on that of social services. These services are part of the local social services offered by local councils.

Read the case studies opposite and think about the potential barriers.

Gareth has a GP but has problems getting to hospital appointments because of poverty.

Both Rose and Paul would face difficulty because they may not have a GP. Rose has no fixed address and Paul is a visitor.

Sometimes prejudice is a barrier to access. Read the next case study to see why.

Case Study

Gareth is 50 years old and lives in a small village in the country. The buses run only early in the morning or late in the evening. He does not have much money and has not got a car. He has been unwell for some time.

What barriers might Gareth face in accessing health care?

When Gareth finally goes to see the GP, he is referred for tests to the local hospital in town. He gets a lift from a friend. A few weeks later, he gets a letter asking him to attend an outpatient appointment. This time, another friend gives him a lift. At the clinic, he is told he will need a course of chemotherapy and will need to attend hospital every other day for several weeks.

What further problems might Gareth face in completing his treatment?

Case Study

Rose is part of the traveller community. She is 30 years old and happily married with one daughter, aged four. Rose is expecting another child. She has no fixed address as they move every few weeks.

What barriers might Rose face in receiving health care?

Case Study

Paul is 20 years old. He is a Polish student and is in this country for the season to help with fruit picking. He has very limited English. One morning, he collapses with severe abdominal pain.

What barriers may Paul face getting immediate health care?

Case Study

Mary is a drug addict. She started experimenting with drugs in her teens, then went on to harder drugs as she got in with the wrong crowd. She worked for a time but, because of her drug habit, she was unable to keep a job. She then turned to prostitution to pay for her habit. Now in her 40s, she lives in a council flat in a rundown area. There is very little food in the flat. She no longer bothers having a wash and the flat is also dirty. One day, she notices a lump in her breast. A friend tells her she ought to get it checked. Mary turns up at the GP surgery in her usual dirty and unkempt state, having had a drink to steady her nerves.

What barriers may Mary face?

Health and social care workers

The health and social care sector requires many people, undertaking a variety of job roles. All of these roles are important for good care practice. The diagram below shows how these roles can be considered.

Role of professional bodies

In health and social care, professional bodies protect the public. These bodies are overseen by the Council for Health Care Regulatory Excellence (CHRE), as we mentioned earlier in this chapter.

Professionals must register with their own organisation before they can work in that field. The General Social Care Council (www.gscc.org.uk) keeps a register of social care workers, while nurses and midwives register with the Nursing and Midwifery Council (www.nmc-uk.org). The Health Professions Council regulates 14 different health professions, including art therapists, dieticians, occupational therapists, paramedics and physiotherapists. These professional bodies keep a register of competent professionals and, in serious cases of misconduct, a professional will be struck off the register. By being on the register, a person agrees to abide by the codes of conduct issued by that professional body.

Career pathways, training and qualifications

Many careers in health and social care require a degree or a diploma from a university. Nursing, midwifery and social work are graduate professions. Operating department practitioners complete a two-year diploma or foundation degree. Youth and community workers may complete a two-year diploma or a three-year degree. Find out more at www.ucas.com/students/coursesearch.

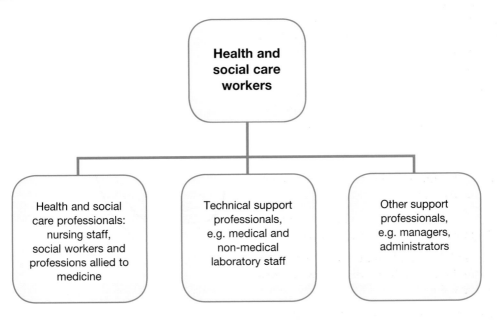

Social work and social care work are governed by the General Social Care Council. Their website gives advice on training and qualifications (www.gscc.org.uk). The type of qualification you aim for will determine the type of job you will be able to get. For example, if you would like to deliver hands-on care, a national vocational qualification will allow you to do this, but if you want to be a social worker or an occupational therapist, you will need a degree.

Apprenticeships give young people and adults a qualification to work in health and social care. The Skills for Care website (www.skillsforcare.org.uk) explains the different training routes for entry into social care work.

Workforce development

Health and social care is continually changing as society changes. Sector Skills Councils (SSCs) plan what workforce is needed and what training is required. These are employer-led but licensed and sponsored by the government. They provide advice on training for jobs in each area.

Skills for Care and Development is the Sector Skills Council (SSC) for social care, children, early years and young people's workforces in the UK. It brings together the following organisations: Care Council for Wales

- Children's Workforce Development Council
- General Social Care Council
- Northern Ireland Social Care Council
- Scottish Social Services Council
- Skills for Care.

Skills for Care represents adult social care. The Children's Workforce Development Council represents children, early years and young people's workforces.

Skills for Health is the SSC for the health sector in the UK.

Codes of conduct

Professional bodies publish codes of conduct. These codes provide guidance on how a professional should behave. Nurses follow the Nursing and Midwifery Code of Practice and Social

Workers follow the General Social Care Council Code of Practice. Codes are downloadable from the relevant websites: for social workers, www.gscc.org.uk, and for nurses and midwives, www.nmc-uk.org.

Roles and responsibilities

Whatever your profession, you have responsibilities towards service users, your employers and others in your profession. Although each individual job is unique, general rules are to respect your service users and their wishes, maintain confidentiality, foster equality and diversity, and promote the rights of service users.

Multi-disciplinary teams

These are professionals working together. Each discipline can bring unique skills and expertise. Multi-disciplinary work pools resources and can reduce duplication of services. A child may be at risk of harm in the family. They may be monitored by a social worker, but the social worker may need to work with the nursery the child attends and with the family's GP to share information and ensure the safety of the child. An elderly person may be admitted to hospital with a broken leg, but as they live alone, they may have no one to help them if they are discharged. The social worker will need to talk to the nurses and occupational therapist about how much the person can do. The social worker may then contact a nursing home manager to find a place for a few weeks until the person is able to cope independently at home. In each case, care is better when professionals work together instead of in isolation.

Activity 13 | P7

Research the roles, responsibilities and career pathways of three health or social care workers and present a slide show to your group.

End-of-unit knowledge check

Personal and professional development draws together everything you learn in other units. Health and social care services are different in England, Scotland, Wales and Northern Ireland and they are changing. This unit requires work placement experience. If you understand learning theories you can learn more effectively. If you know what influences your learning you can make sure you have the best chance of achieving. You can learn how to learn. Study skills are like any skills – practice and you get better at it. Support for learning and deleopment is all round. Remember – we learn formally and informally. Review your skills, make action plans and monitor them to achieve; reflect on your own development and collect evidence that you have developed.

Assessment and grading criteria

In order to pass this unit, the evidence that the learner presents for assessment needs to demonstrate that they can meet all the learning outcomes for the unit. The assessment criteria for a pass grade describe the level of achievement required to pass this unit.

To achieve a pass grade the evidence must show that the learner is able to:	To achieve a merit grade the evidence must show that, in addition to the pass criteria, the learner is able to:	To achieve a distinction grade the evidence must show that, in addition to the pass and merit criteria, the learner is able to:
P1 explain key influences on the personal learning processes of individuals	**M1** assess the impact of key influences on the personal learning processes on own learning	**D1** evaluate how personal learning and development may benefit others
P2 assess own knowledge, skills, practice, values, beliefs and career aspirations at start of the programme		
P3 produce an action plan for self-development and achievement of own personal goals		

To achieve a pass grade the evidence must show that the learner is able to:	To achieve a merit grade the evidence must show that, in addition to the pass criteria, the learner is able to:	To achieve a distinction grade the evidence must show that, in addition to the pass and merit criteria, the learner is able to:
P4 produce evidence of own progress against action plan over the duration of the programme	**M2** assess how the action plan has helped support own development over the duration of the programme	**D2** evaluate own development over the duration of the programme.
P5 reflect on own personal and professional development	**M3** use three examples to examine links between theory and practice.	
P6 describe one local health or social care service provider, identifying its place in national provision		
P7 describe the roles, responsibilities and career pathways of three health or social care workers		

Resources

Atherton, J.S. (2009) *Learning and Teaching: Experiential Learning*. Available online at www.learningandteaching.info/learning/experience.htm.

Department for Children, Schools and Families (2007) *The Children's Plan*. Available online at www.dcsf.gov.uk/childrensplan/.

Department of Health (2007) *Putting people first: a shared vision and commitment to the transformation of adult social care*. Available online at www.dh.gov.uk/en/Publicationsandstatistics/Publications/Publications Policy And Guidance/DH_081118.

Department of Health (2006) *Our health, our care, our say: a new direction for community services*. Available online at www.dh.gov.uk/en/Publicationsandstatistics/Publications/PublicationsPolicyAndGuidance/DH_4127453.

Schön, D. (1991) *The Reflective Practitioner: How Professionals Think in Action*, Aldershot: Ashgate Publishing.

Weblinks

Children's Workforce Development Council (Be the difference):
http://bethedifference.cwdcouncil.org.uk

Children's Workforce Development Council (All together, a better way of working):
http://alltogetherbetter.cwdcouncil.org.uk/

Care Quality Commission:
www.cqc.org.uk

Community Care:
www.communitycare.co.uk

Council for Healthcare Regulatory Excellence:
www.chre.org.uk

Department for Children, Schools and Families (Every Child Matters):
www.dcsf.gov.uk/everychildmatters

Department of Health:
www.dh.gov.uk

Department of Health's Social Work website:
www.socialworkandcare.co.uk/socialwork

DH Care Networks:
www.dhcarenetworks.org.uk/Personalisation

Dyslexia Action:
www.dyslexiaaction.org.uk

General Social Care Council:
www.gscc.org.uk

The Guardian:
www.guardian.co.uk

Health and Social Care in Northern Ireland:
www.hscni.net

NHS Careers:
www.nhscareers.nhs.uk

Nursing and Midwifery Council:
www.nmc-uk.org

Nursing Standard:
http://nursingstandard.rcnpublishing.co.uk

Nursing Times:
www.nursingtimes.net

Prospects:
www.prospects.ac.uk

Safeguarding Children:
www.safeguardingchildren.org.uk

Scottish Government:
www.scotland.gov.uk

Skills for Care:
www.skillsforcare.org.uk

Skills for Health:
www.skillsforhealth.org.uk

Social Care Institute for Excellence:
www.scie.org.uk

UCAS course search:
www.ucas.com/students/coursesearch

Welsh Assembly Government:
http://wales.gov.uk

7: Sociological Perspectives for Health and Social Care

Introduction

Sociology is one of the social sciences, the main focus of which is to understand the behaviour of people in the context of the society they live in. Related social sciences include economics, psychology and human geography, which all examine separate aspects of social life; however, sociology investigates many different areas of social life, including how social groups interact, the role of social institutions and in some instances how whole societies function.

As well as being the study of society, particular methods of sociological enquiry and investigation are used to explain how society works.

This unit provides an introduction to different sociological perspectives and, in particular, the sociology of health and illness. Using the context of health and social care, various sociological perspectives will be examined, and the sociological explanations for health inequalities will be explored in order to gain an understanding of how sociological approaches to study are relevant to health and social care.

Learning outcomes:

On completion of this unit, you should:

1 Understand sociological perspectives

2 Understand sociological approaches to health and social care.

1 Understand sociological perspectives

Sociological perspectives are different explanations of how society works that have been developed over time and are constantly being re-evaluated and re-examined as society changes. A perspective is a particular way of looking at things, seeing things from a certain viewpoint. Each perspective provides a different model of society. The descriptions below provide explanations of some of the terms and definitions used in sociological study. This is followed by a summary of the key sociological perspectives.

Social structures

Sociologists refer to the institutions and organisations through which society is organised and administered for the benefit of the people who live within that particular society, as *social structures*.

However, the actual structure of society is made up of different groups of people, so that the composition of society can also be considered an aspect of social structure. People also have belief systems – the *norms* and *values* they have learnt through *socialisation*, which influence the way in which social structures are organised and administered. All of these are legitimate areas for sociologists to study; each of these social structures, when examined from a different sociological perspective, provide a different explanation of their purpose and role in society.

Social diversity

Society consists of individuals and groups of people who differ according to a wide range of factors – for example, their age, gender, sexual preferences, cultural and ethnic background and economic status. Some people will have a different family background; they may come from big families with lots of siblings (brothers and sisters), or they may be adopted. Others may be single, living with a partner (co-habiting) or married, with or without children.

They will live in different geographical locations – towns and cities, villages or isolated farms – and will have different political and social viewpoints. These differences are referred to as *social diversity* and they affect how individuals see the world. Social perspectives often inform political views and it is important to recognise this. Individuals are likely to form groups with others who share their culture or viewpoint.

> **Key term**
>
> **Economic status** – how wealthy, or not, someone is.

Socialisation

Socialisation is the process through which people learn the social rules and expectations of behaviour in society. Social rules are often referred to as *social or behavioural norms* because they are agreed as the accepted and appropriate way to behave and conduct oneself. These social rules are often unspoken, but reflect what is considered to be important. Social norms are culturally determined – that is, they will often be different in different cultures. For example, it is normal in Japanese society to bow when being introduced to someone; the deeper, the bow, the more respect you are showing, so it is also a way of confirming social status.

Beliefs are convictions, principles or views that an individual or group holds to be true – for example, the view that sex before marriage is wrong. Some beliefs stem from religious principles, whereas others may originate from a non-religious philosophy, such as humanism. Sociology describes religion as a belief system. Other beliefs may be based on opinions formed through experiences.

Values are principles about what is good and bad, right and wrong, whether something is or is not

Table 7.1 Terminology

Social structures	Social diversity	Socialisation
Sociologists generally see society as being organised through social institutions, each having a role in society. They include the family, the education system, the criminal justice system, the church/religion, medical and health care services, and social welfare services.	Diversity is the term used to describe the ways in which people are different from one another. For example, social class, age, gender, culture, ethnicity and location.	Socialisation is the process by which people learn the norms and values of society. *Norms* are social rules about what is important in society. *Values* are what are important to an individual or social group. *Beliefs* are what an individual or group accept as true. *Roles* are the responsibility and functions of someone or a body. *Status* is the importance placed upon someone or something. *Socialisation* occurs initially through parents, friends, family, school and the media, then throughout life by having different experiences.

worth striving for. Values are learned in a cultural context (i.e. through the process of socialisation) and are closely linked to the beliefs and norms that exist within a particular social group. Group values help to explain the way a particular group behaves, for example, football fans consider it of value to chant and sing in support of their team; however, such behaviour in the supermarket by a group of fans would be seen as inappropriate and maybe even threatening.

Roles refer to the responsibilities, actions and duties of an individual or organisation. Roles are socially determined, which means there is general agreement between members of society on what activities should be involved in the role (e.g. the role of education or of parents in society).

Socialisation is a process that takes place in the first instance at home, beginning at birth; for example, the way in which parents treat boys and girls from babyhood is informed by the expectations of society of what it is appropriate behaviour for boys and girls. This is called learning a gender role; the sex of the baby is biologically determined but gender roles are socially determined.

Socialisation continues throughout life at school and work, through the interactions with others, such as parents and teachers, siblings and friends and also through the media and advertising. If you move to a different area, you will become socialised into the norms and values of that area. For example, in some places it is perfectly acceptable to eat fish and chips in the street from the wrappings in which they were purchased. In other areas, this behaviour would attract disapproving looks. When people show such disapproval, it is known as a *social sanction* and is a method of trying to impose the social norm. Laws are rules determined by government, based on the expectations of society, and *formal sanctions* (e.g. fines or jail) apply to people who break them. Non-conformity – refusal to comply with agreed norms – is called deviance. However, not all deviance is criminal; it is only criminal when the law is broken and formal sanctions apply. Laws concerning anti-social behaviour have been brought in to curb behaviour that is unacceptable and where social sanctions have proved ineffective.

> Did you know...
>
> **You can be fined or sent to prison for being an excessively noisy neighbour.**

The health and social care sectors will be examined as social structures, focusing in particular on the sociology of health and illness.

Activity 1

Think about your own situation. What behaviours are the norm in your home? For example, is everyone expected to take off his or her shoes when entering?

Identify three things that are normal behaviour for your home and compare these with those of the others in your group. Complete this sentence:

In our house, we always:

1

2

3

What values are important to you? Look at the following list and identify your top three most important values, then compare with others in your group:

Accomplishment	Honesty	Kindness	Beauty	Determination
Tenacity	Chastity	Compassion	Prosperity	Friendship
Respect for elders	Goodness	Generosity	Security	Success
Justice	Perfection	Status	Strength	Faith

What are your beliefs? Look at the following statements and think about whether you agree with them. Identify two beliefs that you hold personally.

- I believe that war is never justified under any circumstances.
- I believe that men and women have different abilities and should be treated differently.
- I believe that it is acceptable not to tell the truth if it hurts someone's feelings.

You can discuss these with others in your group and try to understand why you hold these beliefs.

Principle theoretical approaches

Although each sociological perspective is essentially a different theory of society and how it operates, there are broadly two main theoretical approaches:

- Structural (macro) approaches, which analyse society as a whole to see how it fits together. They tend to see human behaviour as being primarily shaped by forces within society.
- Social action (micro) approaches, which tend to see society as a product of human activity, with individuals pro-actively creating society through their actions and interactions.

It is important to recognise that sociology has developed over time and within a historical framework, which has influenced theorists, so each school of thought has different intellectual origins and, more importantly, uses different methods to investigate sociological issues (or *phenomena*).

Methodological approaches

Methodology describes the way in which research is undertaken. It includes the tools used to find out information and the way the information is analysed to inform a hypothesis or conclusion. Although it is not simply the case that all sociologists fit into the categories outlined here as

Key term

Hypothesis – a theory or assumption, which needs to be proved or disproved by further research.

methodologies, they provide a broad framework for understanding the different perspectives.

Scientific 'quantitative' methodology

This approach to sociology is known as the 'positivist' or objective tradition. Positivism developed in the early days of sociology as a discipline, when social scientists were keen to replicate the successful discoveries made in the physical and natural sciences (e.g. Darwin's theory of evolution) and sought to give this new discipline credibility as a science.

August Comte (1798–1857) was the first person to use the term sociology. He argued that sociologists should not be concerned with meanings, motives or emotions because they cannot be measured objectively. He held the view that the social world should be studied according to the principles of natural science – by observation, comparison and experimentation. Hence, sociological study should be limited to that which is observable or measureable.

Positivism considers that the world is subject to impersonal laws, which can be discovered by using the same methods that proved successful with the physical and natural sciences; hence, it is concerned with uncovering the 'facts' about society in an objective manner. The methodologies used in this approach are statistical, using, for example, surveys and questionnaires that count and measure responses (quantitative methodology – based on numbers). Emile Durkheim was also regarded as a positivist as he followed this methodological approach in his famous work on suicide. This approach became the orthodox and dominant view. The aim was to produce a body of knowledge of society that was precise, objective and predictive and that demonstrated the laws of human nature.

Key features

- Social facts are regarded as 'things' to be discovered.
- The positivist perspectives use statistical data (e.g. causation, and correlation and multi-variate analysis).
- A hypothesis is developed.
- Laboratory and field experiments are used as comparative methods to test the hypothesis.

This type of methodological approach is used in the discipline of psychology.

Key term

Positivists – positivists believe that social processes should be studied in terms of cause and effect, using scientific methods.

Interpretive and qualitative methodologies

This second school of thought is more concerned with the relationship between the individual and society. This approach is known as 'humanistic' because it is concerned with the way in which individuals make sense of their social experiences and the actions they consequently take (e.g. negotiation of role definitions and boundaries). These actions, in turn, affect the way in which society operates and is changed over time. Hence, this type of approach to sociology is called *social action* or *interactionist theories*. Max Weber (1864–1920) defined sociology as the study of social action.

Interactionist approaches were considered a radical alternative to the scientifically based, quantitative view and were developed much later. Interpretive sociologists argue that the scientific method is only good for studying inanimate matter, which has no consciousness so any observed behaviour can be explained as a consequence of a simple external stimulus. People, on the other hand, interpret the world around them based on their experiences and attach meaning to it on their understanding of this, so constructing their own social reality. They attach meaning to what they experience before responding to it. Sociologists cannot explain actions without understanding what these meanings are.

The methodologies used for sociological enquiry tend to be interactive techniques, such as *participant observation*, a method which involves the researcher observing the social situation long enough for his or her presence to be accepted and normal behaviour to resume. In other situations, the researcher may be able to join – participate in – the group he or she is observing (e.g. football fans).

Ethnography is based upon systematic, long-term observation of people and detailed in-depth interviews with them. It is an account of their way of life and derives from anthropology. Conclusions are drawn, then often checked with the participants. The theories emerge through the investigation (grounded theory), rather than the sociologist devising a hypothesis and testing it.

Phenomenology (phenomena are any things that humans experience) rejects the idea that anything can be objectively measured and classified because people make sense of the world by deciding on what things mean for them subjectively, based on their experiences, values, beliefs, etc. Phenomenologists maintain that there is no social reality other than these subjective meanings. They argue that even statistics are social products, reflecting the meaning and common-sense assumptions of those that create them. For example, measuring the rate of anti-social behaviour depends on defining what anti-social behaviour is. Health statistics depend on agreeing what health and ill health are, but they may mean different things to different people.

Key term

Phenomenology – the philosophical study of lived experience.

Key features

- There are no 'social facts'; individuals make sense of their own world based on their experiences, creating their own social reality/world.

- Sociologists need to understand the meanings individuals and groups of people attach to the social world – how does it feel to be you?
- Interactive perspectives use observation, interviews and participation as research tools to understand social groups and from which to develop theories
- Statistics are social products, created by people with values, beliefs and assumptions.

> **Key term**
>
> **Interactionist** – interactionist perspectives examine how shared meanings and social patterns develop through social interactions within a particular social context.

Feminist methodology

At the core of feminist approaches to sociological enquiry are three key issues:

- Previous sociological research is male dominated. Men have defined the terms, identified the areas of interest to study and the methodological approaches. Feminists argue that, as a consequence, the sociological theory derived from such research is patriarchal and sexist. It is flawed in that it fails to reflect the social reality of women's lives.
- The conventional 'scientific' methods used by men are not helpful as they are unable to reflect the meanings that women attach to their social worlds.
- Feminism has a distinctive theory of knowledge (epistemology) which requires a feminist methodology, e.g. in the way that interviews are approached and conducted, so that the way in which women view and experience the world can be revealed and is equally valid, if different from that of men.

Anne Oakley (1944–) argues that there is a feminist approach to research that rejects the masculine model of interviewing. She studied a range of methodology instruction books which explained how to conduct interviews and identified the key features of what she described as the 'masculine' model of interviewing. The techniques stressed:

- objectivity
- detachment
- hierarchy – the interviewer as superior in knowledge
- a scientific approach which prevents emotional or social engagement with the subject.

Oakley promotes a more collaborative approach to interviewing; using unstructured interviews in order to break down the barriers between researchers and their subjects, and minimising the potential harm and control exercised by the researcher in order to enhance understanding of the subject's experiences.

> **Key term**
>
> **Feminist** – feminist theory focuses on how gender inequality has shaped the social world.

Sociological perspectives 1: structural theories

Functionalism

Key people: August Comte (1798–1857), Emile Durkheim (1858–1917), Talcott Parsons (1902–1979)

Functionalism is a structuralist theory, looking at society as a whole. It is based on the idea that society operates rather like an organism or a mechanism, with each separate part having a distinct role to play in maintaining the overall functioning of the whole. Functionalism (sometimes called structural functionalism) states that the social structure – society – consists of norms, customs, traditions and institutions whose main function is to maintain social order and stability.

Functionalists observe that behaviour in society is structured according to agreed norms and values, which inform particular roles, guiding and limiting individual behaviour. Hence, function-alism examines the role played by social structures and institutions in maintaining stability in society. It considers that each social structure is essential for the interests of a stable society, which is considered desirable. For example, the role of the family is to socialise new members of society (children) in order to maintain social order and stability.

Durkheim agreed with Comte that sociologists should study social facts, such as the belief systems, customs and institutions of society, considering them as things – social structures. Functionalism is sometimes referred to as a *systems theory* because society is seen as a complex system whose parts work together in a relationship that needs to be understood.

For example, factors such as inequality are seen as functional to society; they are helpful to the smooth running of society. Because people are given rewards such as higher wages and better status if they are successful, this acts as an incentive for people to become educated, work hard and train so that they can obtain high-status jobs and hold positions seen as crucial within society.

There have been criticisms of functionalism. For example, it ignores individuals and the fact that individuals can make their own choices. It also does not take account of conflict and diversity; behaviour that is seen as non-conforming is considered to be deviant. Functionalism essentially reinforces the existing order of things, promoting the status quo rather than challenging it.

Marxism

Key people: Karl Marx (1818–1883), Freidrich Engels (1820–1895)

Marxism is a structuralist theory because it takes a view of society as a whole. It is also a conflict theory, seeing class conflict as the key to understanding society.

Karl Marx was a German philosopher, historian, political and economic theorist and one of the first sociologists. He was also the revolutionary founding father of communism and, as such, his complex theories and writings have been much misunderstood and misinterpreted.

Under Marxism, economic (financial) structures and systems and social class are central to Marxist thinking. The key principles underpinning Marx's theories are:

- That human beings need to produce things such as food, shelter and material goods in order to survive. In order to do this, human

> **Did you know...**
>
> Marx was lifelong friends with Engels, who contributed to Marx's thinking with his observations of working-class life in Manchester, which was at the forefront of the Industrial Revolution during this time. Engels, the son of a German textile manufacturer, had been sent to Manchester to look after the family business interests there and he was shocked by the conditions of the workers, writing a detailed account in *The Condition of the Working Class in England in 1844*. Engels took on the responsibility for finalising and editing Marx's work after his death and also contributed to sociological thought in his own right, informing feminist theories with his observations and writings on the family in *The Origin of the Family, Private Property and the State.*

beings need to work together, forming social relationships. Production is therefore a social activity or enterprise.

- That there is a distinction between the *means of production* – physical things (such as land), natural resources (such as minerals), technology and labour – which are necessary for the production of material goods, and the non-physical *relations* of production – the social relationships people engage in to acquire and use these means of production. Together, the means of production and the relations of production are known as the *mode of production* (the way in which the physical and non-physical aspects work together to produce goods).

Marx observed changes in society as the relationship in the mode of production changed over time. As society moved from early hunter-gatherer groups, with each member producing food for the whole community, to an industrialised society in which people no longer owned or had access to the means of production, they were forced to sell their labour for wages in order to buy the food, shelter and material goods they needed to survive. The advancement of industrialisation and the desire to expand caused the working class to be exploited by being forced to produce more than they were paid for – surplus value (profit).

To Marx, this private ownership of the means of production was the source of conflict. The ruling class is based on ownership, and conflict – class conflict – is founded on inequality. Marx saw society as being based on conflicts of interests. He described those owning the means of production as the bourgeoisie and the working class as the proletariat. Capitalist societies are based on these principles and Marx thought that, just as the other stages had progressed and the relations of production altered, capitalism would also come to an end when the workers became sufficiently dissatisfied that a revolution took place, as it had in France and, subsequently, Russia, and the workers took over the means of production.

To summarise:

1 History is a product of material class struggle in society.
2 In a capitalist society, an economic minority (bourgeoisie) dominate and exploit the working class (proletariat) majority.
3 Capitalism is exploitative in the way that it extracts unpaid labour (surplus value or productivity) from the working class.
4 Production is socialised but ownership is private, remaining in the hands of the minority bourgeoisie.
5 In order to overcome this, the working class must seize political power through social revolution and bring production back into collective ownership.
6 Material class distinctions would then disappear and inequality would be eradicated.

The critics state that this theory gives little freedom to individuals. The emphasis is on conflict; yet not every society is in conflict all the time. As Marxism considers that conflict is normal, it comes under criticism for this. Marxism also omits gender and ethnic inequality.

Post-modernism

Post-modernism stresses the uncertain natures of societies. A modern society is considered to be one in which a study of the world was scientific and traditional. Post-modernism believes that we have moved on from this and can point to various aspects of changes in society, such as shifts in work patterns, globalisation and the growth of multi-national companies. Post-modernism looks at a range of theories and considers that they all have a part and something to say about society – for example, some post-modernists argue that areas of social life, such as the family, have become *commodified* (a commodity is something which can be traded). Post-modern approaches are highly individualistic; the emphasis is on flexibility, diversity, distinction, mobility, communication, etc. Society is increasingly dominated by signs and images, such as brands, which help to shape individual self-identity. Society is *pluralistic* and diverse and much of life has become commodified.

> ## Key terms
>
> **Commodified** – turned into something that can be bought and sold.
> **Pluralistic** – diverse, with multiple variations of reality (cultural differences).

An example of an attempt at commodification is the Human Genome Project. This was publicly funded research to identify the chemical construction of DNA (the basic building block of human existence) and to identify the 20,000–25,000 genes carrying specific DNA information that make up a human being. At the same time, commercial biotechnology firms were also mapping the human genome, with the aim of completing before the public programme, patenting the information (being given ownership of the information) and only making it available to researchers if they paid for it. They aimed to 'own' pieces of the human genome to sell for commercial profit – in effect; human genes would have become commodified.

> ## Key term
>
> **Capitalism** – an economic and social system in which the means of production are privately owned. Labour, goods and services are bought and sold and the profits distributed to the owners.

Post-modernism has been criticised for not taking into account the role of individuals or between social institutions. Some sociologists also disagree that we are living in a post-modern society.

Sociological perspectives 2: interactive theories

Social action theory

The emphasis in social action theory is how the thoughts and actions of individuals create society through their social interactions. Shared meaning is created through the interactions people have with each other.

This theory recognises that individuals are not just passive but have a role within society, but it fails to acknowledge why some groups have the power to label others or put constraints on individuals.

The interactionist perspective considers that a person's *self-concept* is shaped and developed by interactions with others. For example, when meeting someone for the first time, we make tentative judgements about him or her based on:

- their appearance – are they dressed conservatively or not, are they scruffy, clean, etc?
- their speech – do they speak like us in terms of accent, style of speech, language?
- facial expression – are they smiling, stern, indifferent?
- whether they are likeable, friendly, interested
- what we already know or have been told about them – personal history.

> ## Key term
>
> Self-concept – our awareness of ourselves and our beliefs about ourselves.

We develop a working hypothesis about the person, but are willing to amend these views initially until they are either confirmed or contradicted. However, once we have made up our mind about a person, we will view all further interactions and contact with the person from this position and act towards them accordingly. We will label them, even if only in our minds. This is why it is so difficult to get someone to change their opinion of another person once they have made up their mind. For example, we might establish that a person is homosexual. We will then tend to think of them as a homosexual first, with all that this means to us, rather than a loving son, gifted intellectual or hard worker.

Labelling theory suggests that once a label has been given to someone, they tend to see themselves in terms of that label, especially if it is a negative one, and act accordingly. Other people then begin to see them in terms of the label and act towards them based on assumptions or stereotypes suggested by the label. This cycle is called a *self-fulfilling prophecy*. Those in authority can use labels as a control method.

Symbolic interactionism/interactionism

Key people: George Herbert Mead (1863–1931), Herbert Blumer (1900–1987)

This perspective states that people impose meaning on the world through the use of symbols, especially language. Communication is able to take place because these meanings are shared; however, each person involved in an interaction must interpret not only the meanings, but also the intention of others. In order to do this, people engage in 'role taking'. In other words, they imagine the situation from the other person's position in order to interpret meaning. Mead called the people engaging in interactions *social actors* and argued that role taking was important in the development of self-concept. Symbolic interactionism was further developed by Mead's student, Herbert Blumer, who stated that symbolic interactionism shows society as an ongoing process of interaction, involving people (actors) constantly interpreting situations and adjusting to one another.

It has been criticised for not being able to explain power structures in society or to recognise the influence of the historical context in which interactions take place.

Phenomenology

Key people: Edmund Husserl (1859–1938), Alfred Schultz (1899–1959)

Phenomenology is slightly different from social action theory because it is mainly concerned with explaining how people make sense of the world, rather than examining the causes of human behaviour.

Phenomenologists believe that the world is experienced mainly through the senses. In order to understand this sensory input, people start to organise and classify, divide and sub-divide these experiences according to their common features – phenomena (observable facts or experiences). When people communicate their understanding of these phenomena to others, 'common-sense knowledge' is created, shared and subsequently modified during interactions.

Activity 2

In groups, think of the labels we might attach to people who use health and social care services. How helpful or unhelpful are these labels? Give three ways in which labels might affect the relationship between health professionals and their patients.

Sociological perspectives 3: feminist sociological theories

Key people: Betty Friedan (1921–), Shulamith Firestone (1945–), Anne Oakley (1944–), Sheila Rowbotham (1943–)

Feminist sociological perspectives start from the understanding that, because men and women have dissimilar experiences and see the world from different viewpoints, they do not construct their knowledge and understanding of the social world in the same way.

Generally feminism provides a critique of other sociological theories, considering their examination of society to be informed primarily from the male perspective, which fails to take into account women's different social experiences such as childbearing, and is therefore incomplete. By putting forward theories of the social world that exclude women's roles and experiences, the knowledge that it creates serves the interests of male power and privilege.

Feminist sociological theories observe that there are clear inequalities between the position of women and men within society (gender inequalities) and that these have shaped social life. They seek to find sociological explanations for these inequalities and feminist sociological perspectives consist of a number of theoretical approaches to examine society from the point of view of women's experiences.

Feminist sociological theories have been informed by the long history of the struggle for women's rights and independence, first documented publicly in the 1700s. Feminism, and the sociological perspectives it helped to shape, cannot be fully understood without some reference to the history of the Women's Rights Movement.

Women's rights can be described as the freedoms and entitlements of women and girls of all ages, and of equality with men. They are generally considered to include (but are not limited to) the following:

- the right to bodily integrity and autonomy (i.e. the right to have control over one's own body)
- the right to be educated
- the right to vote (suffrage)
- the right to hold public office (e.g. as a councillor or MP)
- the right to work
- the right to be paid equally
- the right to enter into legal contracts
- the right to own property
- the right to be in the military or be conscripted (fight for one's country)
- to have marital, parental and religious rights.

Whilst these have a great deal of similarity to basic human rights, they are not entirely the same. It is important to recognise that for many years these rights were denied to women in Western societies, who were not able to exercise them independently of men, and they continue to be denied to women in other societies and cultures.

Feminism has a long history, beginning in the eighteenth century with women starting to write about their situation and place in the social world.

Simone De Beauvoir, in *The Second Sex* written in 1949, stated:

'Representation of the world, like the world itself, is the work of men; they describe it from their own point of view, which they confuse with the absolute truth.'

Feminists saw women's cultural and political inequalities as inseparably linked and encouraged women to understand aspects of their personal lives as deeply politicised and as reflecting male-dominated power structures in society. Sociologists examined areas such as housework, inequalities in the labour market, the family, childbirth, sexual politics and male violence and a number of theories emerged.

Radical feminist theory

Radical feminism is a conflict theory and argues that men gain the most advantage from women's unequal position in society; they therefore exploit women to maintain their superior position.

Radical feminism maintains that gender inequality in society is not natural or functional but is a result of *patriarchy*. Patriarchy is regarded as the systemic domination of women by men. From this perspective, men are seen as the ruling class and women the subordinate class. Patriarchy is maintained through social systems and structures, particularly the family, in which men exploit women's free, domestic labour, asserting that this is part of women's role, thus allowing them the time to pursue careers and hold positions in public life. Similarly, many radical feminists argue that men aim to control women's reproductive rights and exploit women's biological function of giving birth – for example, by making child rearing the primary responsibility of women and thus denying them equal opportunities in the workplace. This can be described as 'biological inequality'.

Other radical feminists argue that patriarchy, and hence male supremacy, has been sustained by male violence, particularly sexual harassment, rape and domestic violence. The failure of social institutions such as the police and the legal system to address these issues is seen as evidence for a patriarchal system that exploits and oppresses women.

Patriarchy gives an imbalance of power, which is expressed publicly when women are exploited in the economic market, and privately, such as when woman are the victims of violence. Women will not be free from oppression until patriarchy as a system is overcome.

Key term

Patriarchy – a form of society or social system, which is dominated and ruled by men, who are seen as being in authority. Power is passed from father to son.

Liberal feminist theory

Liberal feminists are concerned with achieving economic and political equality within a capitalist system.

The theory starts from the position that traditional gender roles disadvantage both men and women because women's role as homemaker keeps most of her efforts in the private sphere and disadvantages her economically, whereas men's role as breadwinner keeps him in the public sphere and prevents him from interacting with his children. The domestic division of labour, based on gender roles, thus alienates men from the full range of human experiences. Gender roles are socially determined; sex roles are biologically determined and there are clear physical differences between the sexes. However, gender is learnt through socialisation – for example, giving girls dolls and miniature domestic appliances such as kitchens and ironing boards prepares her for domestic labour, like an apprenticeship. Boys, on the other hand, are encouraged to play sports and aggressive games.

In addition to the physical labour that housework entails, liberal feminist sociologists argue that women provide emotional labour in the form of caring activities, taking responsibility for ensuring the mental well-being and happiness of family members, being responsible for health care and acting as carer for older family members.

Because gender roles are learnt and socially determined, they can be reduced or erased. The ideal society would be one based on the best characteristics of both men and women, in which women had equal access to power and resources.

Marxist feminist theory

Marx viewed gender differences in power and status as reflecting other divisions. He maintained that there were no gender or class divisions in pre-capitalist societies but as capitalism and the ownership of private property became important, women became the private property of men through the social institution of marriage. This was important in order for men to ensure they produce children whose paternity cannot be disputed so that the male heirs can inherit private property, and the females can be used to consolidate wealth through appropriate marriages, forming strategic alliances. The monogamous family is therefore a tool used by capitalism to reinforce class relationships.

Marxist feminists are concerned with the relationship of women to production and highlight the role of production – public and domestic – in women's oppression. They argue that the capitalist system exploits women by making them sell their labour in order to survive, providing a reserve army of labour. However, they criticise traditional Marxist theories for neglecting the role of women's unpaid domestic labour in supporting the economy, reproducing the labour force through childbearing and providing unpaid labour to support men and children. Engels' work on the family helped to inform this theory, as he maintained that history was concerned with the production and reproduction of life, i.e. the production of the things needed for existence such as food, shelter and tools required for production and also the reproduction of human beings to maintain the species. Marxist feminists believe that women will not be liberated until capitalism is overthrown.

Socio-political perspectives

These theoretical perspectives outline a set of political beliefs that have been very influential, particularly in the development of social policy and approaches to the provision of welfare and social care.

Collectivism

Collectivism stresses the importance of a shared approach to society and the inter-dependence of human beings. There is an emphasis on group as opposed to individual goals and a focus on community and society. Jacques Rousseau (1712–1778) in his work *The Social Contract* stated that there was, in effect, a contract between members of society covering the powers of government and the rights and responsibilities of citizens (citizenship means collective belonging). The people are represented by the government they elect. This is known as democracy.

Collectivist economic principles argue that some things should be group owned and used for the benefit of everyone in society, rather than a few individuals. At its most extreme, this is how a communist system operates; the state owns the means of production. A less extreme version of collectivism is social democracy, in which the inequalities caused by unrestrained capitalism are reduced through government regulation, redistribution of income, government planning and public ownership of vital social structures such as health care, education, utilities (gas, water, electricity, etc.) and transport systems.

Trades unions are an example of collectivism; they were set up to collectively negotiate terms and conditions of employment on behalf of their members with employers, to ensure a *living wage*. Another example is the Co-operative Society, which is the application of collective principles to business. The Co-operative Group is owned by its members, democratically run by members on behalf of its members. (www.co-operative.coop). John Lewis is another example of a collective organisation (www.johnlewispartnership.co.uk).

Key term

Living wage – defined as sufficient income to provide adequate nutrition, physical activity, housing, social interaction, transport, medical care and hygiene for an average family.

A collective approach to society in Britain developed after the Second World War with the development of the welfare state, when the government was looking at how Britain should be re-built (post-war reconstruction). Collectivist principles informed the implementation of the welfare state; people in work made contributions through the system of National Insurance, as did their employers, and everyone contributed through the tax system so that everyone could benefit.

Did you know...

Sir William Beveridge (1879–1963) produced a report recommending that the government should find ways of eliminating the 'five giant evils' of 'want', 'disease', 'squalor', 'ignorance' and 'idleness'. The result was the welfare state with free health care and education, together with a national system of social security (now called welfare benefits) intended to protect people from 'cradle to grave'.

Key term

Welfare services – universal services provided by the government and funded from individual contributions so all individuals within a society can expect to benefit from them. This is an example of collectivism.

New Right

This is a term commonly used to describe economic and political *liberalism* (neo-liberal economics). The key features are as follows:

- Individualism – this is concerned with a focus on the self, rather than the group, an emphasis on self-sufficiency and control and the pursuit of individual, rather than collective, goals. People are motivated by self-interest to achieve personal goals and derive a sense of pride from their achievements. Individual rights are promoted.
- Liberty – individuals have a right to act according to their free will, without being compelled or coerced into action.
- Laissez-faire politics – the role of the state (government) is minimal, defending the right to property and free enterprise through maintaining the rule of law. People succeed according to ability and hard work. (Laissez-faire means let it be, or leave alone.)
- Free market economics – one in which the trading (buying and selling) of goods and services is not subjected to regulation by government except to enforce ownership (property rights) and contracts. Prices are negotiated and agreed, with people paying what they believe the product is worth. All these individual buying and selling decisions lead to the theory of supply and demand – if people don't think the product is worth the price, they won't buy or they buy from elsewhere. Because of this, it is believed that free markets are self-regulating (the invisible hand).
- Deregulation – the abolition of regulations that restrict competition except when justified on the grounds of safety, environmental or consumer protection.

This approach was influential in shaping social and economic policies in the 1980s and 1990s. It was influenced by the economic theories of Freidrich Von Hayek (1899–1992), who wrote *The Road to Serfdom*. Hayek favoured some regulation but saw liberty as a prerequisite to wealth and growth, rather than the other way round. Another key figure was Milton Friedman (1912–2006) who advocated *monetarism* and stated that there was a natural rate of unemployment. The New Right is closely linked to functionalism because it is a structural theory, based on consensus.

The New Right theorists believe that capitalist society should be based on choices; individuals have a choice as to how they spend their money and what services they want to pay for. They believe that state provision, such as the welfare state, interferes with the smooth running of the market economy because competition is the best way of ensuring efficiency. There is an assertion that the free market produces wealth and freedom and that for it to operate effectively it is essential to minimise the state and maximise the private sector. The theories of the New Right introduced market principles into society, especially in areas of public life, through the privatisation of state enterprises in order to open them up to competition and promote choice in line with free market principles. There is a belief that the private sector will be able to provide services more efficiently; that is, better and cheaper. The New Right approach considers that traditional values (such as the family, education and nationalism) are being threatened by too much state intervention and that the availability of welfare benefits is a disincentive to hard work.

However, this theory has been criticised for destroying community and collective ideals due to its emphasis on market principles, which only deliver wealth and freedom for a minority of individuals. By imposing a set of social, cultural and political policies and practices that use the language of markets – choice, efficiency and individual autonomy – financial risk is shifted from government and corporations and onto individuals and families.

> ## Key terms
>
> **Individualism** – emphasises liberties in terms of 'freedom from', e.g. government control – negative liberties.
>
> **Collectivism** – emphasises 'rights to', e.g. health care – positive liberties.

> ## Activity 3
>
> **In groups, carry out research and identify three ways in which market principles are applied to health and care services in Britain.**

2 Understand sociological approaches to health and social care

There is clearly a social aspect to health and illness, since illness happens in the everyday world, not in social isolation. For clarity, some sociologists have categorised human disorders as:

- disease – this describes the physiological malfunctioning of the body
- illness – refers to the individual's subjective awareness of disorder

> ## Key term
>
> **Physiological** – the functioning of the different parts of the body and their relationship to the efficient functioning of the whole organism.

- sickness – describes the social role of the unwell.

Sociologists have studied these different aspects as well as the impact of the medical professions and the role of knowledge in shaping health and health beliefs.

Understanding different concepts of health and illness

The concept of health has always been more difficult to define than that of illness, mainly because illness is usually associated with symptoms that can be seen and/or described. However, the definition of health is important because health is desirable, and therefore has implications for promoting health. Several different ways of defining health have been put forward over time. For example:

- Negative definition – health is seen merely as the absence of any physical illness or disease.
- Positive definition – health is seen as a process; a person achieves a healthy state through their own efforts in maintaining themselves.
- Holistic definition – this definition considers the whole person rather than specific parts or aspects and would include, for example, mental health.

The World Health Organisation offered the following definition in 1946:

> 'Health is a state of complete physical, mental and social well-being and not merely the absence of disease or infirmity.'

This is the most commonly accepted definition but it can be problematic as it is difficult to achieve.

Models of health

Based on these definitions, health can be considered in two ways; the bio-medical and socio-medical models.

Bio-medical model

The bio-medical health model originates from the belief in *mind–body dualism*. Influenced by the philosopher Descartes in the seventeenth century, this is the belief that the mind is distinct from, and operates separately to, the body. The bio-medical model is one of the main features of modern, Western society, which promotes science and reason over religious or superstitious explanations for health and illness, and has been accompanied by the rise in power of the medical profession. The emphasis within the bio-medical model is on the treatment of ill health. The human body is regarded as a machine and illness as a malfunction of the machine. Ill health is treated as an external attack on the body and symptoms are the evidence; it is a temporary state that can be fixed. The bio-medical position on health sees it as resulting from specific diseases, which are diagnosed by a health professional. This professional is the only person with the expertise to tell whether a person is sick or healthy. Within the bio-medical model, illness occurs naturally and independently of social behaviour or social influences.

The bio-medical model has been criticised for failing to address illness and disease which has no obvious physical symptoms, such as mental illness, and diseases for which there does not appear to be a biological explanation, such as anorexia, and chronic diseases, which are not time limited. It also fails to adequately address disability.

Socio-medical model

This model recognises the links between the social life and the body – for example, the effects of social change on the body, particularly the role of social and environmental influences on health and disease. Health and illness are therefore not distributed evenly across the population. In order to define illness within this model, it is necessary to understand the social context of the illness.

The social model of health and illness considers that the medical profession has high status and is in a dominant position within society and, in order to remain dominant, uses the strategies of limiting access to medical knowledge and legitimising the role of doctors diagnosing ill health and disease.

Key term

Social determinants of health – the genetic, social, lifestyle, cultural and environmental factors that influence health and the likelihood of ill health and disease.

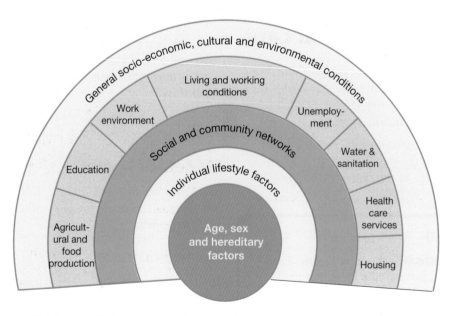

Dahlgren and Whitehead's (1991) social determinants of health

Dahlgren and Whitehead developed a model in 1991 that mapped the *social determinants of health*. The model shows how health is influenced positively or negatively by a range of factors – the 'causes of the causes' of ill health (Dahlgren and Whitehead, 2006).

This social model emphasises the importance of factors such as lifestyle, poverty, education, housing and social support in determining the health outcomes of populations.

Medicalisation

'Medicalisation' refers to the tendency to see normal life stages, experiences or events as needing medical intervention because they are considered to be risky and problematical. Because of their superior knowledge, doctors define what is normal – for example, in mental illness; they define the boundaries of normal and abnormal thinking and behaviour.

Ivan Illich (1976) examined the issue of medical-isation and claimed that the medical profession has created the belief that it has special knowledge and skills that cannot be provided by anyone else, and that people know less about their own bodies and the best ways to care for themselves than doctors. He concluded that there was convincing evidence that medicine not only has limited success in treating many conditions but, in many cases, is actually harmful. He then looked at these detrimental effects and considered that these go beyond direct clinical harm. He claims that the medical profession actually harms public health by causing increased levels of illness and social problems through medical intervention. He called this *iatrogenesis*.

Illich considered three types of iatrogenesis:

- Clinical – refers to the harm done due to wrong diagnosis or treatment, and the serious side effects of many drugs, which often need other drugs to counter such side effects.
- Social – doctors have extended their activities into areas of social life, have more control over people's lives and tell them how to adopt a 'healthy lifestyle'. People are passive and expect pills and cures for social and physical ills.
- Structural – the medical profession has reduced the ability of people to deal with

normal bodily and life changes (e.g. the female menopause). People no longer feel responsible for or able to deal with pain, sickness and death.

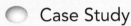

Activity 4

Case Study

Thalidomide was prescribed in the 1960s for pregnant women to overcome morning sickness. The consequences were unknown at the time, but the drug left children with severe deformities.

Discuss this in relation to Illich's theory of iatrogenesis. How does this fit with Illich's theory?

The clinical iceberg

This refers to the amount of unreported and undocumented illness, which is either time limited and self-medicated or ignored. For example, Epsom (1978) carried out a study into the health of adults using a mobile clinic. He found that some patients had major diseases, such as cancer, which had not been detected by their general practitioner (Haralambos and Holborn, 2008). It is called the clinical iceberg because the amount of unreported ill health is far greater than that which is reported (i.e. the tip of the iceberg).

Application of sociological perspectives to health and social care

Functionalist perspective

This perspective is concerned with the smooth running of society, and examines how health and illness help society to function by looking at the relationship between the sick person and society as a whole.

Talcott Parsons suggested that in Western societies,

sickness is socially determined. He described the 'sick role': the patterns of behaviour adopted by the individual to minimise the disruptive impact of illness whilst they are unable to carry out their normal functions. Adopting this sick role provides the sick person with rights but also obligations. Parsons suggested that:

- By adopting the sick role, the individual is exempted from normal duties, obligations and work activities, depending on the seriousness of the illness and other people's acceptance of this. Often, the doctor is consulted to legitimise the illness through diagnosis and treatment.
- The sick role is seen as something that happens to the person. The individual has no choice, is blameless and therefore has a right to be cared for by others.
- The sick person has a responsibility to try and get better as soon as possible, accepting that being ill is undesirable and temporary.
- In order to do this, it is expected that the sick person will consult the doctor, use available healthcare resources and comply with all treatment in order to regain their health.

Because the medical profession has a key role in legitimising illness, acting as a gatekeeper, it allows people who are ill to withdraw from society whilst at the same time protecting the public from people who want to abuse the system. This explanation helps us to understand how society benefits and how people are expected to behave when they are ill.

This perspective looks only at the response to illness, not how people experience, construct and identify illness. For example, some people do not have the option of withdrawing from society and others may deny or fail to recognise their ill health (e.g. in the case of mental illness).

Marxist perspective

This approach considers how health and illness benefit capitalism. Vincente Navarro (1986) identified three ways in which capitalism benefits from medicine:

- Medicine contributes to maintaining a healthy workforce and therefore the profits of the ruling class (bourgeoisie). Doctors ensure that people are fit to work – for example, by

treating illness and by making sure that those claiming incapacity benefits are actually unable to work.
- Medicine is a social structure and part of the capitalist system; many people are employed either directly by the medical and healthcare establishment, such as doctors and nurses, or indirectly, such as manufacturers of medical technology and the pharmaceutical industry.
- Work within a capitalist system is unrewarding and a major cause of ill health. For example, workers receive minimal reward for their labour in order to extract maximum profit, rather than being paid for the true value of their labour. This means that there are significant socio-economic inequalities and low socio-economic status leads to poorer health.

Navarro claimed that the dominant bio-medical model of health is similar to capitalism as it stresses individual responsibility for health and, by ignoring the social causes, it obscures the exploitative nature of capitalism.

Post-modernist perspective

In the twenty-first century, people are living longer, thanks to a range of different factors such as better nutrition, preventive medicine and safer working practices. Post-modernists believe that in a media-dominated age we create meaning from the images we are subjected to. Consequently, post-modernists suggest that there is increasing emphasis on the quality of life, self-determination (the idea that the individual is in charge of and is able to shape their own life) and healthy living. For post-modernists, health care has hence become a commodity to be traded for profit. Examples include:

- The building of new hospitals and clinics using private finance (Private Finance Initiative); the state (the taxpayer) pays the money back, with interest, over many years.
- The growth of plastic surgery, in which people undergo clinically unnecessary medical interventions to aspire to a commercially induced ideal of beauty.
- The development of polyclinics, in which not only the buildings, but the health care of patients is delivered by private medical insurance companies.

● The growth of the leisure industry – gyms, spas – holistic medicine, well-being centres and alternative medicine; these are about the individual exercising health choices.

Symbolic interactionist perspective

An interactionist looks at health and the meaning, impact and consequences that illness can have on people's lives. Interactionists focus on how people come to define themselves as ill, including the interactions between doctors and patients, aimed at reaching agreed definitions of illness. They suggest that disease is a social construction, particularly those diseases which do not have an obvious cause, or obvious symptoms, and that it can be seen as a form of social deviance. The label 'ill' is only applied to certain groups and not to others. For example, people with long-term conditions and disabilities learn to live with illness and may choose not to describe themselves as ill, even though other people might.

The 'clinical iceberg' exists because not everyone chooses to define themselves as ill and visit the doctor. The 'health belief model' was developed by the US Public Health Service in the 1950s (Becker, 1974), which considers:

● Motivation – what makes someone more likely to define themselves as ill?
● Estimation – the individual's perception of the likely harm to themselves of an illness, balanced against the level of interference with their daily lives and social activities.
● Compensation – what benefits will they obtain from being ill and receiving treatment?

Other factors for consideration within this model include the age of the individual, the social, physical and social costs of treatment, attitude of the medical professionals and the influence of others in recommending action.

Phenomenological perspective

Phenomenologists focus on the meaning of a phenomenon; in this case, what health or illness means to the individual, and the development of shared meanings.

Phenomenology is concerned with human understanding. Differences in the meanings that people attach to experiences are possible because everyone interprets their world separately from everyone else. The ability to enable others to share one's understanding depends on language and the ability to describe experiences in a way that is meaningful for others.

For example, this is why some conditions experienced by individuals are difficult for doctors to accept, e.g. chronic fatigue syndrome (myalgic encephalomyelitis or ME). Because the cause of this condition is unknown, some doctors have difficulty diagnosing the condition, leading to problems in the relationships between doctors and ME patients.

Feminist perspectives

Feminists are concerned with women's unequal position in society relative to men and sociological approaches seek to explain how this situation arose and has been maintained. Considerable attention has been paid to medicine, health and illness and, in particular, reproduction, maternity and childbirth, which are conditions exclusive to women.

Radical feminist perspective

Radical feminists start from the assertion that, in Western society, women are oppressed and exploited by men. They see medicine as a male-dominated, patriarchal agent of social control, designed to keep women in a subordinate position. The medical establishment has exclusive knowledge and power – knowledge is power.

Medicine has historically been used to control women's behaviour, particularly in relation to sexuality, reproduction and childbirth (Ehrenreich and English, 1978; Turner, 1987). It is argued that medicine has taken over from religion in the regulation of women's bodies, in which sex outside the institution of marriage is seen as deviant and punished accordingly. The difficulties experienced by young women in accessing contraception and abortion and the controversy over the availability of the morning-after pill in pharmacies are examples of this type of regulation. Similarly, in relation to rape and domestic violence, all these issues are presented as the woman's individual problem and not social problems of male violence.

The medicalisation of pregnancy and childbirth is another way in which control over women is demonstrated. Examples include strict guidelines on what pregnant women should eat and drink and the lack of accurate information on the actual level of risk posed by these rules. Despite the availability of information on the internet, the information offered is often confusing and contradictory (e.g. the safety of alcohol during pregnancy). Messages disguised as 'scientific' are often about scaring women into behaving in a particular way; in other words, they are social messages.

Liberal feminist perspectives

Liberal feminists look at how men dominate aspects of health and illness and how women within health and social care are assigned what are perceived to be lesser roles. Medicine and medical institutions are dominated by men, and the institutions themselves are gendered, i.e. female doctors are most likely to be found in areas associated with women's role such as paediatrics (children's health), and those areas that are seen as less attractive (Cinderella services), such as geriatrics (older people) or psychiatry. There are fewer women in professorial roles or surgery.

Women lack power and influence in their dealings with the medical profession and are often positioned as responsible for maintaining the health of the whole family, including that of men. For example, a sign in a local GP's surgery aimed at

Activity 5   P2

Read the case study below and explain what this means from two different sociological perspectives.

 Case Study

In New York, under a system introduced in 1992, qualified midwives wishing to offer a home birth service are obliged, under state law, to be approved to practise by a hospital or an obstetrician, in addition to their professional training.

Only one of the city's hospitals was prepared to underwrite (insure) the midwives and now it has gone bankrupt, the midwives are unable to practise legally – within the law – and could theoretically be arrested for undertaking the work they have been trained for.

This means that mothers in New York who wish to deliver their babies at home under the care of a trained midwife are unable to do so.

In the USA, less than 1 per cent of babies are born at home, compared with 30 per cent in the Netherlands and 2.7 per cent in the UK.

Obstetricians in the US are trained to offer intervention in childbirth and may not even have seen a natural birth. They are in charge of 92 per cent of births and under the private medical system see midwives as competition.

The US spends more money on pregnancy and childbirth-related hospital costs than any other type of hospital care, with one in three deliveries being by caesarean section.

The US has one of the highest rates of maternal mortality (women dying in childbirth or as a direct result of childbirth) in the industrialised world, at 16.7 deaths per 100,000 live births, compared with 8.2 in the UK and 7.6 in the Netherlands.

Source: *Guardian*, 14th May 2010

women asked them to encourage the men in their lives to attend the Well Man clinic.

Certain conditions are more likely to be ascribed to women than men (e.g. depression and anxiety, sleeplessness, migraine). Women with these symptoms are more likely to be diagnosed with a mental illness than men. Men presenting with the same symptoms tend to be identified as suffering from stress. Despite this there are strong links between mental health and economic well-being and women suffer from income inequality compared with men.

Marxist feminist perspectives

Marxists see medicine as a way of maintaining the existing social order and oppressive power relationships. For feminists, this means that capitalism benefits from women's role in reproduction by reproducing the workforce. Childbearing is associated with childrearing and women are given responsibility for both roles. Women are also expected to do the domestic tasks associated with running a household and act as a reserve army of labour as required, so they need to be healthy. Women support capitalism through both production and reproduction.

The Marxist view is that the dominant bio-medial model of health stresses the individual nature of illness, ignoring the social aspects of ill health, which for women, includes the stresses of managing the conflicting demands of the 'double day' (i.e. how to fulfil their multiple responsibilities as homemakers, mothers and workers). They are more likely to work part-time in order to do this, which has an impact on both their physical and financial health, perpetuating women's financial inequality since they get paid less than men and part-time work tends to pay less than full-time work in any case.

Medicalisation of pregnancy and childbirth also allows capitalism to profit through new technologies and drugs.

Understanding patterns and trends in health and illness among different social groups

There are many ways in which sociologists can measure patterns and trends in health and illness. Sociologists argue that the way in which health is measured indicates how health is considered, and reveals different perspectives on health and illness.

Morbidity rates

Morbidity looks at sickness rates, whether temporary (acute), long term (chronic) or without cure (terminal). It is measured statistically

Table 7.2 Standard mortality rates, 1971–1998

Males	All causes	Cancer oesophagus	Cancer lung	Cancer breast	Cancer prostate
1971	111	84	106	n/a	92
1981	100	99	100	n/a	100
1991	84	130	82	n/a	140
1995	79	140	70	n/a	137
1998	73	143	63	n/a	128
Females					
1971	110	91	69	94	n/a
1981	100	98	98	101	n/a
1991	86	114	89	105	n/a
1995	84	120	78	80	n/a
1998	81	118	72	75	n/a

(e.g. through GP sick notes, hospital records or prescriptions dispensed). Some diseases are notifiable in law to the authorities because they pose a threat to public health (the health of the population). Doctors must report incidences of these diseases to the local authority (e.g. tuberculosis and meningitis), so statistics are more likely to be accurate. Morbidity statistics examine the frequency and prevalence of diseases within population groups.

The advantage of these statistics is that they are reliable. However, a large number of people who are ill do not contact doctors and are therefore not taken into account when statistics are examined – the clinical iceberg. A patient may also visit the doctor on several occasions for the same symptoms. There is no real way of filtering these out and therefore this may distort the statistics. In addition, some diseases are not necessarily recorded as they depend on an accurate diagnosis, which is difficult in controversial cases such as chronic fatigue syndrome, where there is no agreement about the condition.

Mortality rates

The mortality rate compares the number of people who die of a particular disease or condition with those who would be expected to die of all other causes – all other deaths. The calculation is done per 100,000 of a population for each year. The standard mortality rate (SMR) assumes the average risk of death for those aged 16–65 years to be 100. Those with an SMR of 100+ have a higher risk of an early death.

The advantage of mortality rates is that they are objective. They can also give scope for comparing countries. However, a mortality rate does not reflect the quality of life the person has. For health and social care professionals, this would be an important consideration.

From Table 7.2, it is possible to see that life expectancy has gone up because deaths from all causes have gone down.

Similarly, cancer of the oesophagus was less likely to kill you than other causes in 1971, but more likely in 1998 because death from all causes had decreased, so cancer of the oesophagus made up a greater proportion of all deaths.

Men are less likely to get cancer of the breast; the numbers are so small that it is statistically insignificant. Women do not get prostate cancer.

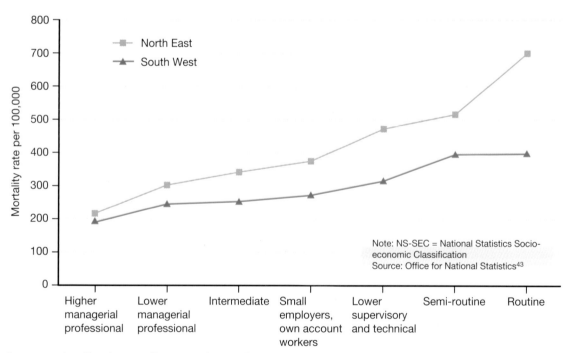

Note: NS-SEC = National Statistics Socio-economic Classification
Source: Office for National Statistics[43]

Age standardised mortality rates by socio-economic classification (NS-SEC) in the North East and South West regions, men aged 25–64, 2001–2003

However, the figures tell us that better progress has been made in treating breast cancer than prostate cancer because the higher proportion of all deaths from prostate cancer has increased whereas the proportion of all deaths from breast cancer has decreased.

Current mortality rates are shown in the graphs on page 189.

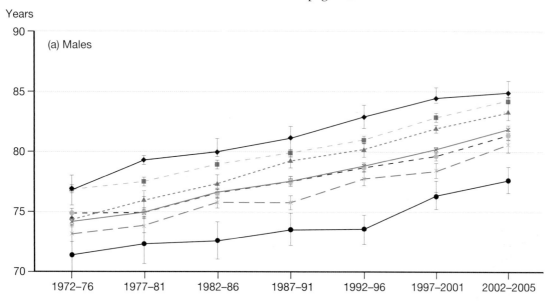

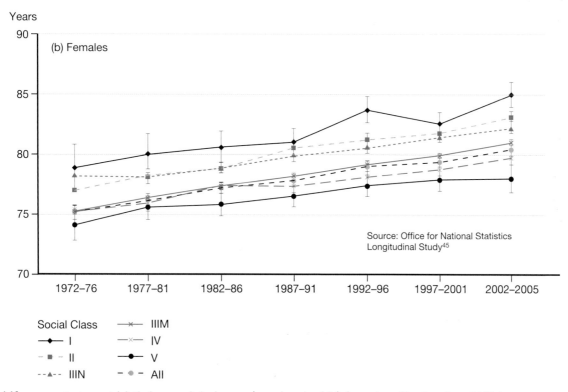

Life expectancy at birth by social class, a) males and b) females, England and Wales, 1972–2005

Key term

Standardised mortality rate – this is a calculation based on the number of actual deaths compared with the expected number of deaths in a particular group.

Health surveillance

This measures the frequency of health and illness revealed by screening results (e.g. cervical screening). It can predict symptoms and illness that may occur. However, health professionals are not able to screen for all illnesses, which means that this way of measuring health and illness is not a true representation. In addition, not everyone who is entitled to screening procedures will use them.

Health inequalities

Much of the statistical data available is based on a functionalist approach and the bio-medical model of health. It has focused on individuals' responsibility for their own health and the role of disease, telling us nothing about the causes of these diseases, or people's experiences. Of course, statistics only tell us what has been measured and take no account of the actual level of ill health – for example, in relation to unreported and undiagnosed ill health (the clinical iceberg).

However, there is a well-documented link between social class and health. The Black Report (Townsend and Davidson, 1982) was the first and most influential. The report examined the differences in mortality and morbidity according to social class, and used the Registrar General's five occupational categories, as was used by government at the time. They found that there was an inverse relationship between social class and health; in other words, the higher the social class, the lower the mortality rate. Four possible explanations were offered:

1 The differences were a result of the way mortality and social class are measured – *artefact explanation*. The accuracy of statistics has been questioned, as has the relevance of the categories of social class in modern society; some sociologists have argued that these categories ignore the huge differences in wealth and power between the 5 per cent who own most of the wealth and the rest of the population.

2 Social class differences are explained by the fact that healthier people are more able to be socially mobile and improve their social class – *social selection explanation*. Sociologists have argued that the evidence shows that those from poorer backgrounds suffer economic, social and employment obstacles and this causes ill health, affecting opportunities to improve their life chances.

3 Lower social classes (working class) are more likely to adopt unhealthy lifestyles – *cultural explanations*. This explanation has been criticised for blaming the individual and ignoring the social factors affecting health – for example, the fact that healthier food is more expensive and capitalism obtains profit from selling a greater volume of unhealthy foods.

4 Economic differences lead directly and indirectly to higher mortality rates for those with less income – *material explanations*. Sociologists argue that it is the structure of capitalist society which creates inequalities in the pursuit of profit and, although most people in capitalist societies have enough to eat, the quality of their food and the circumstances in which they live cause them to be less healthy and die younger. Social factors are a significant factor in determining health.

Activity 6   M1

In small groups, discuss the advantages and disadvantages of the bio-medical model of health and the social model of health for two different groups (e.g. disabled people, older people or mothers). Compare your answers with your group and agree conclusions.

Health inequalities are based on income inequalities, and explanations of other inequalities linked to, for example, ethnicity or gender have, at their source, income differences.

For example, health differences based on gender are explainable in terms of income inequality. More women than men work part-time in order to combine paid work with childcare responsibilities and part-time work is less well paid. Secondly, the gender divisions of labour mean that women receive only 80 per cent of male wages on average. In addition, when families break down, women are usually left with the responsibility of bringing up children; over 90 per cent of single parents are women. Where women are not able to combine work with childcare responsibilities (e.g. due to the high cost of private nursery provision), they have to rely on welfare benefits. These factors all cause women to be economically disadvantaged and less healthy as a result.

Health inequalities have, more recently, been seen as an issue of social justice and there has been a gradual recognition of the social determinants of health – a move away from the bio-medical model and towards the social model of health. This has been influenced by the World Health Organisation's focus on European health inequalities in the report by Goran Dahlgren and Margaret Whitehead (*European Strategies for Tackling Social Inequalities in Health*, 2007). Dahlgren and Whitehead produced a visual model of the social factors affecting health (see figure on page 180).

Whilst there has been an improvement overall in the health of the people in the UK, there remains

Activity 7   P3   M2   D1

Using the categories in Dahlgren and Whitehead's model, explain the patterns and trends in health and illness between those in higher managerial and professional occupations and those in routine occupations, with reference to one or more sociological perspectives.

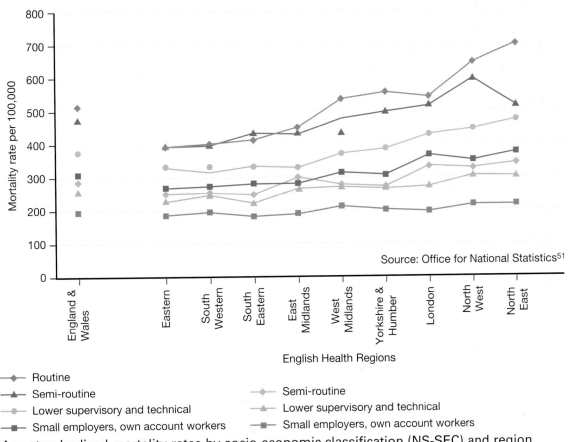

Source: Office for National Statistics[51]

English Health Regions

- ◆ Routine
- ▲ Semi-routine
- ● Lower supervisory and technical
- ■ Small employers, own account workers

- ◆ Semi-routine
- ▲ Lower supervisory and technical
- ■ Small employers, own account workers

Age standardised mortality rates by socio-economic classification (NS-SEC) and region, men aged 25–64, 2001–2003

a gap between the healthiest and wealthiest and those who are relatively poor. In fact, the gap between the healthiest and the least healthy has widened (see graph on page 187).

> 'In the poorest neighbourhoods of England, life expectancy is 67 years, similar to the national average in Egypt or Thailand, and lower than the average of Ecuador, China and Belize, all countries that have a lower Gross Domestic Product and do not have a national health service.'
>
> Source: *Marmot Review: Fair Society, Healthy Lives*, DH, 2008)

As a result, inequalities have been examined at neighbourhood level so that the social and environmental factors affecting health can be more easily identified and local authorities can take action to improve health.

Favourable and less favourable environmental conditions include, for example, river water quality, air quality, green space, habitat favourable to bio-diversity, flood risk, litter and rubbish, housing conditions, road accidents and regulated sites such as landfill and industry.

Summary

Sociology provides a useful approach to evaluating information on health and social care and an understanding of the advantages and disadvantages of statistical data.

Sociological perspectives enable a theoretical evaluation of the health and care sectors of society and the reasons for persistent health inequalities and trends in health and illness among different groups in society.

Assessment and grading criteria

In order to pass this unit, the evidence that the learner presents for assessment needs to demonstrate that they can meet all the learning outcomes for the unit. The assessment criteria for a pass grade describe the level of achievement required to pass this unit.

To achieve a pass grade the evidence must show that the learner is able to:	To achieve a merit grade the evidence must show that, in addition to the pass criteria, the learner is able to:	To achieve a distinction grade the evidence must show that, in addition to the pass and merit criteria, the learner is able to:
P1 explain the principal sociological perspectives	**M1** assess the bio-medical and socio-medical models of health	
P2 explain different sociological approaches to health and ill health		
P3 explain patterns and trends in health and illness among different social groupings.	**M2** use different sociological perspectives to discuss patterns and trends of health and illness in two different social groups.	**D1** evaluate different sociological explanations for patterns and trends of health and illness in two different social groups.

Resources

Becker, M. (1974) *The Health Belief Model and Personal Health Behavior*, Thorofare, N.J.: C.B. Slack.

Dahlgren, G. and Whitehead, M. (2006) *European Strategies for Tackling Social Inequalities in Health: Levelling Up Part 2*, WHO Collaborating Centre for Policy Research on Social Determinants of Health: University of Liverpool.

Ehrenreich, B. and English, D. (1978) *For Her Own Good: 150 Years of the Experts' Advice to Women*, Garden City, N.Y.: Anchor Books.

Giddens, A. (2009) *Sociology, 6th edition*, Cambridge: Polity Press.

Haralambos, M. and Holborn, M. (2008) *Sociology Themes and Perspectives*, London: Harper Collins.

Illich, I. (1976) *Limits to Medicine. Medical Nemesis: The Expropriation of Health*, London: Marion Boyars.

Navarro, V. (1986) *Crisis, Health and Medicine: A Critique*, New York and London: Tavistock.

Townsend, P. and Davidson, N. (1982) *Inequalities in Health: The Black Report 1980*, London: Pelican.

Turner, B. (1987) *Medical Power and Social Knowledge*, London: Sage Publications.

Introduction

This unit provides an introduction to different psychological approaches and shows how these can be used in study and in health and social care.

Psychology was studied in Ancient Greece over 2,000 years ago. 'Psychology' refers to the study of how mental processes influence behaviour. When you study this unit, you are learning about a subject that has fascinated people for thousands of years: why do we behave the way we do?

The Acropolis in Athens dates from the time of Ancient Greece

Did you know...

The Greek word 'psyche' means 'mind' or 'soul'.
A word that ends in 'ology' refers to the knowledge of a subject.

Learning outcomes:

On completion of this unit, you should:

1 Understand psychological perspectives

2 Understand psychological approaches to health and social care.

1 Understand psychological perspectives

In this section, we will look at six major perspectives, or approaches, of psychology. These are outlined in the diagram on page 193.

Key term

Perspectives – views or approaches. There are six main psychological perspectives: behaviourist, social learning, psychodynamic, humanistic, cognitive/ information processing and biological.

Did you know...

Although there are several psychological perspectives, many psychologists now think that there is no one correct approach, but that a combination of views may explain behaviour.

Ivan Pavlov (1849–1936) studied dogs and found that, when a bell was rung at feeding time, the dogs salivated. Gradually he withdrew the food but rang the bell and noticed that the dogs still salivated. He called this classical conditioning. The dogs associated the sound of the bell with food and were conditioned to respond to the bell.

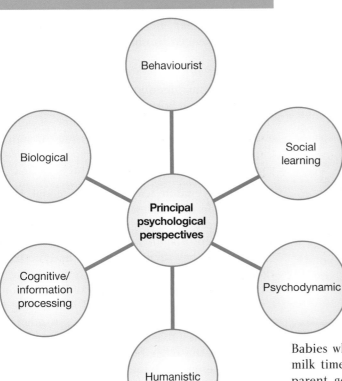

Ivan Pavlov

The behaviourist approach

Babies who are bottle fed often know when it is milk time because they recognise the signs of a parent getting the bottle ready. They may start salivating too. This is a conditioned response. Sometimes if the parent is getting the bottle ready for later in the day, the baby gets confused and wonders where the milk is.

Key terms

Behaviourist – focuses on behaviour as a learned response.
Conditioning – a learned response to a stimulus.

B.F. Skinner (1904–1990) researched operant conditioning. This is where conditioning is used to modify behaviour. Key terms are:

● Reinforcement – where a consequence causes behaviour to occur more often; a child who is praised for picking up his toys will do so again in the hope of being praised again.
● Punishment – causes behaviour to occur less often, so a young person who is caught shoplifting and charged with the offence will think carefully before shoplifting again.
● Extinction – a term to describe no consequence following a response. Experienced parents may use this with

Behaviourists believed that there is a scientific explanation for behaviour and that behaviour can be learned and shaped scientifically. They used methods such as scientific experiment and observation to explain how people behaved. Two of the main theorists were Ivan Pavlov and B.F. Skinner.

B.F. Skinner

a toddler to reduce pester power in the supermarket. If the parent does not respond to the child's demands, the child gets bored and stops asking.

Key term

Reinforcement – this causes behaviour to occur more often.

Skinner used positive reinforcement and negative reinforcement with rats. He also used positive punishment and negative punishment. See Table 8.1 for an explanation.

Skinner believed that behaviour could be changed or modified, but he did not believe that punishment worked. He reasoned that if punishment worked, people would not go back into prison.

Skinner believed in positive reinforcement, rewarding the desired behaviour. Some teachers and social workers use this technique to manage behaviour in young people. Parents find this method effective too.

The social learning approach

Key term

Social learning – we learn behaviour from others.

Social learning means learning from others. We learn from other individuals and from groups. We are influenced by our culture and by society. The desired behaviour is observed, then modelled symbolically, in play, then acted out for real. Words, images and an identity help fix the behaviour. Bandura used a Bobo Doll experiment to show that children will copy the behaviour of adults, even if the behaviour is aggressive. You can watch the experiment described by Dr Bandura on www.youtube.com/watch?v=vdh7MngntnI.

A child may watch television and model their behaviour on a character they admire. For some, the influences are nearer home. People are more likely to adopt a modelled behaviour if it results in outcomes they value and if they have nothing else in their life that offers recognition. Being a member of a gang gives status and protection. It is more probable that they will join a gang if members are similar to themselves. An admired older brother is a role model for younger brothers to follow. If the older brother joins a gang, the younger ones may join too. This is why gangs such as the Johnson Crew and the Burger Bar Boys still attract recruits in Birmingham and why there were 29 teen murders in 2008, prompting extra police measures. Despite this, by May 2010, ten teenagers had died violent deaths on London streets (www.guardian.co.uk/uk/2010/may/06/nick-pearton-london-teenager-killed).

Social learning may be positive too. Children learn to respect older people by modelling the

Did you know...

In 2009, London Metropolitan Police ran an anti-knife campaign 'Choose a Different Ending'. Watch the video and choose the ending:
www.met.police.uk/campaigns/anti_knife_crime/index.htm.

Table 8.1 Reinforcement and punishment

	Positive	Negative
Reinforcement	Desired behaviour gets a positive reward. Skinner used rats. When rats pressed a lever, they got a reward of sugar.	Desired behaviour gets the removal of discomfort. Skinner sounded a loud noise in the rat's cage. When the rat pressed the lever, the noise stopped.
Punishment	Undesirable behaviour gets an unpleasant response, so a rat showing undesirable behaviour may get a mild electric shock. A child who runs into the road may get shouted at.	Undesirable behaviour results in the removal of something pleasurable, so a rat showing undesirable behaviour may have food withdrawn. A child who hits another child may have a toy taken away.

behaviour of others around them, so in cultures where age is respected, young people will model the behaviour of their elders and learn to respect them. Children learn good manners from their parents and from those they admire.

Another type of social learning is the self-fulfilling prophecy. This is a prediction that originally may be false but becomes true. Robert King Merton first used the term. In a famous educational experiment conducted by Meichenbaum (1969), a teacher was told that, in their new class, certain students had high academic potential. In fact, this was not true at the start of the experiment, but at the end, when performance was measured, the students labelled as potentially better had in fact become better performers. This was due to the teacher's expectations of them.

Role theory implies that if we know the role expectations for a specified position much of the behaviour of the person in that role can be predicted. We may expect a teacher to be fair and to explain a subject. We do not expect a teacher to provide us with clothes or bus fare because that is not part of a teacher's role.

Key terms

Self-fulfilling prophecy – if you believe something will happen, you sometimes make it happen.
Role theory – the idea that certain behaviour is associated with certain roles, such as a doctor wears a white coat and has an air of authority.

REMEMBER

Telling yourself you are good at something may help you become good at it!

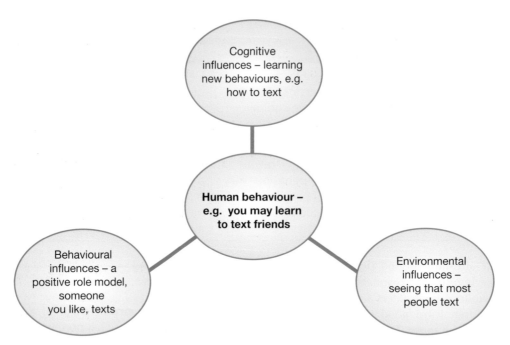

Albert Bandura's social learning theory says human behaviour is a result of continuous interaction between cognitive, behavioural and environmental influences. The diagram above may help you understand this.

The stages of social learning are as follows:

1 Attention – recognising a behaviour. For example, you watch someone doing a creative activity at placement.
2 Retention, including rehearsal of the behaviour. You imagine what you would say or do in that situation.
3 Motor reproduction – you try the behaviour out, use reflection and feedback to check how it went.
4 Motivation – you are praised by your tutor for getting involved, get positive comments from individuals and you feel a sense of achievement in overcoming your nerves.

Key terms

Psychodynamic – our unconscious mind influences our behaviour.
Unconscious mind – the part of our mind we are not aware of.

The psychodynamic approach

The psychodynamic approach emphasises the importance of the unconscious mind and of early experiences. Sigmund Freud (1856–1939) developed the psychodynamic school of psychology. His theory states that there are three parts to our mind:

● The 'id' (fully unconscious) contains drives and basic instincts. A baby passes urine without thinking about it.
● The 'ego' (mostly conscious) deals with external reality, so the child learns the rules of society – for example, to use the toilet.
● The 'super ego' (partly conscious) is the conscience or the internal moral judge, so a child who knows where the toilet is and how to use it but has an 'accident' may feel ashamed.

You may be able to think of a case study from placement that involves a similar situation.

Freud also said that early experiences shape us. He described the following stages of development:

● Oral (0–18 months). In this stage, the baby puts everything to the mouth.
● Anal (18 months–3½ years). During this phase, the child learns to control bowels and gains pleasure from this.
● Phallic (3½–6 years). In this phase, children

are working out what it means to be a girl or boy. Freud said that children fall in love with the parent of the opposite sex. Boys love their mothers most at this stage – the Oedipus complex – while girls love their fathers – the Electra complex.

- Latency (6 years–puberty). This is a period of calm in a child's life.
- Genital (puberty–adulthood). This is a period of creativity when work and love are balanced. The person is psychologically well adjusted and balanced. The child grows into the adult and is no longer 'in love' with the opposite-sex parent but may identify with their values, so a girl who loved her father because he was kind will, as an adult, adopt this as her own value and will try to be kind.

If a person does not work through a stage, they may revert to that stage when stressed. In health and care situations, you may see individuals who revert to a previous stage of behaviour when they are upset, so an adult may behave childishly.

Freud believed that personality is formed by the age of five, whereas Erik Erikson believed that changes happen throughout life. Erikson's theory

Table 8.2 Erikson's eight stages

Stage	Age	What happens
Trust versus mistrust	Birth to 1 year	The baby learns to trust the world if someone responds to their cry. If the child is neglected, they will be frustrated, withdrawn, suspicious and will lack self-confidence.
Autonomy versus shame and doubt	2–3 years	The child needs a supportive atmosphere so it can develop a sense of self-control without a loss of self-esteem. If a child does not trust the world, or is labelled as naughty, they experience shame and doubt. A child opens a cupboard and pulls out glasses. A carer who says the child is naughty will instil shame and doubt. A carer who encourages exploration also encourages independence and autonomy. Of course the carer must make sure the environment is safe for the child by removing breakable objects.
Initiative versus guilt	4–5 years	The child develops a sense of responsibility, which increases initiative during this period. If the child is made to feel too anxious, they will feel guilty.
Industry versus inferiority	6 years–puberty	The child starts school and learns about the wider world. The child learns from every aspect of the environment and is eager to learn. Success and mastery bring a feeling of achievement and encourage further industry. Failure at this stage makes them feel inferior.
Identity versus role confusion	Adolescence	The child emerges as an adolescent and forges a new identity or remains confused about their role, sometimes acting childishly.
Intimacy versus isolation	Young adulthood	The young person either remains isolated or enters a close and intimate relationship.
Generativity versus stagnation	Adulthood	This creative and nurturing phase encourages the younger generation in developing and leading useful lives too. An unfulfilled life is stagnant.
Integrity versus despair	Older age	This is when the individual looks back and evaluates their life. Some feel they have had a good life and have few regrets. They experience integrity. Some people feel bitter and betrayed by life. They are full of regrets and may despair.

of life stages is widely used in health and social care. This is a psychodynamic theory which looks at how emotional and motivational forces affect behaviour. Erikson described eight stages that humans pass through (see Table 8.2).

The humanistic approach

> ### Key term
>
> Humanistic – our behaviour is driven by needs.

The humanistic approach includes theories by Maslow and Rogers. Abraham Maslow published *A Theory of Human Motivation* in 1943, after studying high achievers. His theory states that there are five levels of need and they are hierarchical – that is, one must be fulfilled before the next one can be. The needs are usually represented in a triangle called a hierarchy of needs (see page 8).

> ### Key term
>
> Hierarchy of needs – some needs are more important to our survival than others. We need food, water and oxygen. These are basic needs we must satisfy if we are to survive. Higher-level needs, such as the need for love and belonging, come only after basic needs have been met.

The top level of needs is a growth need. The bottom four needs are deficiency needs. Only when all the deficiency needs are met can an individual self-actualise, be spontaneous and confident in who they are and be truly creative. Some people achieve self-actualisation later in life. Some people never achieve this stage, while others may achieve it early. A person may be self-actualising, but if they are suddenly plunged into a situation where they are in danger, with no food or water, they can no longer self-actualise but must focus on basic needs.

> ### Key term
>
> Self-actualisation – self-fulfilment, meeting one's full potential.

Self-concept is a person's knowledge and understanding of his or her self. Self-concept has physical, psychological and social aspects, which can be influenced by the individual's attitudes, habits and beliefs. These form self-image and self-esteem.

Social psychologist Erich Fromm (1900–1980) described self-concept as 'life being aware of itself'.

A baby is not born with a self-concept. The child gradually learns who he or she is and where they fit in the family. Self-concept is learned. A child may be physically active, psychologically confident and socially confident. These aspects are organised by the child into a self-concept. As the child grows, self-concept changes. A confident toddler may become a shy teenager. A shy teenager may later become a confident adult. Self-concept is learned, organised and dynamic.

Self-concept and self-esteem are closely linked. Self-esteem refers to how much we value ourselves. A person who feels good about themselves may also have high self-esteem.

> ### Key terms
>
> Self-concept – our awareness of ourselves and our beliefs about ourselves.
> Self-esteem – how much we value ourselves.

Carl Ransom Rogers (1902–1987) worked with Abraham Maslow and founded the humanist approach to psychology. He developed the idea of a person-centred approach to psychotherapy. The person or individual is the focus, not the therapist. In *On Becoming a Person: A Therapist's View of Psychotherapy* (1961/1977), he said: 'It is the client who knows what hurts, what directions to go, what problems are crucial, what experiences have been deeply buried.'

A key factor in the development of personality is whether a child is raised with unconditional positive regard. 'Unconditional positive regard' means that the child is accepted for itself, with no conditions attached. A child who is loved in this way will develop freely and self-actualise. A child who is told 'we won't love you if…' receives conditional regard and is scared to experiment or be creative in case affection is withdrawn.

Rogers believed that self-actualisation was not just about happiness but about experiencing a rich and full life where the individual is not afraid to live and may experience pain as well as happiness. According to Rogers, a fully functioning person is open rather than defensive, lives each moment fully rather than thinking about what comes next, trusts their own judgement of a situation, makes choices and takes responsibility for their behaviour. The fully functioning person is creative and reliable. They experience the good life which, according to Rogers, 'involves the courage to be. It means launching oneself fully into the stream of life' (Rogers, 1961).

The cognitive/information processing approach

> ### Key term
>
> **Cognitive/information processing** – how we understand the world. Cognitive refers to our thinking processes. A child starts by calling everything red, but as they develop cognitively, they can tell the difference between red, pink and orange.

Jean Piaget (1896–1980) described four stages of cognitive development:

- Sensori-motor stage: from birth to two years, where children experience the world through movement and through their senses. They learn that objects covered over by a blanket do not disappear.
- Pre-operational stage: from ages two to seven, where children develop motor skills, such as hopping, skipping and writing.
- Concrete operational stage: from ages 7 to 11, where children begin to think logically about concrete events and can see that 12 sweets shared between four children gives three sweets each.
- Formal operational stage: after age 11, children can reason that 13 sweets shared between four children will leave one sweet remaining. They will not need to physically have the sweets to work through the problem. They use abstract reasoning.

- Some people with learning difficulties may be at a different stage, even though by chronological age they are considered adult.

George Kelly's personal construct theory (PCT) is widely used in education and management to help make sense of how an individual views the world or processes information. The individual interprets the world around them by seeing patterns of events, similarities and contrasts. They refine these constructs in the light of further events. Information processing involves filtering out some information and selecting that which we consider important.

Core constructs govern the processes by which people maintain their identities. These super-ordinate constructs tend to be more fixed and the individual may be reluctant to change these ideas. For example, a person may see themselves as unattractive even though others do not.

> ### Key term
>
> **Information processing** – refers to how we make sense of all the stimuli around us. We see, hear, taste, touch and smell the world around us. Most people can filter out the information they do not need but people with autism have difficulty filtering and processing. They may get information overload, and crash out, just like a computer crashing.

An individual may not be aware of their personal constructs. Kelly devised a 'role construct repertory test' to help people identify some of their personal constructs. Here is an example of how it works:

- Compare and contrast your mother, your father and yourself.
- How are two of them the same?
- How do two of them differ?

The individual may say that they are like their mother and have a trusting nature, but their father is not as trusting as their mother. This then identifies that 'trusting' is one of the individual's core constructs.

These results can be noted on a repertory grid, such as the simplified one in Table 8.3. Constructs are the attributes to be measured.

Table 8.3 Simplified repertory grid

Construct	Elements			Construct
	Mother	Father	Self	
Trusting	1	7	1	Suspicious
Emotional	1	7	5	Logical
Attractive				Unattractive
Popular				Unpopular

Groups of three are presented each time, so the individual can say how they are like someone and how they differ from someone. They can then say how each element would score on a rating of 1 to 7, with 1 being the most. A trusting mother would score 1. A suspicious father would score 7.

The individual may score themselves as being very trusting like their mother, so they both score 1. The individual may decide that their mother is very emotional, but they themselves are logical, but father is even more logical. Repertory grids can be complicated.

The biological approach

Key term

Biological – how the physical body influences behaviour – for example, through genetic inheritance.

Did you know...

MRI scans can identify regions of high brain activity.

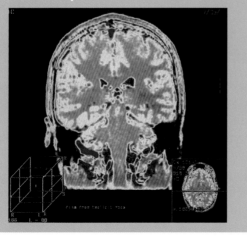

Maturational theory states that development depends on maturation, especially of the nervous system. Psychologist and paediatrician Arnold L. Gesell said that behaviour seems to follow a set developmental pattern. For example, there is a critical period when humans learn language. This cannot happen until the nerve pathways in the brain have developed enough for the baby to distinguish sounds. Similarly, walking happens only when the child develops control of the muscles in the legs and back. Reading happens only after a child has learned to focus and control eye movements.

Key term

Maturational theory – states that our brain has to mature to be able to shape behaviour. It is no good expecting a one-month-old baby to speak in sentences. The language part of their brain is not sufficiently developed to enable it to form words.

Recent research on the development of teenage brains provided evidence to support the view that teenagers cannot help their emotional outbursts. The adolescent brain undergoes massive changes as it matures. Find out more about the teenage brain on the US website National Institute of Mental Health: www.nimh.nih.gov/health/publications/teenage-brain-a-work-in-progress-fact-sheet.

Did you know...

The brain does not reach maturity until 20 or 30 years old.

Although Gesell believed in the importance of genetic influences on behaviour, he was also aware that nurture or upbringing has an effect on how children develop. Several twin studies have been carried out to try to find out how much of behaviour is due to genes and how much is due to nurture. Monozygotic (MZ, identical) twins share all of their genes, while dizygotic (DZ, fraternal) twins share only half of their genes. Therefore, identical twins should be more alike than fraternal twins.

One famous study of twins separated at birth suggests a strong link between genes and behaviour. Thomas J. Bouchard is director of the Minnesota Center for Twin and Adoption Research, University of Minnesota. In 1979, Bouchard came across a pair of twins, Jim Springer and Jim Lewis, who, separated from birth, were reunited at the age of 39. Bouchard later wrote:

> 'The twins were found to have married women named Linda, divorced and married the second time to women named Betty. One named his son James Allan, the other named his son James Alan, and both named their pet dogs Toy.'

The importance of genetic influences on autism, bipolar disorder and other mental health issues is being researched at the Maudesley Hospital in London. Sometimes endocrine or hormonal imbalance may cause depression. Seasonal affective disorder (SAD) is thought to be due to a lack of serotonin in the brain. Boosting serotonin levels relieves the disorder. Read more about this on the NHS website: www.nhs.uk/conditions/seasonal-affective-disorder.

Another biological reason for changes in health and behaviour may be lack of sleep due to disrupted sleep rhythms. Circadian rhythms are our body's natural pattern and are linked to light levels, which in turn are linked to hormones. When we work shifts or do not sleep regularly, our circadian rhythm is disturbed. Pilots have to cope with the effects of jetlag on their health.

Activity 1   P1   M1

Split into four groups of six and research the six psychological perspectives, with one person in each group taking a different perspective. Present your findings in the following ways:

- **Red group presents using a PowerPoint presentation.**

- **Blue group presents using posters.**

- **Yellow group makes leaflets.**

- **Green group develops and performs short scenarios to illustrate each perspective.**

To achieve M1, you should discuss the perspectives and assess each of the different psychological approaches to study.

2 Understand psychological approaches to health and social care

In the first part of this unit, we looked at psychological approaches, but to fully understand them, we need to apply these ideas to health and social care. This section deals with the application of psychological perspectives to health and social care practice.

The behaviourist approach

Skinner believed that behaviour could be changed or modified, but he did not believe that punishment worked. He believed in positive reinforcement, rewarding the desired behaviour. He also believed that the reinforcement should be immediate so the child associates the behaviour with the pleasure of being rewarded. A child who is often disruptive will respond to praise for listening during story time and will subsequently repeat good behaviour. A young person who is destructive of his own and other people's work will respond to praise when they try to create something. Further positive reinforcement will shape and change their behaviour. A person on an anger management course will respond positively if you acknowledge positively when they deal with a situation calmly. This behaviourist technique can be used when dealing with challenging behaviour.

The social learning approach

> ### Case Study
>
> Jake is on placement at a residential care home. He is not sure how to talk to the residents but he sees the senior care assistant asking each person what they would like to drink mid-morning. He notices that she gives them a free choice and makes sure everyone is asked. When he has to do the mid-morning drinks, he does the same, having learned from watching the senior care assistant.

Positive role models influence behaviour and are used in health education campaigns.

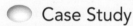

Did you know... ❓

Diversity, the winners of Britain's Got Talent 2009, teamed up with the Department of Health in a competition to get children active and combat obesity.

The psychodynamic approach

A Freudian psychodynamic approach to understanding challenging behaviour would look at a person's early life and relationship with parents to explain why they now have this behaviour. Understanding the role of ego and super ego may help the person understand their own behaviour, but this approach must be used with caution as many people find Freud's ideas difficult. Using the concepts of id, ego and super ego, a mental health nurse may work with a service user to help them understand why they have challenging behaviour. The 'id' (fully unconscious) contains drives and basic instincts.

> ### Case Study
>
> Rob, a teenager with challenging behaviour, lives in a residential unit as his parents can no longer cope with him at home. After a visit from his parents, he is angry they will not take him home and he throws his television out of the window.

A mental health nurse or counsellor may talk with Rob and help him to understand that, when he acts this way, it is the id driving his behaviour. Working with him, the counsellor may help him develop the ego, consciously learning the rules of society. Eventually, Rob may go on to internalise the rules and develop a conscience through the 'super ego'. He can then understand what impact his behaviour has on others. As his super ego develops, he becomes his own moral judge. A social worker may help a young person such as Rob to reflect on their life and compile a 'life story' book. This may help him understand why he feels and acts as he does.

Understanding Erikson's eight stages may also help someone understand why they feel as they do.

Case Study

Jane has obsessive compulsive disorder (OCD), an extreme form of anxiety. When she was a little girl, her mother always dressed her in pretty dresses and told her off if she got dirty. Since then, Jane has had a dislike of dirt and feels she has to wash her hands several times a day. Even then, she does not feel clean, sometimes scrubbing her hands until they bleed.

According to Erikson's theory, Jane may not have successfully worked through the stage of initiative versus guilt and so feels guilty if she gets the slightest speck of dirt on her hands.

Did you know...

You can find out more about mental health on these websites:
www.nhs.uk/livewell/mentalhealth
www.mind.org.uk

The humanistic approach

The humanistic approach underpins the values of health and social care. All care workers need to have empathy, to be able to understand how individuals and service users feel. By applying Maslow's theory of needs, a care worker can understand better what a person needs and why they need it.

Case Study

Mary is 80 years old and recently went to live at Sunnydene care home. She had lived in her own home for 50 years very happily until one day a burglar broke in, stole what money she had and assaulted her. She was unable to live alone after that as she was too frightened, so she moved to Sunnydene. She stays in her room and does not like to leave it, even for meals.

Jenny, the care manager, knows about Maslow's hierarchy of needs and realises that Mary still needs security. She tells the carers to be friendly and supportive, and to listen to Mary and her needs. Eventually, when Mary has learned she can trust people again, she will start to mix.

A person-centred approach, such as that described by Rogers, will ensure that service users are treated with understanding and respect. Carers need to use active listening, not just listening while they are doing other things. A person-centred approach links in with helping people self-actualise.

Case Study

Jenny is a good manager and she organises time in the afternoon when carers sit with individuals and encourage them to talk. Previously, individuals used to sit in the lounge doing nothing, staring into space or falling asleep. Jenny realised this was not helping them be happy. Some of the people were in fact very unhappy. She organised a variety of activities, based around their hobbies, and offered them as alternatives to falling asleep after lunch. After a few weeks, the home was transformed. People laughed and smiled. They even talked to each other. They helped with tasks such as setting the table or collecting cups. Everyone, including the carers, looked ten years younger.

Of course not everyone wants to join in activities. Jenny explains to the staff why a non-judgemental approach is an important part of care. Mr Smith, who has dementia, does not realise he is offending others with his swearing, and carers should not judge. Mary is still in her room, although she does venture out to join in some activities.

The cognitive approach

Piaget described four stages of cognitive development. Look back to page 199 if you have forgotten them.

Case Study

When Sazia goes to her placement at Toddle Tots nursery, she spends some time observing the children. She notices that some of the babies like to play peek-a-boo. They are learning that objects are still there even when they cannot see them. The three-year-olds are much too busy to play peek-a-boo. They like songs with actions, like Head, Shoulders, Knees and Toes. Sazia recognises that the babies are in the sensori-motor stage, while the three-year-olds are in the pre-operational stage that Piaget described.

At her next placement, Sazia works with people with learning difficulties. One of them, Sophie, who is 30 years old, is putting out the biscuits for coffee. There are five people for coffee and they need two biscuits each. She needs to put two biscuits on each plate, then count them all to find out how many biscuits she used. She cannot work it out in her head.

Which stage is Sophie at according to Piaget's theory? Did you recognise the concrete operational stage?

Kelly's personal construct theory is another cognitive approach.

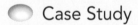

Case Study

A resident in a care home was staring out of the window. The sun was shining, birds were singing and the first flowers of spring were in bloom, but the person with depression saw only blank emptiness stretching ahead.

How could Kelly's personal construct theory be used to help them?

First, it is important for carers to be aware of their limitations. Unless a person is employed as a trained and qualified counsellor, they should not attempt to counsel a person. Yet carers do interact with individuals and want to help. Sitting with an individual or resident, just being with them if they do not want to talk, can be supportive.

A person who is emotionally upset after trauma may want to talk and they may need someone to listen. A depressed individual may need more specialist help, but getting them to talk may be a way of establishing contact and giving support. They may offer their view of how they are 'as unlucky as my mother in picking men'. This tells the skilled helper that the individual's view of themselves is as unlucky. They may say that they 'get walked over just like their dad' or 'I'm not like my sister, who is a money-grabbing career woman with no time for her family'. The person is showing their values in the way they talk about others.

An individual with depression may have a view of themselves or the world which others do not recognise. The person seeing a blank emptiness is not seeing the flowers that others see. Sometimes a carer can point out the positive aspects of a situation and help the person reframe their view of life. Sometimes this is a role for a skilled counsellor.

The biological approach

This approach looks at the effect of biological development on behaviour.

Certain illnesses and health-related behaviours are believed to be linked to biological causes. The NHS website (www.nhs.uk/news) has several examples of the genetic link between illnesses and health-related behaviours. Below are some of the research studies reported on the NHS website.

Obsessive compulsive disorder (OCD) is thought to be linked to a reduced amount of grey matter in certain parts of the brain. Researchers performed tests and MRI scans on people with a certain type of OCD and found a difference between OCD patients and the control group ('OCD brains are different', 26th November 2007, www.nhs.uk/news/2007/november/pages/ocdbrainsdiffer.aspx).

Case Study

Lisa has a placement with a health visitor. Mothers bring their babies in to clinic for routine checks, but today the health visitor is visiting a new baby at home. Lisa has special permission to accompany her. The baby is due for a hearing check. The health visitor puts a small, soft-tipped earpiece in the baby's ear, which sends a clicking sound to the inner part of the ear. Screening equipment picks up the echo response. This test is the automated otoacoustic emission (AOAE) screening test. The test result was normal.

Mum is particularly worried because her oldest child has a hearing impairment and this was only found when he was late speaking. At nursery, he was labelled as 'naughty' because he ignored the staff when they called him to come for story time. Her oldest child had also not reached the developmental norms for smiling and interacting with others. The GP referred him to a specialist for autism.

Did you know... ❓

One study suggests that those who achieve highest grades may be at an increased risk of bipolar disorder later in life ('Bipolar risk greater for bright children', 4th February 2010, www.nhs. uk/news/2010/02February).

A study by the World Health Organisation International Agency for Research on Cancer suggests that working night shifts could slightly increase women's risk of breast cancer. The Health and Safety Executive have commissioned a report on the effect of night working on health. Results are due in 2011 (www.nhs.uk/news/2009/03march/pages/nightshiftandbreastcancerqa.aspx).

Seasonal affective disorder (SAD) is thought to be due partly to a lack of sunlight. SAD is more common in winter when days are short and there is not much sunlight. One theory suggests that light is needed to stimulate the hypothalamus, which controls mood (www.nhs.uk/conditions/seasonal-affective-disorder).

Case Study

Jane is staff nurse on a busy casualty department. She works nights so that she can be home during the day to pick her children up from school. In winter, she sees the sun only on her days off. According to the research, how might this affect her health?

She could be at a slightly higher risk of developing breast cancer and seasonal affective disorder.

In this unit, you have seen how our mind influences our behaviour and health.

Activity 2 P1 P3

Work in pairs with someone who is at a different placement from you, so if you are in a health care placement, work with someone who is in placement in a social care environment.

Make a list of the six psychological approaches on a flip chart. Person A goes first and has to say how each psychological approach can be seen in their placement. Some approaches are easier than others to link to practice. Then, person B has a turn and says how each approach links to their placement.

You may have to help each other out with ideas. Make notes on the flip chart and write notes after your discussion.

Hint: if you do not know where to start, try to finish this sentence about social learning: *A social learning approach says that a carer learns what is good care by...*

Activity 3 M2 D1

Draw round your hands so you have two outlines.

Label one hand with the name of one psychological approach, such as humanistic. Write the key points of this theory on the hand. Label the other hand with another psychological approach, such as social learning. Write the key points of this theory on the hand.

Compare the theories. What is the same? What is different?

You could start:

- 'On the one hand, a humanistic approach looks at individual people and their future needs.'

- 'On the other hand, the social learning approach looks at how we learn to be social workers or nurses, by copying the behaviour of professionals.'

Once you have compared two psychological approaches to health and social care service provision, say how useful each one is in helping you understand how health and social care is provided. Remember, you can say one approach is more useful than another. You can also say if an approach is very helpful, partly helpful or not at all helpful in health and social care provision.

Summary

In this unit, you should have learned that there are six main psychological approaches. Behaviourists such as Pavlov and Skinner look at reinforcement and conditioning. Social learning theory says we learn from others. Bandura's Bobo Doll experiment shows that children copy the behaviour they see.

Psychodynamic theorists such as Freud and Erikson look at early influences on behaviour. Freud developed the idea of the id, ego and super ego, while Erikson thought we pass through eight stages of development.

Humanistic approaches include the work of Maslow and Rogers. A cognitive or information-processing approach looks at how we understand ideas. A biological approach looks at how maturation changes behaviour, how genes can affect our health and how hormones can affect behaviour.

Applying these approaches helps us understand challenging behaviour, depression, anxiety and other behaviours.

Assessment and grading criteria

In order to pass this unit, the evidence that the learner presents for assessment needs to demonstrate that they can meet all the learning outcomes for the unit. The assessment criteria for a pass grade describe the level of achievement required to pass this unit.

To achieve a pass grade the evidence must show that the learner is able to:	To achieve a merit grade the evidence must show that, in addition to the pass criteria, the learner is able to:	To achieve a distinction grade the evidence must show that, in addition to the pass and merit criteria, the learner is able to:
P1 explain the principal psychological perspectives	**M1** assess different psychological approaches to study	
P2 explain different psychological approaches to health practice	**M2** compare two psychological approaches to health and social care service provision.	
P3 explain different psychological approaches to social care practice.		**D1** evaluate two psychological approaches to health and social care service provision.

Resources

Maslow, A. (1943) 'A theory of human motivation', *Psychological Review*, 50: 370–396

Meichenbaum, D. (1969) 'The effects of instructions and reinforcement on thinking and language behaviours of schizophrenics,' *Behavior Research and Therapy*, 7: 101–114.

Merton, R.K. (1968) *Social Theory and Social Structure*, New York: Free Press.

Rogers, C. (1961/1977) *On Becoming a Person: A Therapist's View of Psychotherapy*, London, Constable.

Weblinks

www.met.police.uk/campaigns/anti_knife_crime/index.htm:
Metropolitan Police – Anti Knife Crime
www.nhs.uk/news: NHS news page
www.nhs.uk/conditions/seasonal-affective-disorder:
NHS – seasonal affective disorder

www.nimh.nih.gov:
National Institute of Mental Health
www.youtube.com/watch?v=vdh7Mngntnl:
Bandura's Bobo Doll experiment

10: Caring for Children and Young People

Introduction

This unit is concerned with the arrangements made for children and young people who need to be cared for by people other than their parents, and reasons why this might be necessary.

It looks at the types of care arrangements available for children and young people, and the roles and responsibilities of the people who look after children when the parents are unable to. This includes the legal responsibilities and arrangements for keeping children and young people safe.

Since some children need to be looked after because of maltreatment, the implications and effects of trauma, neglect and abusive or exploitative behaviour for children and young people will be examined, together with strategies to minimise the consequences and long-term damage, including to the life chances of such children and young people.

The unit also covers aspects of safeguarding and protecting mechanisms, systems, policies and procedures relevant to understanding how and why children and young people need to be cared for by people other than their birth parents.

Learning outcomes:

On completion of this unit, you should:

1 Know why children and young people might need to be looked after

2 Know how care is provided for looked after children and young people

3 Understand the risks to children and young people of abusive and exploitative behaviour

4 Understand the strategies used to safeguard children and young people from abusive and exploitative behaviour.

1 Know why children and young people might need to be looked after

Key term

Stigmatise – to label as socially undesirable.

Looked after children

This term was chosen by children and young people in the care of the local authority because their parents are unable to look after them properly. Such children were known as 'children in care', but they felt it was *stigmatising*, and the term 'looked after children' better reflected the fact that they needed to be cared for, showing that the adults in their lives had a responsibility for their health, well-being and interests.

More looked after children are now accommodated in foster homes (foster care) than in residential care. This is part of the safeguarding and child protection system and before children and young people are taken to be looked after by the local authority (LA), efforts are made by the authorities to support parents and families; taking a child away from the parents' care is a last resort. Under the Children Act 1989, LAs have a duty to safeguard and promote the welfare of all children and families in their area who are 'in need'. According to the Act a child is 'in need' if:

- S/he is unlikely to achieve or maintain, or to have the opportunity of achieving and maintaining, a reasonable standard of health (physical or mental) or development (physical, intellectual, emotional, social or behavioural) without the provision for her/him of services by a local authority.
- His/her health or development is likely to be

significantly impaired, or further impaired, without the provision for her/him of such services.

- S/he is disabled (is blind, deaf or dumb or suffers from a mental disorder of any kind, or is substantially and permanently handicapped by illness, injury or congenital deformity or other such disability as may be prescribed).

Children may be 'in need' temporarily or more permanently, depending on their family circumstances. LAs provide support to families in various ways, providing advice, guidance or counselling, access to other services such as respite care, or home help. They can also provide help for a family to have a holiday – if they have a disabled child, for example. The LA must work in partnership with parents and families to prevent family breakdown and minimise the need for the courts to intervene.

Although it is usually best for the child or young person if their families look after them, it is clearly stated in the act that the welfare of the child is *paramount*, that is, of primary importance (the 'paramountcy principle'), so it is up to the LA to ensure that it is safe and in the best interests of the child to remain with the family. The Children Act 1989 replaced the concept of parental rights with parental responsibilities towards children, and defined parental responsibility as 'all the rights, duties, powers, responsibilities and authority which a parent has in relation to the child and the child's property'.

Key term

Paramount – of principal and supreme importance.

Whoever has parental responsibility has the legal authority for the child; they are the decision makers and must be consulted. When a child becomes looked after, the LA shares parental responsibility for the child or young person who is subject to a care order. If the child or young person is 'accommodated' (i.e. if they go into care on a voluntary basis), the parents retain full parental responsibility for their child. Teachers who are responsible in school for looked after children should discuss arrangements regarding parental responsibility with the child's social worker.

The LA must make a distinction between children who are defined as in need and those requiring protection – children at risk of 'significant harm'. The LA has a duty to investigate when there is reasonable suspicion that a child or young person is suffering, or is *likely to suffer* significant harm, for example in situations where they are being ill treated, or where their health or development is being impaired. The act defines suffering as:

- ill treatment – includes sexual and emotional abuse as well as physical abuse and neglect
- ill health – includes physical and mental health
- delayed development – includes physical, intellectual, social and behavioural/emotional development.

If the child or young person is less developed in any of the above areas compared to others of the same age, or suffers abnormal (continuous, repeated or complex) health problems they have suffered significant harm. Local authority services are therefore provided with the intention of safeguarding and promoting the child or young person's welfare.

A care order by the court is required before the LA can remove a child or young person from parents. However, a court will only make an order if, by not doing so, the child is likely to suffer significant harm – in other words, if it is better for the child than making no order.

Under the Children Act 1989, there are two main routes into care:

- **Compulsory care orders** – these are made by the court under Section 31 of the Children Act 1989 and are enforced. They account for 63 per cent of all looked after children and young people and are used for children who are at risk if they remain with their families. In some cases, the court may make an interim care order, which lasts for eight weeks so that the LA can investigate the child's home circumstances.
- **Voluntary accommodation** – around 30 per cent of looked after children are admitted to care on a voluntary basis with agreement of the parents. They can be removed at any time, unlike children who have a care order. This option is more often used for children in need.

Key concept

The welfare of the child or young person should be the main and most important consideration, not the rights of parents.

Potential reasons

There are many reasons why children and young people become looked after by the LA and it is important to recognise that:

- not all of them will have been maltreated or abused
- not all of them will need to be looked after permanently.

However:

- all their parents will be unable to care for and/or protect them at the time they are received into care
- they will all be suffering a crisis in their lives, and some will have been suffering for a long time.

Facts and figures

On 31st March 2009, the government found that there were 59,500 children in the care of their LA in England, representing about 0.5 per cent of all children. Of these, 62 per cent were there because of abuse or neglect. Other reasons included:

- family dysfunction
- acute stress
- absent parenting
- parental illness or disability
- socially unacceptable behaviour.

In addition, four per cent of children were looked after because of their own disability and around six per cent of children in care were unaccompanied asylum seekers (House of Commons Children, Schools and Families Select Committee, 2009).

All children who need to be looked after by the LA share the fact that their parents are *unable or unwilling* to fulfil their responsibilities towards them. The reasons may be family related. For example:

- **Bereavement** – if a child or young person loses a parent and no other family members are able to care for them.

- **Parental illness or incapacity** – If a parent is admitted to hospital and they are the sole carer with no one else who could step in, the LA would need to take action. Sometimes parental ill health means that the parent cannot look after their child properly (e.g. mental ill health or substance abuse). Some children and young people become responsible for the care of their parent and are in need because of this.
- **Suspected or actual maltreatment** – The LA has a duty to investigate and initiate child protection procedures if the suspicions of maltreatment or abuse are confirmed.
- **Domestic violence** – in families where there is a history or suspicion of domestic violence, the children are at risk and their parents are in need of support. Although domestic violence is often hidden, when it becomes known, the children and the non-violent partner need protection. There is a well-documented link between domestic violence and child maltreatment, particularly child deaths (Saunders, 2004). LAs can offer advice and support, including help to find a refuge. Unfortunately, the link between domestic violence and child abuse and child murders is not always recognised.

The reasons for becoming looked after may be concerned with the child or young person. For example:

- **Health problems** – a child may be suffering from a chronic, complex or long-term condition (e.g. cancer or some congenital syndromes). The LA can provide short-break respite care to provide relief for parents to give some time to other children in the family.
- **Behavioural problems** – these may be congenital and associated with other health problems, or acquired (e.g. as a result of injury). Some children develop behavioural problems as a result of poor, inadequate or inappropriate parenting and may need to be looked after for their own safety and well-being. Some young people rebel against their parents and may put themselves in danger.
- **Learning difficulties** – children with learning difficulties may be easy or more difficult for parents to manage. As with health problems, short-break respite care can provide

a break for parents and child alike, as they may benefit from interacting with others.

- **Disability** – the LA can provide specialist support services, home helps and care assistants to help parents manage the care of their disabled child or young person, depending on the family's needs. Disabled children can be at higher risk of maltreatment and are considered to be both in need and possibly at risk.

- **Offending behaviour** – This may be a behavioural response to poor or inadequate parenting, or a consequence of peer pressure. If the offending behaviour cannot be managed within the family, the young person may be subject to a care order. This is usually a last option, after efforts by the youth offending team, for example, to work with the family.

2 Know how care is provided for looked after children and young people

Legal framework/legislation

Laws designed to protect children have existed for many years; the first Act of Parliament was passed in 1889. Despite this, children are still maltreated and even killed by their parents or carers. For example, in 2007/2008, 55 children were killed by someone known to them (Lord Laming, 2009).

An overview of child protection legislation can be found at http://www.guardian.co.uk/society/2004/apr/23/childrens services.childprotection (Timeline: a history of child protection, *The Guardian*).

Main principles of the Children Act 1989

The Children Act 1989 remains the key legislation for safeguarding and protecting children and young people and was strengthened by the Children Act 2004. You must understand the key principles of the 1989 Act if you are working with children or young people. An overview of the principles can be found at The National Teaching and Advisory Service website: www.ntas.org.uk/resources/childrenact.htm.

The framework for protecting and safeguarding children and young people also includes treaties (agreements), such as the United Nations Convention on the Rights of the Child (UNCRC). This international human rights treaty grants all

Activity 1   **P1**

Why might looked after children feel stigmatised for being in care? Search the internet and see if you can find out why children and young people are received into care and what they say about their experiences.

Identify three reasons for being in care and three positive and three negative things people who have been in care have to say about it. Try looking at: www.anational voice.org. Discuss your findings.

children and young people (aged 17 and under) a comprehensive set of rights. The UK signed up to the Convention which came into force in 1992.

In Wales, the Welsh Assembly Government has seven core aims which underpin all their work with children and young people, based firmly on the UNCRC. (For more information, go to www.wales.gov.uk/children.) In Northern Ireland, responsibility for looked after children lies within the Department of Health, Social Services and Public Safety (DHSSPSNI) (see www.dhsspsni.gov. uk). Arrangements in Scotland are different from those in England.

The Convention gives children and young people over 40 substantive rights. These include:

- the right to special protection measures and assistance
- the right to access to services such as education and health care
- the right to develop their personalities, abilities and talents to the fullest potential
- the right to grow up in an environment of happiness, love and understanding
- the right to be informed about and participate in achieving their rights in an accessible and active manner.

Articles 1–41 of the Convention set out the rights of children and governmental obligations to safeguard these rights. Article 42 requires states to publicise the principles and provisions of the Convention to children, young people, parents and carers, and everyone working with children and young people (source: www.dcsf.gov.uk/ everychildmatters).

The UNCRC gives the same rights to children and young people as the Human Rights Act 1998 provides for adults, plus additional rights to protection and care, recognising that they require support from adults to exercise their rights. The Human Rights Act 1998 has its origins in the European Convention on Human Rights.

In England, following the death of Victoria Climbié, the government published a green paper called 'Every Child Matters', with the intention of strengthening children's services. The Children Act 2004 implemented the recommendations of the Laming report. The Every Child Matters

green paper identified five outcomes that are most important for all children and which have been the focus of successive work in children's services, aimed at helping children and young people reach their potential. The five outcomes are:

1 Be healthy.
2 Stay safe.
3 Enjoy and achieve.
4 Make a positive contribution.
5 Achieve economic well-being.

(For more information, see www.everychildmatters. gov.uk.)

The government initiated research to see what worked in improving outcomes for children and young people in care and leaving care, leading to the Children and Young Person's Act 2008.

Main principles of the Children and Young Person's Act 2008

This important act made changes to the statutory (legal) framework for the care system, placing a duty on the Secretary of State for Children and Families to promote the well-being of children in England.

Summary of key areas:

- Improve stability of placements for looked after children, ensuring more consistency.
- Improve the school experience for looked after children, increasing their educational attainment.
- Give pilot local authorities the power to test different ways of organising social care by commissioning services from 'social work practices' and to enable regulation of these.
- Increase the focus on care planning ensuring the child's voice is heard when making important decisions that affect their future.
- Increase schools' capacity to address the needs of looked after children, including placing the role of the designated teacher on a statutory footing and ensuring that children in care do not move schools in Years 10 and 11, except in exceptional circumstances.
- Ensure that young people are not forced out of care before they are ready, by giving them more say over moves to independent living and ensuring they retain support and guidance as long as they need it.

This act aims to ensure that children and young people who are looked after in the care system have the same chance of achieving as any other.

Data protection

Professionals working with families and children must be aware of the Data Protection Act 1998, the main law protecting the personal data of individuals. Whilst personal data should clearly only be processed fairly and lawfully, in order to ensure this, at least one of these six conditions must be applicable to that data:

1 The data subject (the person whose data is stored) has consented ('given their permission') to the processing.
2 Processing is necessary for the performance of, or commencing, a contract.
3 Processing is required under a legal obligation (other than one stated in the contract).
4 Processing is necessary to protect the vital interests of the data subject.
5 Processing is necessary to carry out any public functions.
6 Processing is necessary in order to pursue the legitimate interests of the 'data controller' or 'third parties.

Some people and organisations have refused to share information for fear of breaking the law in relation to the Data Protection Act but the act should never be used to withhold information that might prevent a child or young person suffering harm – this is an exception to the rule. If in doubt, consider the 'need to know' rule – why is the person asking the question and do they need to know the answer to carry out their responsibilities or are they just being curious? (For more information, see the flowchart 'What to do if you are worried a child is being abused' on page 230.)

Following the 2004 Children Act, agencies providing *universal services* for children and families, such as health and education, were required to work together with LAs in children's trusts (see 'Organisation of care provision' on page 216). Integrated working aimed to identify children with additional needs for care, protection or support earlier – early intervention. A simple process was therefore designed to enable any practitioner in the children's workforce to carry out a holistic assessment of children's needs and strengths. This is the Common Assessment Framework, used to

- identify what support children and families need
- improve integrated working
- form the baseline for a formal referral to social services where a child or young person is thought to be in need or is at risk.

(For more information go to www.cwdcouncil.org.uk/integrated-working.) It is based on the parameters of the *Framework for the Assessment of Children in Need and their Families* (see diagram on page 216).

> ## Key term
>
> **Universal services** – those services within health and education that are provided for all children, e.g. immunisation and school services.

The assessment framework

Social workers use the *Framework for the Assessment of Children in Need and their Families* when social services have concerns about a child or young person (e.g. for initial assessment following referral). It is a way of considering the child or young person's situation and circumstances to decide whether the child is in need or requires safeguarding. All the factors that affect the child or young person are assessed systematically and holistically to determine the level of risk to the child's health and well-being.

The framework triangle shows:

- factors relating to the child and how well their developmental needs are being met
- factors relating to the parents' ability to provide care for the child
- factors affecting and relating to the family as a whole.

Assessment of risk must be thorough, requiring a dynamic approach to the collection and analysis of family information. Assessment is carried out by a qualified social worker, although other agencies in contact with the family, such as health visitors, may have useful information to add.

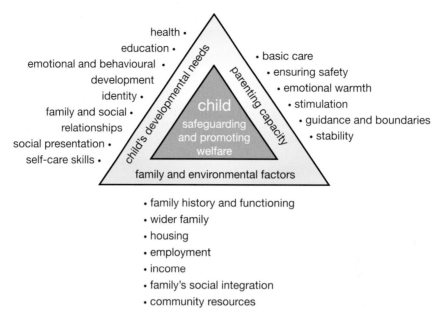

Framework for the Assessment of Children in Need and their Families

Care available

The type of care provision offered will depend entirely on the assessed needs of the child or young person and their family. Care is planned in partnership with parents and the child's 'voice' is heard, meaning the child discusses their care with the social worker representing them who puts those views forward on the child's behalf. Sometimes an advocate is appointed to represent the child's views and young people may be able to represent themselves. If foster care is considered the most appropriate option, the fostering agency is included in the discussions. Different types of care are:

- *Foster care* – These are ordinary people, who offer to give a temporary home to a child or young person in need. The LA approves them and pays them enough to cover care expenses and a little extra.
- *Respite care* – some foster carers offer short-break or respite care, usually to families of disabled children, those who are sick or have complex care needs. These foster carers are experienced and some might even be professionals or practitioners in health or care.
- *Residential care* – some children will live in a residential care home, maybe because there insufficient suitable foster parents

available or because they are difficult to care for (e.g. if their behaviour is disturbed and unpredictable as a result of their experiences). Institutional care can cause emotional difficulties, but improvements in residential care include smaller, more specialist homes that provide specific care and treatment, such as psychological therapy or family therapy.

- *Adoption* – there is an increasing tendency to place children and young people up for adoption more quickly, depending on their circumstances, as an alternative to different foster placements; however, it remains easier to place babies than older children or disabled children with adoptive parents.

Organisation of care provision

Each UK country has slightly different arrangements for the care and responsibility for looked after children. In England and Wales, each LA has a department responsible for looked after children, safeguarding and ensuring that children and young people in the local area are supported to meet their full potential.

In Northern Ireland, responsibility for children and young people's care lies with the Department of Health, Social Services and Public Safety (HSSPSNI). In Wales, it is the Welsh Assembly

Did you know...

Approximately 7,000 British children from deprived backgrounds were sent to Australia after the Second World War. Around 150,000 children were forced to migrate to Commonwealth countries and promised a better life, but they often found themselves in foster homes, abused or used as slave labour. Some left brothers and sisters behind and some have grown up not knowing their parents were still alive (source: **www.myheritage.com**).

Government and, in Scotland, the Scottish Government Education Directorate (Children, Young People and Social Care).

As well as government (statutory) care provision, much care is provided through voluntary or charitable organisations that may provide some services independently, such as holidays for disabled children, or may be contracted by LAs and paid to deliver services for children and young people on behalf of the LA. Barnardo's and the National Society for the Prevention of Cruelty to Children (NSPCC) are examples. The NSPCC has an emergency helpline and is the only non-statutory (non-government) agency allowed to take direct action to protect children at risk. There are also a number of fostering organisations, such as the British Association for

Fostering and Adoption (BAFF) and the Fostering Network – an organisation for everyone involved in fostering, whether personally or professionally. Most third-sector organisations are registered charities, obtaining their income from various sources, including individual donations, national and local government. They may have to bid for contracts to carry out work for local or national government (contracting).

Did you know...

A Yorkshireman, the Reverend Benjamin Waugh, founded the NSPCC in 1899 after seeing first hand the suffering of children in London's East End, where he had his parish.

Victorian England was harsh for children who were forced to work in hazardous conditions (e.g. as chimney sweeps). They were often abused at home. Reverend Waugh was so shocked to realise that there was a law against cruelty to animals but not children that he set up the NSPCC.

Types of services

Health education and social services are provided for all children and young people; however, some services are provided to all children, others specifically for those needing additional help.

There are three main types of health services available to children and young people; *universal services*, *specialist services* and *targeted services*. Universal services are the health, education and social services available for all children and young people. Specialist services are for all those with particular health or care needs and targeted services are only available to a few children and families with specific needs. There is considerable overlap because some children and families have different needs at different times.

Health

Universal health services are mainly primary care services, focusing on the prevention and detection of ill health and early intervention. They consist of the early years and health visiting service, and the school health services for the whole child population.

Early years and health visiting services

Deliver family-centred preventive and public health services to pre-school children and their families. The key aims are to promote health and well-being and to intervene early where health or development may be at risk. Settings where universal services are provided include:

- community health centres
- GP practices
- Sure Start settings/children's centres
- specialist Child and Adolescent Mental Health Services (CAMHS)
- hospital accident and emergency departments
- hospital outpatient departments
- hospital-based maternity services.

School health services

Offer a needs-based approach to the provision of health care in schools for children and young people aged 4 to 18 years. Key aims are to promote health with school children, their families and the wider community, carrying out school-based activities and working with partner agencies to address health inequalities within the context of public health. School health services are often provided in:

- community health centres
- GP practices
- other health settings
- special schools
- mainstream schools
- extended schools and extended special schools
- other education premises.

A small percentage of school health services are offered in residential children's homes and children's day care services (e.g. Sure Start children's centres). Universal services are usually delivered by primary care trusts (PCTs).

Specialist health services are for children and young people with particular health problems.

Paediatric therapy services

Deliver interventions by allied health professionals, such as speech therapy, physiotherapy and occupational therapy, often within multi-disciplinary teams. They may work in specialist settings, such as child development centres, or with particular groups of children, such as those with a disability. Children are referred for treatment by another health professional.

Community paediatric services

Consist of teams who provide services in non-acute (hospital) settings. They deliver public health services, disability and mental health support services (CAMHS) and community-based *palliative care*, as well as support for sick children and families (e.g. following hospital discharge).

Key term

Palliative care – this is care for people who are not going to recover from their illness and for whom no further treatment is available. It consists of making sure they are pain-free and comfortable, enhancing the quality of life.

Services for children with special needs

Are provided specifically for children with long-term or life-threatening conditions, those with a disability, (including learning disability, autistic spectrum disorder, physical disability, sensory impairment) and children with complex health needs.

Targeted health services are aimed at children with particular needs, focusing on prevention and early intervention.

Services for children in special circumstances

Are concerned with supporting vulnerable children with specific needs, who are at risk of health problems due to their circumstances. This would apply to homeless children, substance misusers, teenage parents, looked after children, children with blood-borne illnesses, asylum seekers and children of travellers.

Safeguarding children services

Are concerned with child protection. Specialist

teams are configured to respond to concerns, provide advice, support and information to a range of professionals and organisations, and respond to requests for clinical examinations. These teams provide additional support to all childcare workers in a given locality, all of whom have a duty to protect children.

Mental health services (outside CAMHS)

Are described as Tier 1 mental health services, concerned with early intervention and prevention of mental ill health. They include counselling services, services for children with behavioural problems, such as attention deficit hyperactive disorder (ADHD), and services for children who have been abused.

The children's health workforce overlaps with education, through the provision within schools and support for children and families, with social services in relation to safeguarding children, supporting CAMHS and through support for children with special needs and learning disabilities. Looked after children is a significant area of partnership work focused on the needs of the child or young person.

Social care

Social care is only provided to children and families who need support and assistance, so there is no universal provision of social care, only specialist and targeted services. Social care is vital to achieving the integration of services for children in England, aiming to improve the overall outcomes for children's health, development and well-being; hence the children's social care workforce is identified separately from that of adult social care.

There are two primary groups of workers within the children's social care workforce; social workers and social care workers. They are employed across a range of settings and contexts within the statutory, voluntary and independent sectors; their skills and levels of qualifications reflect the different levels of responsibility and accountability within particular job roles, which are linked to registration and regulation. Social care workers provide specific social care services within the health, education and justice sectors.

Whilst some staff deal exclusively with vulnerable children and families, others are employed in specialist areas such as mental health or substance misuse, and also engage with children and families in situations where these issues lead to children becoming vulnerable.

Family support workers are usually social work assistants, teaching assistants or healthcare assistants and so span different parts of the childcare workforce, working across the statutory, independent and voluntary sectors.

It is important to recognise that other LA departments, such as housing, can also help to support families, especially through an integrated working approach, such as the Family Intervention Projects, which are aimed at preventing family breakdown and social problems (see the case study on page 232).

Education

Through the Children Act 2004 and the Children and Young Person's Act 2008, schools have responsibility for promoting the well-being and achievement of all children, especially the outcomes for looked after children and young people, in line with the Every Child Matters agenda. They also have a duty to cooperate with other agencies to ensure children remain healthy, safe and protected.

Partly because of this, many schools work closely with children's trusts, and there are now people working in schools who have particular responsibility for working with families and children, especially when problems occur (e.g. due to a change in the child's circumstances). An increased focus on attendance has helped identify potential or actual problems earlier and family support workers can develop and maintain links with families. Support services in schools aim to improve a child or young person's capacity to learn when circumstances make it difficult, recognising the wider factors impacting on education and subsequent life prospects.

Programmes such as Social and Emotional Aspects to Learning (SEAL) are becoming integrated into teaching and learning strategies to help equip children and young people to recognise and manage their feelings and emotions and ask for help.

Extended schools and 'wrap around' care have been implemented in many schools to provide after school care, when parents or carers are working; they also provide a refuge for children whose home lives are not supportive.

Children's centres and Sure Start provision, which provide early years childcare, and additional services aimed to support the most disadvantaged, providing a range of integrated provision from health, social care and education to try and prevent problems. By all working from a central point, integrated working and information sharing is easier.

Activity 2 | P2 | M1

In small groups, find out what provision is available in your area for looked after children. Make a map identifying whether the provision is universal, specialist or targeted.

Take three different services and find out how they provide care for looked after children and young people. Explain how they deliver high-quality care.

Job roles

Because looked after children are part of safeguarding and child protection systems and processes, the jobs and roles associated with looked after children are wide-ranging, with some having a specialist focus and others concerned with delivering universal services. Safeguarding and child protection is the responsibility of everyone who works with children and young people, although levels of responsibility and accountability differ according to role. The creation of children's trusts in each LA area, bringing the work of health, social care and education together, is intended to strengthen integrated working and support children and young people to meet the Every Child Matters outcomes.

Health

Medical staff within universal services are likely to be specialist community child health physicians and GPs. Nursing staff include health visitors who are specialist child health practitioners, but may also include children's nurses, early years practitioners and general nurses. Non-qualified support staff may be support workers without medical or nursing qualifications.

Each healthcare trust has designated roles for safeguarding children/child protection. For example, a named doctor, nurse, midwife or health visitor and paediatric social worker are likely to work as a team, holding strategic responsibility for ensuring policies and procedures are in place, followed and that all staff are appropriately trained.

Social care

The LA is the lead organisation for protecting and safeguarding children and young people. Within each LA, there is a designated councillor whose role is Lead Member for Children's Services. Together with the Director of Children's Services, they take a strategic view of children's services, including child protection services for the local area. Managers, their deputies and assistants involved in the provision of social care for children and young people include:

- registered managers of children's homes, their deputies and assistants and all residential childcare workers
- children and families social workers, employed in the statutory, voluntary and independent sectors (e.g. fostering and adoption teams)
- family court advisers – Children and Family Court Advisory and Support Service (CAFCASS)
- outreach/family support workers
- education welfare officers
- foster carers (including private foster carers)
- lead inspectors of registered children's services
- support workers
- volunteers.

LAs contract with other organisations for the delivery of services to support children and families; however, they directly employ children and families social workers. There is always a duty social worker on call to receive child protection referrals and act on concerns from members of the public.

Education

Schools and colleges have increased services to support children and families in recent years due to a desire to improve educational standards, and in recognition of the difficulties that some children face in engaging with school and the process of learning due to their home circumstances.

Support services in schools have the following broad job roles, although their titles can vary:

- Attendance officer/educational welfare officer – responsible for school attendance (and enforcement, where necessary, since education is compulsory until 16 years). They may be first to spot a problem and alert colleagues or, in certain circumstances, the child protection authorities.
- Learning mentors – responsible for helping children with their learning and recognising when external factors affect this.
- Personal assistants – support children with their educational choices and provide support for vulnerable children and young people.
- Family support workers/family liaison workers – help parents engage with their child's education.
- Non-teaching heads of pastoral support – have a strategic role for arranging support for children and young people struggling with education.

Regulation of care provision

Services provided for children and young people are regulated in two main ways:

- Regulation of the individual worker.
- Regulation of the organisation.

Regulation of the individual worker

Individuals are checked to ensure they are safe to work with children and young people. The Criminal Records Bureau searches for information on individuals to ensure they have not been in trouble with the law for abusing, exploiting or otherwise harming children. Many job advertisements ask applicants to provide a CRB check or undergo one.

Regulatory councils or bodies regulate all health and social care professionals. These include:

- *General Social Care Council (GSCC)* – regulates qualified social workers, social care workers and social work students on approved degree courses in England. Equivalent bodies in the other UK countries are the *Northern Ireland Social Care Council (NISCC)*, the *Care Council for Wales (CCW)* and the Scottish *Social Services Council (SSSC)*.
- *Nursing and Midwifery Council (NMC)* regulates nurses, midwives and specialist community public health nurses (health visitors, district nurses and community psychiatric nurses).
- *The General Teaching Council* is the professional body for teachers, responsible for awarding Qualified Teacher Status (QTS) and regulating teachers.

All of the medical and associated professions also have their own regulatory councils. Most have a set of standards of good practice that practitioners should follow. Foster carers also have a set of standards, the UK National Standards for Foster Care, which explain best practice for foster carers, their supervisors and managers. These are used to provide an induction framework for foster care training and development.

Regulation of the organisation

Regulating organisations occurs through a focus on good practice and legal minimum standards. Regulatory bodies inspect organisations to ensure that the minimum standards are upheld. The standards cover things such as minimum staffing levels, the number of qualified staff and the type of qualifications that are acceptable. They also say, in the case of residential organisations, what type of accommodation is acceptable – for example, the size of rooms to ensure privacy and safety. (See the Care Standards Act 2000, Health and Social Care Act 2008 and National Minimum Standards.)

In the health service, the standards are called the National Service Framework for Children, Young People and Maternity Services. There are five standards in the framework:

1 Promoting health and well-being, identifying needs and intervening early.
2 Supporting parents and carers.
3 Child, young person and family-centred services.

4 Growing up into adulthood.
5 Safeguarding and promoting the welfare of children and young people.

These health-focused standards cover both physical and emotional health and well-being, a holistic approach, recognising the wider factors impacting on health.

The Care Quality Commission (CQC) is responsible for regulating and inspecting health services and adult social care. It has stated how it will improve standards for the care of children and young people receiving health services, including young women having babies (see www.cqc.org.uk).

Ofsted inspects early years, education and children's social care, including foster care agencies. It carries out three-yearly inspections of the council's performance with its partners in relation to child protection and looked after children. LAs are subject to Comprehensive Area Assessments, measuring the authority's performance against a set of criteria, including Ofsted ratings.

Key concept

Integrated working is in place to help children meet their full potential.

---

3 Understand the risks to children and young people of abusive and exploitative behaviour

Types of maltreatment

Maltreatment means physical, emotional, intellectual or sexual abuse, neglect, bullying or harassment. Anyone working with children or young people must be familiar with the signs and symptoms of abuse, and know what action to take. If unsure whether a child or young person is being maltreated, it is better to take action than not. It is important to recognise that some signs will be age related and not all will be present.

Physical abuse

Physical abuse is sometimes called non-accidental injury because it is deliberate injury caused to a child or young person by hitting, punching, scalding, burning or throwing them (e.g. down the stairs). Shaking or throwing can cause non-accidental injury in babies who are not yet mobile. Some parents use physical means to discipline their child and there are cultural differences in childrearing practices; however, if this causes injury, it is disproportionate and unacceptable.

Emotional abuse

Emotional abuse is continuous verbal abuse (swearing, insults and name-calling), inconsistent parenting (one minute warm and the next hostile) and emotional withdrawal (using affection to manipulate the child's behaviour). In children who are too young to speak, the signs of emotional neglect are often difficult to spot without seeing the parent and child together; however, developmental delay, e.g. speech, will be evident. They may seem clingy or withdrawn, showing passive/aggressive behaviour in older children. They may have temper tantrums and be difficult to toilet train. Children who have achieved bladder and bowel control may regress due to either physical or emotional abuse.

Sexual abuse

Sexual abuse can occur to a child of any age, even infants. The child becomes an object on which an adult expresses his (or her) sexual fantasies. Most perpetrators are male. Issues of power and control, stemming from emotional or social inadequacy or immaturity, can also cause sexual abuse.

Neglect

Neglect is the 'hidden abuse', it is difficult to detect, tending to happen over time as the child's circumstances gradually deteriorate. Therefore, it is vital to be alert to the signs of neglect. A child may be subjected to more than one type of maltreatment, and neglect is often accompanied by emotional, physical or sexual abuse. Some indicators of maltreatment are common across more than one type of abuse.

Children struggle to talk about maltreatment;

believing they have done something to deserve it and that no one will believe them. They often have confused feelings about the adult abuser – they may love them and the maltreatment may be offset by treats and happy times, so they don't want the family to break up by the perpetrator going to prison, for example. They will also have ambivalent feelings about being taken into care, even if it is for their safety. They may be relieved that the abuse has stopped, but may also feel responsible and that they are being punished. Foster carers must be aware of these conflicting emotions likely to be brought to placement.

Risk of maltreatment and wider factors suggesting risk of maltreatment

When professionals assess the risk of maltreatment, they take an objective but holistic view, including 'emotional histories' just as a doctor takes a medical history. They enquire about family relationships, close associates and feelings, *family dynamics*. They also look at the current stresses within the family.

> ## Key term
>
> **Family dynamics** – the relationships within the family and how family members relate to one another, especially in relation to who has the power and control.

Table 10.2 on the next page shows risk factors in the child and family, and positive protective factors.

Maltreatment in residential care

Whilst family members, including extended families and step-families, cause most maltreatment, children have also been abused in residential care. Unfortunately the data to determine the level and likelihood of abuse in residential care is lacking; the NSPCC suggests that UK research shows children in residential care to be more at risk from physical and sexual assault from other residents than staff.

Several high-profile cases in the media have highlighted abuse in residential care (e.g. the 'Pindown' punishment regime in Staffordshire, 1989), often also highlighting the sexual abuse of boys and young men. For example, in Leicestershire, the officer in charge of a children's home was convicted in 1992 on 17 counts of physical and sexual assault of children and young people in his care, and a social worker was convicted in 1999 of 24 indecent assaults of boys in his care. These cases led eventually to the tighter regulation of children's homes and the development of national standards. More recently, information on systematic abuse carried out in Catholic children's homes in Ireland has emerged. More research is needed to establish the extent and predisposing factors of abuse in residential childcare.

Predatory child abuse, often involving the child being abducted, is relatively rare, but often attracts more media attention. Children and young people are actually more at risk from people known to them.

Profile

Overlapping themes identified from analysing child deaths include neglect, physical assault and lack of support for older children from helping agencies.

Typical features of neglect suggested that the families were known to social services for many years and had complex and confusing family histories. Engagement with the agencies – education, health and social services – tended to be ambivalent and sometimes hostile, particularly the men, with frequent missed appointments and difficulties in engaging with the family. There were often mental health issues and links with mental health agencies. There was almost always a family history of domestic violence with the police involved and frequent contact with A&E departments.

Children and domestic violence

Statistics show a strong link between child maltreatment and domestic violence, which is sometimes overlooked. However, it is extremely important and wherever domestic violence is identified, child maltreatment must be considered. Children who have witnessed domestic violence have effectively been emotionally abused by this.

- In 90 per cent of domestic violence incidents, children are present in the same or next room.

Table 10.2 Risk factors and positive protective factors

Risk factor	Positive factor
Child	
• Specific learning difficulties • Communication difficulties • Specific developmental delay • Genetic influence • Difficult temperament • Physical illness • Academic failure • Low self-esteem	• Secure early relationships • Being female • Higher intelligence • Easy intelligence as an infant • Positive attitude, problem-solving approach • Good communication skills • Planner, belief in control • Humour • Capacity to reflect • Religious faith
Family	
• Overt parental control/domestic violence • Family breakdown • Inconsistent or unclear discipline • Hostile or rejecting relationships • Failure to adjust to child's changing needs • History of physical, sexual or emotional abuse • Parental psychiatric illness • Parental criminality, alcoholism • Personality disorder, substance misuse • Death or loss, including friendship	• At least one good parent–child relationship • Affection • Clear, firm and consistent guidelines and fair discipline • Support for education • Supportive long-term relationship, absence of severe discord
Community	
• Socio-economic disadvantage • Homelessness • Disaster • Discrimination • Other significant life events	• Wider supportive network • Good housing and standard of living • High-morale school with positive policies for behaviour, attitudes and anti-bullying • Sport and leisure activities • Opportunities at school

Source: Early Intervention, Department for Children, Schools and Families

- 75 per cent of mothers reported that their children had directly witnessed domestic violence, 33 per cent had seen their mothers beaten up and 10 per cent had witnessed sexual violence.
- In 25 per cent of cases of domestic violence, the male perpetrator has also been violent towards the children in the home.
- One in three child protection cases also show a history of domestic violence in the home.

Source: Action for Children (www.actionfor children.org.uk)

Indicators of maltreatment

Signs of *physical abuse* include:

- Unexplained injuries or explanations that sound untrue or don't fit the injury (e.g. child says he fell over but the injury is on the inside of the forearm). Bald patches where hair has been pulled out or circular burns from a cigarette.
- Injuries in a non-mobile baby; head injury in a child under one year.
- Nervous behaviour, jumpy, watchful and cautious. Fear of physical contact – shrinking back when touched.
- Difficulty making friends and trusting others.

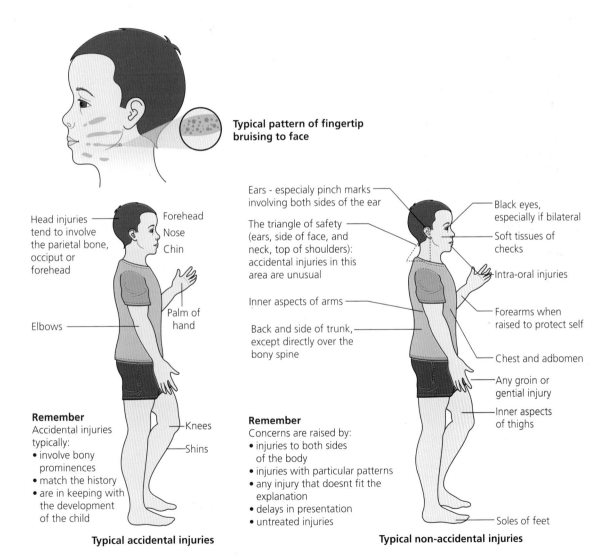

Typical pattern of fingertip bruising to face

Head injuries tend to involve the parietal bone, occiput or forehead

Forehead
Nose
Chin

Palm of hand

Elbows

Remember
Accidental injuries typically:
- involve bony prominences
- match the history
- are in keeping with the development of the child

Knees

Shins

Typical accidental injuries

Ears - especialy pinch marks involving both sides of the ear

The triangle of safety (ears, side of face, and neck, top of shoulders): accidental injuries in this area are unusual

Inner aspects of arms

Back and side of trunk, except directly over the bony spine

Remember
Concerns are raised by:
- injuries to both sides of the body
- injuries with particular patterns
- any injury that doesnt fit the explanation
- delays in presentation
- untreated injuries

Black eyes, especially if bilateral

Soft tissues of checks

Intra-oral injuries

Forearms when raised to protect self

Chest and adbomen

Any groin or gential injury

Inner aspects of thighs

Soles of feet

Typical non-accidental injuries

Sites of accidental and non-accidental injury

- Refusing to undress for PE or medical examination, wearing too many clothes in warm weather to cover injuries, covering up.
- Chronic running away and school absences, truanting.
- Repeated attendance at A&E.
- Self-harm or self-destructive behaviour, being bullied.
- Aggression towards others, bullying others.
- Lying, stealing, getting into trouble with police.
- Admitting they have been punished but it seems excessive.
- Frightened that the perpetrator will find out.

Behaviour demonstrated by the child who is being *emotionally abused* include the following:

- Delayed development – emotionally immature for age, physically small and intellectually behind peers (failure to thrive).
- Nervous behaviour, such as rocking, hair twisting, self-harm.
- Speech disorders.
- Extremes of passive or aggressive behaviour, often alternating.
- Fear of making a mistake and over-reaction to mistakes – own and others'.
- Extreme fear of new situations but can be over-friendly with strangers.
- Continually putting themselves down – 'I'm stupid, ugly, clumsy', etc.
- Inability to play or be spontaneous – may be in the corner of the playground, watching.
- Inability to concentrate.

Behaviour demonstrated by the child who is being *sexually abused* may include the following:

- Medical problems, such as itching, infections or pain in the genital area, even sexually transmitted infections, bed-wetting, soiling.
- Being overly affectionate and sexually knowing – demonstrating sexually inappropriate behaviour, flirting or graphic, sexualised play.
- Changes in behaviour – withdrawn, sad, or more extreme, such as depression, self-harming, attempts at suicide, overdosing.
- Eating disorders – anorexia, bulimia, loss of appetite or compulsive over-eating.
- Being withdrawn, isolated, and unable to concentrate. Disturbed sleep, inability to sleep.

- Regressing – behaving as a much younger child (e.g. thumb-sucking or having a cuddly toy).
- Thinking badly of themselves and at the same time trying to be 'ultra good' – over-reacting to criticism.
- Being afraid of someone they know, not wanting to be alone with them, lacking trust, or showing aggressive behaviour towards them.
- Being frightened of physical contact and fear of undressing.
- Running away, abusing drugs and/or alcohol, becoming promiscuous.

Neglected children often demonstrate a combination of the following behaviours:

- Poor personal hygiene – smelly.
- Underweight and constantly hungry, may steal food.
- Always tired and cannot concentrate to learn or play.
- Clothing inadequate for weather, dirty, too small, threadbare.
- May have untreated medical conditions (e.g. constant cough, cold). These children are at risk from many infectious diseases, including TB.
- No friends, may be bullied, isolated socially.
- Destructive tendencies.

Child survivors of *domestic abuse* often exhibit similar signs to those for physical abuse. However, boys tend to become aggressive, regressing and demonstrating behaviour problems whilst girls become withdrawn, have low self-esteem and display signs of anxiety and depression, exhibiting vague physical symptoms, such as tummy ache, and starting to self-harm or develop eating disorders. In particular, both will show symptoms of post-traumatic stress disorder, such as nightmares and flashbacks. They will be easily startled.

(For further information, see 'When to suspect child maltreatment', NICE Clinical Guideline, 2009, available here: http://guidance.nice.org.uk/CG89.)

Consequences of maltreatment

These vary depending on the child's age, the duration and type of abuse and the protective factors the child or young person has available. The long-term consequences of maltreatment on children and young people who are not helped effectively have a personal cost and a cost to society as a whole.

Personal costs

Emerging research suggests that the constant fear experienced by abused children can affect brain development, with lifelong consequences. Academics conclude that every child needs secure attachments to carers, quality childcare provided by people who are interested in them and love and attention from parents and carers. If unavailable within the family, action must be taken to ensure that it is provided elsewhere. The faster this happens, the better the outcome for the child, as less damage is done to the brain's development. Brain scans show the difference in brain development and activity between abused and non-abused children.

Bonding is of particular importance. From conception to at least three years of age, a child needs to bond – develop a secure and trusting relationship – with their main caregiver (usually the mother) in order to develop physical, psychological and emotional health. Subsequent ability to feel empathy, compassion, trust and love, the foundation for all other relationships, is based on these early experiences. If early bonding is disrupted, damaged or broken, the child may develop reactive attachment disorder (RAD), caused by failure to form normal attachments with the main caregiver, often resulting from severe early experiences of neglect, abuse, abrupt separation, lack of responsiveness by carer to child's efforts at communication and socialisation or frequent changes of carer.

Children vary in the likelihood and severity of attachment disorder and some develop stable attachments and positive social relationships; however, some children are particularly vulnerable to developing RAD.

Indicators of RAD in infants may include:

- Non-organic failure to thrive – slow growth and development without obvious physical cause.
- Constant whining or grizzling but a weak crying reflex.
- Sensitivity to touch/cuddling (e.g. baby goes rigid).
- Poor sucking reflex.
- Poor eye contact.
- Not smiling in response to others.
- Indifference to people.

Indicators in older children may include the following:

- Failure to develop a social conscience – lies and steals.
- Superficially charming with incessant chattering aimed at control.
- Inability to give or receive affection.
- Extreme control issues – demanding and wants own way. May be violent if refused.
- No impulse control – risk taking and apparently unaware of danger.
- Lack of eye contact, except when lying.
- Destructive to self, others, animals and property.
- Unusual eating patterns – hoarding, gorging, refusal to eat.
- Unusual speech patterns – mumbling to self, robotic speech, talking softly to self, except when in a rage.

Source: adapted from www.psychnet-uk.com

Attachment problems and RAD are often the cause of frequent placement breakdowns. It is difficult and costly to treat because of the neurological damage to brain development.

Social costs

These are the long-term costs to both the individual and society of failing to intervene early enough or effectively enough to prevent or modify the problems resulting from abuse.

For more information, see *Early Intervention: securing good outcomes for all children and young people* (DCSF, 2010).

There is a direct cost to society of maintaining a child welfare system to investigate and respond to allegations of abuse – for example, the cost of residential and foster care and the cost of support for families.

Indirect costs include health costs and economic consequences, the juvenile court system and detention, mental illness and the costs of policing and dealing with domestic violence.

Theories of maltreatment

Medical theories

These include the impact of childhood abuse and domestic violence on the brain development of infants, and the effects of stress on the mother during pregnancy causing the release of the stress hormone cortisol, thought to cause unborn babies to be more sensitive to stressors in the environment (e.g. less calm). It is likely that such a baby would cry more frequently and need much reassurance. Crying babies are more likely to be abused. A mother who drinks heavily during pregnancy can cause the baby to suffer *foetal alcohol syndrome*, a condition causing multiple problems, including low IQ and delayed development.

Sociological theories

These suggest that poverty and economic deprivation can lead to child maltreatment, either due

Table 10.3 Personal and social costs of maltreatment

Issue	Social cost	Personal cost
Physical ill health in adulthood – particularly chronic conditions such as allergies, asthma, arthritis, high blood pressure and ulcers.	All of these are long-term stress-related conditions that are difficult and costly to the NHS to treat.	Low income due to inability to work as a result of ill health.
Mental ill health – found even in very young children. Depression, anxiety, eating disorders, self-harm, suicide, anger management problems, and RAD or other attachment problems.	Cost to the NHS of treatment and support. Cost to the economy of inability to work. Cost to society in terms of likely relationship breakdown.	Low income due to inability to work as a result of ill health. Poor relationships with others. Poor quality of life. Loss of life.
Cognitive difficulties – lower IQ, delayed language development and poor academic achievement.	Cost to the economy of inability to work.	Low income due to inability to work as a result of ill health.
Social problems – anti-social behaviour, violence and aggression, teen pregnancy, drug and alcohol misuse, risk-taking behaviours and becoming abusive parents themselves.	Cost of offending behaviour to victims and the economic cost to the criminal justice system. Health costs of substance misuse. Welfare costs of family breakdown.	Poor relationships with others. Poor quality of life.

to stress or neglect. Socialisation may also play a part – for example, failure to bond and form attachments will affect the development of relationships. Similarly, the process of socialisation can lead to abuse being seen as the norm, and bullying may occur.

Psychological theories

These focus on an individual's self-esteem and self-worth. It is difficult to parent if parenting becomes a challenge to your self-esteem. For example, some mothers believe that the baby doesn't like them when they are unable to soothe them and stop them crying. This can lead to hostile feelings towards the baby. Parents are emotionally damaged.

Feminist theories

Feminists believe domestic violence and child abuse are about men's need to maintain control over women and children.

> ### Key concept
>
> Child maltreatment is damaging to children and young people in terms of their physical, social, intellectual and emotional health and development and costly to society in terms of the economic and social consequences.

Activity 3   P3 P4 M2 M3 D2

Case Study

Iain is six years old. Iain's parents split up when he was three and his dad left the family home. He now lives with his mum and new step-dad Steve in a flat owned by a housing association and has no contact with his biological father. Iain's mum works part-time at the local supermarket and Steve is a care assembly worker at a local car factory. Steve is quite strict with Iain and expects him to do jobs around the house.

Last month, the factory shut down and Steve was made redundant. He has refused to sign on the dole and has been trying to get work doing odd jobs. The rent is in arrears and Iain's mum has taken a second job cleaning in the mornings. Steve is drinking heavily in the evening and is increasingly short tempered. He has started hitting Iain for small mistakes and once he knocked him downstairs and threatened to kill him if he told his mum. Iain has to get himself up and dressed and off to school in the morning because Steve won't get up and his mum has to go to work. He has missed school on several occasions.

You are a teaching assistant at Iain's primary school. What behaviours might Iain show that would lead you to suspect abuse? What action should you take?

Identify the key responsibilities of your role and one other professional in contact with Iain (e.g. attendance officer/educational welfare officer).

Using the Assessment Framework, assess whether you think Iain is a child 'in need' as per the Children Act 1989.

What strategies might be used to help Iain and his family to minimise the effects of abuse?

4 Understand the strategies used to safeguard children and young people from abuse and exploitative behaviour

Procedures where maltreatment is considered, suspected, confirmed or excluded

All organisations dealing with children and families have policies and procedures in place for safeguarding children and young people. Whilst these may differ slightly, all have clear arrangements for referring a child or young person who is suspected of being at risk to LA social services for follow-up.

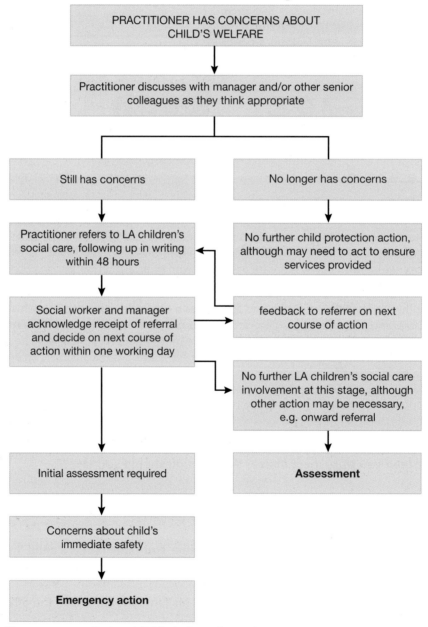

What to do if you are worried a child is being abused

In each LA area, there is a Local Safeguarding Children's Board (LSCB), responsible for coordinating all the relevant organisations in each area and ensuring they cooperate with each other to safeguard and promote the welfare of children and young people effectively.

When working with children you must know, understand and be able to follow your organisation's policies and procedures for safeguarding and protection, including reporting arrangements and safe working practices (e.g. making sure you are not alone with a child when carrying out intimate tasks such as toileting or nappy changing). You can also contact agencies such as the NSPCC or social services yourself, if necessary.

from an appropriate person; ensuring you respect confidentiality.

> ## Key concept
>
> You must understand and be able to follow the correct procedures, including the reporting arrangements and documentation, if you suspect abuse of a child, including by a colleague.

Responding to direct or indirect disclosure

You may find that a child or young person confides in you, disclosing maltreatment or abuse. This may be indirect, e.g. a small child may 'act out' a scene during play that suggests they have been ill treated. An older child may confide in you directly.

You must show you absolutely believe them, listening carefully and attentively to what the child or young person is saying, using active listening skills and giving them plenty of space and time to say what they want. Privacy must be respected and the child or young person controls what is disclosed and how much information is revealed. You should provide reassurance and unconditional acceptance of what they are telling you making it clear that you will have to share it with people who can help. Disclosure requires specialist support to deal with the feelings and issues that inevitably arise and this should be left to the professionals who are trained to manage such situations – social workers and mental health professionals, not teachers, midwives or even health visitors. You may need to seek support for your own feelings

Support for children or young people who disclose

You need to provide access to professional support for the child or young person who discloses in line with your organisation's policies. All children who have been maltreated will have issues of self-esteem, even if they appear to be the most outgoing and loud in the group. It is likely that, at some level, they feel responsible for what has happened to them and will need much calm reassurance that it is not their fault.

You must be able to bolster children's self-esteem and empower them to act on their own behalf – for example, by calling ChildLine or the NSPCC, in addition to following the settings policies and procedures. Make sure you give them praise when they have done something well, or when asked, or when they have spontaneously helped someone, for example. Giving the child or young person some responsibility in line with their capabilities can help. Be lavish and genuine with praise (a child can spot phoney praise immediately) and sparing with rebukes – be sure to criticise the behaviour not the child. The child or young person needs to feel accepted for themselves

Strategies with children and young people

When working with children and young people, develop an open and honest child-centred approach, which is respectful to them and expects respect in return – recognising that respect must be earned, especially from children who do not trust adults. To gain trust, you must be scrupulous about respecting confidences, unless it is a safeguarding issue, being aware of your organisation's information-sharing policy. Adopt strategies that will boost children and young people's assertiveness skills and self-esteem. Demonstrate that issues can be sorted out amicably, without violence and provide them with straightforward, easily understandable information.

Strategies for working with parents and families

In response to legislative changes and high-profile child death investigations, there is more emphasis on integrated working, with agencies using different and innovative ways of working together to help children and young people who are at risk. As a practitioner, you can develop supportive and helpful relationships with parents and carers, relatives and friends of the children and young people you work with. Engaging with parents and involving them in assessment of their child's needs, shows that you recognise and value their

input. Support for the development of parenting skills is also important, perhaps providing information or getting a parent's group together to share experiences or arranging a speaker. Formal parenting classes may be available.

Minimising the effects of abuse

Developing a warm and welcoming approach that is open and honest enables you to encourage children and young people to express their feelings in a safe environment within acceptable boundaries. This means making sure children and young people have the opportunity to 'let off steam' safely. Opportunities to improve their self-image and self-esteem should be provided by listening to what they say and involving them in care arrangements.

Formal support for children and young people who have been abused includes play therapy, psychological therapies and outdoor development opportunities. Several voluntary organisations specialise in helping children and young people recover from their traumatic experiences.

Activity 4   **P5**

Read the case study below and identify the agencies involved in helping this family. What do you think would have happened if the family had not been referred?

 Case Study – Family Intervention Project (FIP)

The police, social services and education services agreed to refer a family to the FIP following reports of regular anti-social behaviour, non-school attendance, concerns about child neglect and a threat of eviction.

The four eldest children had not been attending school for the past 18 months and the two youngest children, who were accessing education, were at risk of permanent exclusion due to their very challenging and aggressive behaviour.

The children's parents showed little evidence of being able to set boundaries, exercise discipline methods and could not communicate well with their children. The father had acute mental health difficulties and the mother was alcohol-dependent and suffered depression.

A multi-agency conference was convened and the family's support needs were prioritised and arrangements for the coordination of a number of other services agreed.

The FIP prioritised the family's housing situation and secured the local authority housing provider's agreement to suspend plans to evict the family while the FIP worked with family members.

The FIP worker visited the family daily, early (7 am) and late (midnight) to help establish parenting routines. Both parents were also asked to sign parenting contracts and anti-social behaviour contracts were served on the children.

Alcohol services and counselling were arranged for the mother. Education/training was arranged for all the children, including a statement of educational need for one child. Specialist emotional and mental health support was provided by child and adolescent mental health services and adult mental health services. Tenancy support and debt management were provided.

A multi-agency team around the family met every six weeks to review progress in dealing with their many complex needs.

In the last six months, there have been no complaints of anti-social behaviour. All the school-age children are now in full-time education with over 90 per cent attendance.

The mother has benefited from the specialist counselling support, her confidence has risen, the household is now functioning in a structured manner and she has attended employment training. There have been major improvements in parenting, including by some of the children (who are also parents) and little evidence of the squalor previously found in the household. This family has now left the FIP and these positive changes have been sustained.

Activity 5   P2   D1

Research the care options for children and young people and, using reports and information, evaluate the success of different placements for different children

Read the case study above. If the Family Intervention Project had not taken place, what other options for quality care would there have been to ensure the health, safety and well-being of the two youngest children? Which do you think would be most successful? Give your reasons.

Summary

When working in health or social care, you need to be aware that some children and young people may be looked after children. They may be cared for outside the family and will have particular needs. This unit helps you to understand the issues faced by such children, the policies and procedures in place to keep them safe and help them achieve their potential.

Assessment and grading criteria

In order to pass this unit, the evidence that the learner presents for assessment needs to demonstrate that they can meet all the learning outcomes for the unit. The assessment criteria for a pass grade describe the level of achievement required to pass this unit.

To achieve a pass grade the evidence must show that the learner is able to:	To achieve a merit grade the evidence must show that, in addition to the pass criteria, the learner is able to:	To achieve a distinction grade the evidence must show that, in addition to the pass and merit criteria, the learner is able to:
P1 outline why children and young people may need to be looked after away from their families	**M1** discuss how policies and procedures help children, young people and their families whilst the child is being looked after	
P2 outline the arrangements for providing quality care for looked after children and young people	**M2** explain the roles and responsibilities of two members of the children's workforce in relation to looked after children and young people	**D1** evaluate the regulation of care provision for looked after children and young people
P3 explain the factors that would lead to suspicion of child maltreatment or abuse	**M3** assess strategies and methods used to minimise the harm to children, young people and their families where abuse is confirmed.	**D2** justify responses where child maltreatment or abuse is suspected or confirmed, referring to current legislation and policies.

To achieve a pass grade the evidence must show that the learner is able to:	To achieve a merit grade the evidence must show that, in addition to the pass criteria, the learner is able to:	To achieve a distinction grade the evidence must show that, in addition to the pass and merit criteria, the learner is able to:
P4 explain appropriate responses when child maltreatment or abuse is suspected		
P5 explain the strategies and methods that can be used to support children, young people and their families where abuse is suspected or confirmed.		

Resources

Department for Children, Schools and Families (2010) *Early Intervention: securing good outcomes for all children and young people* (available at http://publications.dcsf.gov.uk/default.aspx?PageFunction=productdetails&PageMode=publications&ProductId=DCSF-00349-2010&).

House of Commons Children, Schools and Families Select Committee (2009) *Looked-After Children*, London: The Stationery Office Ltd.

Lord Laming (2009) *The Protection of Children in England: A Progress Report*, London: The Stationery Office.

Saunders, H. (2004) *Twenty-Nine Child Homicides: Lessons Still to be Learnt on Domestic Violence and Child Protection*, Bristol: Women's Aid.

Weblinks

www.cwdcouncil.org.uk:
Children's Workforce Development Council
www.nspcc.org.uk:
NSPCC

www.directgov.org.uk:
Directgov

Introduction

In this unit, we focus on safeguarding adults. You will learn how to recognise different types of abuse and abusive situations, and see how professionals working together can promote the rights of adults through a person-centred approach to care. At an organisational level, adults are protected by laws, regulations, strategies and procedures. At a personal level, they are protected by supportive relationships.

Note: this unit considers issues which some may find distressing. If you are affected, please talk to your tutor or a healthcare professional.

This unit links closely with Unit 2: Equality, Diversity and Rights in Health and Social Care, Unit 6: Personal and Professional Development in Health and Social Care, Unit 26: Caring for Individuals with Additional Needs and Unit 28: Caring for Older People. In each unit, you can also work towards Functional Skills ICT and English at Level 2, as well as personal, learning and thinking skills.

Key term

Safeguarding – protecting.

Learning outcomes:

On completion of this unit, you should:

1 Know types and indicators of abuse

2 Understand factors which may lead to abusive situations

3 Know legislation and regulations which govern the safeguarding of adults

4 Know working strategies and procedures to reduce the risk of abuse of adults

5 Understand the role of supportive relationships to promote the rights, independence and well-being of adults using health and social care services.

1 Know types and indicators of abuse

Key term

Abuse – a violation of an individual's human and civil rights by any other person or persons. Source: No Secrets (www.dh.gov.uk)

People abuse others. People also abuse and harm themselves. In this section, we will examine how people are abused or treated in a way that harms them. There are at least ten types of abuse. We will examine each in turn but first here is the official guidance from the Department of Health:

'Abuse may consist of a single act or repeated acts. It may be physical, verbal or psychological, it may be an act of neglect or an omission to act, or it may

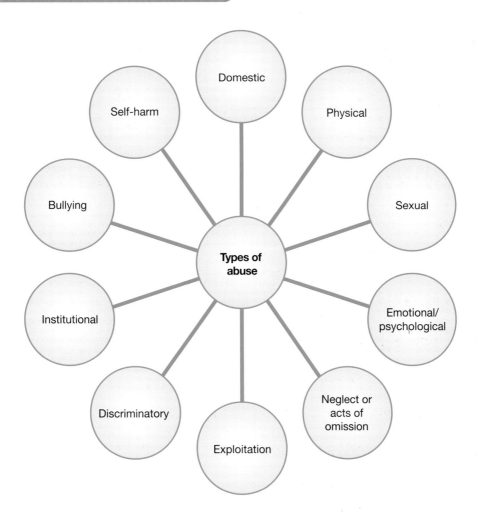

occur when a vulnerable person is persuaded to enter into a financial or sexual transaction to which he or she has not consented, or cannot consent. Abuse can occur in any relationship and may result in significant harm to, or exploitation of, the person subjected to it.'

> Source: 'No Secrets: Guidance on developing and implementing multi-agency policies and procedures to protect vulnerable adults from abuse'

The types of abuse outlined in this unit are shown in the diagram on page 237.

Types of abuse

Physical

This is harm caused to someone physically. It may be obvious if a person has bruises or broken limbs, but it may be less obvious if the bruises are covered by clothing, or if the person is immobile.

Sexual

This is harm caused to a person through a sexual act. This may happen on several occasions over a period of time, or it may happen just once.

Emotional or psychological

This occurs when a person is harmed emotionally, perhaps by being treated in a disrespectful manner.

Neglect or acts of omission

This occurs when the abuser causes harm by not doing what should be done – for example, by not giving an older person enough to drink or to eat, or by not changing soiled clothing and bed linen.

Exploitation

This may be financial – for example, an abuser may persuade a vulnerable adult to hand over their life savings – but it is not just financial. It occurs whenever a person is used for another person's gain.

Discriminatory

This type of abuse may be based on gender, race, ability, sexuality or age. A person who is denied membership of an organisation because of their ethnicity or their gender experiences discriminatory abuse. A person who uses a wheelchair suffers discriminatory abuse if they are denied a job because of their reduced mobility.

Institutional

This occurs when routines work for the benefit of the organisation, not for the person they are supposed to care for. In poor-quality care homes, service users are not given choice about when they eat, when they sleep or even when they go to the toilet. Where there is institutional abuse, the needs of the individual fit in with the routines of the home; everyone has to get up at the same time, have breakfast at the same time and go to bed at the same time. In 1961, Erving Goffmann published his classic study on asylums, where he described a regime that left little choice for residents. Their lives and choices were determined by routine, what he termed 'batch living'.

Bullying

Bullying is unfortunately common in organisations. Bullying may be name calling or sending threatening text messages. Bullying can be physical and/or emotional. Often there is more than one type of abuse present in a situation, as shown in the following case study.

Case Study

X is a 20-year-old woman with learning difficulties. She lives with two other people in a house. Support workers are on duty at all times. Nav, a support worker, finds X crying in the kitchen one afternoon. The others are watching television in the sitting room. X tells Nav that one of the people she shares the house with has been borrowing money to buy cigarettes and, when she asked for it back, he threatened her and twisted her arm up her back. X is scared of what he might do if she does not give him money.

Nav tells X that it must be reported. This is financial, emotional and physical abuse.

Activity 1 — P1

List the different types of abuse, then write few sentences in your own words to describe each type, giving an example. Use journals such as *Community Care* and government websites such as www.direct.gov. uk to find examples. You may wish to make notes under these headings but remember to write your notes out in full later:

Type of abuse:

Description:

Example:

Self-harm

Self-harm takes many forms. People may cut themselves or take an overdose of tablets. Mind, the mental health charity, suggests that more women than men self harm (www.mind.org.uk).

Domestic

Domestic abuse may be physical, sexual, financial or emotional but, like bullying, it is aimed at controlling another person. Often domestic abuse is aimed at a partner, but children also may suffer from domestic abuse. Women's Aid, a national domestic violence charity, provides help and advice for men and women who are in abusive relationships (www.womensaid.org.uk).

Did you know...

At least two women a week are killed by current or ex-partners. One in four women in the UK will experience domestic violence.

Indicators of abuse and self-harm

We have looked briefly at types of abuse, but how do we know it is happening? Many victims of abuse are reluctant to say they are being abused. Some people may not even know they are being abused and just accept that they are beaten up for no reason. In this section, we look at indicators of abuse and self-harm.

Key term

Indicators – signs.

Disclosure of abuse does not always happen. Sometimes people who are being abused make excuses for the abuser. A woman may say of her partner, 'He works long hours, he is stressed. It's only natural he lost his temper'. People find it difficult to admit that the person they love is hurting them. If and when a person does disclose they are being abused, it is important to listen but also to let them know that if someone is at risk of harm, the authorities must be told.

If a person wishes to proceed with the disclosure, support must be given and they must be referred to a health and social care professional or the police, who are trained to manage such situations. It is important to let the person know what help is available.

Unexplained injuries, such as fractures, bruising, burns, scalds, cuts and scars, can be signs of abuse but they may also be signs of other things. Fractures may occur if a person has osteoporosis (thinning of the bones). Bruising may occur easily if they are taking tablets to thin their blood. Someone living alone may have burns or scalds because they no longer see as well as they did. Cuts and scars may be a sign of self-harm, but may also be a sign that someone has been playing with an unruly cat or clearing a garden of brambles.

It is important not to jump to conclusions, but to look for a cluster of signs that might indicate abuse. Malnourishment and weight loss may occur in older people if they have health problems. It is important to keep records, and to note whether a loss of appetite happens just once or persists. Poor hygiene may be due to neglect.

Changes in behaviour may indicate abuse. Someone with low self-esteem, mood swings and social withdrawal may be experiencing bullying. They may become passive or compliant, hoping to appease the abuser. If an adult is fearful of certain people and does not want to be left alone with them, make a note and observe the person's behaviour with different people. Sometimes an abused person may react by seeking attention or react with inappropriate behaviour, perhaps of a sexual nature. Occasionally a person who has been abused feels suicidal.

Difficulty with finances, especially when there has been no problem in the past, may indicate the person is being financially abused. If they are unable to pay bills or lack food and basic necessities, it may be a case of abuse. Sometimes people do not always realise they are being abused financially.

Stress that triggers health problems may indicate abuse. Heart conditions, breathing problems and ulcers are all worsened by stress. Someone being abused may have difficulty sleeping.

2 Understand factors which may lead to abusive situations

Activity 2   P2

Case Study

Mrs M lives alone in her council bungalow. She is partially sighted and finds it difficult to get to the shops. Agnes, her personal assistant, pops in every morning to help her get washed and dressed. Sometimes Agnes does her shopping for her too. One day, Mrs M tells Agnes that her nephew Jack has been to visit her. Agnes is surprised as he has not been to see his aunt for years. Over the next few weeks, Jack visits regularly. Mrs M does not seem to have as much money for groceries and, when Agnes asks if she needs any shopping, she says 'No', despite the fact that there is very little food in the fridge. Agnes also notices that Mrs M does not like to talk about her nephew and, when Agnes asks about him, Mrs M goes very quiet. She says she is tired – she has not been sleeping well lately.

What indicates that abuse may be happening?

What other indicators of abuse may there be that are not apparent here?

Adults most at risk

Adults most at risk are those who are vulnerable. A vulnerable adult is someone over the age of 18 years:

> 'who is or may be in need of community care services by reason of mental or other disability, age or illness; and who is or may be unable to take care of him or herself, or unable to protect him or herself against significant harm or exploitation.'
>
> Source: No Secrets (www.dh.gov.uk).

People with learning disabilities may not be assertive enough to say no to an abuser. People with physical disabilities may not be able to stop an abuser.

People who have ill health are at risk of abuse because they do not have the strength, physically or mentally, to complain. Those with dementia or with mental health needs may not realise they are being abused. People who are aphasic and cannot speak may know they are being abused, but may not be able to communicate that to others. Those who are sensory impaired, perhaps visually or hearing impaired, may not know they are being abused. A visually impaired person may not see relatives take money from her purse. A hearing impaired person may not hear the rough way a carer talks to them or even swears at them.

Comatose or semi-comatose people are especially vulnerable to physical and sexual abuse. The

Case Study

Mrs T lives alone and has limited mobility because of her arthritis. She relies on carers to get her out of bed and to help her shower and dress. Her carers are always in a hurry. One carer never changes the incontinence pad that Mrs T wears, even when it is soiled. Mrs T cannot manage to do this herself and so has to wait until another carer comes. This is abuse by neglect and omission – not doing what should be done.

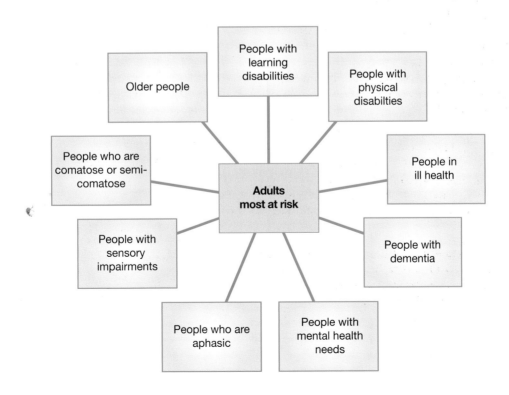

film *Kill Bill* hints at such abuse experienced by the comatose bride played by Uma Thurman. Older people who are lonely and poor are again vulnerable. They may not have a social network of friends to help them and lack of money may mean they rely solely on the care provided by local authorities. They may be scared to complain in case they lose that care.

Environments

Sometimes the environment is a factor in abuse. Care takes place in a variety of environments.

A person expects to feel safe in their own home, but that is not always the case. Family members may exploit an older person's vulnerability and visit only to steal or borrow money. Abuse can remain undetected for a long time in a person's own home because there are no regulations governing informal carers.

Community care services are the care services provided in any setting or context. This includes domiciliary care, where paid carers go into a person's own home to help them with activities such as dressing and showering.

Day care centres provide physical and mental stimulation for people. They also provide information and social interaction for vulnerable adults.

Abuse can take place anywhere. Hospitals can be places of neglect. Food and water may be served, but if no one helps the frail old lady to eat, she may starve. If no one helps her to pour a glass of water, she may as well be in the Sahara desert. In a residential home, carers who are tired and short of time may not give resident choices about what to wear. They may rush the person into the shower and scrub them roughly. People in independent living are at risk of abuse from others sharing their home and from staff.

Abuse can also occur in health services, such as GP surgeries, dental surgeries and physiotherapy practices, particularly neglect or omissions. A common abuse is when a person is asked to change into a gown that is too skimpy. Not offering a

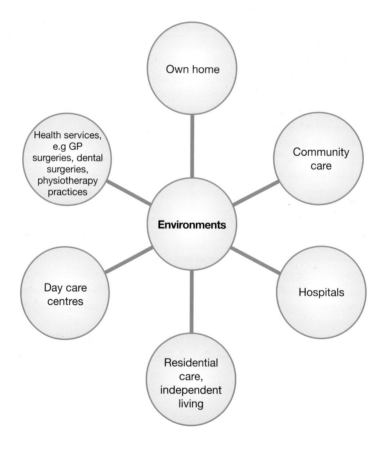

larger gown or a dressing gown, leaving the person exposed, is neglect.

Contexts

The contexts or situations where abuse may happen are numerous. Usually the context is influenced by power relationships. If a person who uses a service is empowered, they will complain and abuse is less likely. If a person feels they will not be listened to, and feels powerless, they will not complain and abuse is more likely to happen.

People who are dependent on others for personal care or who are socially isolated may know they are being abused but may be too ashamed to report it.

 Case Study

Mr Z lives near his married daughter. She is his main carer. She helps him take a shower in the morning and prepares his meals. She is very impatient with him because he is slow and she has to get to work. One day, she slaps him across the face, causing a large bruise to develop. His neighbour pops in for a chat, notices the bruise and asks him what happened. Mr Z is too ashamed to say his daughter hit him so makes up a story about tripping over the rug.

Sometimes people may lack the mental capacity to consent to sexual relationships or may not have the social awareness that abuse has taken place. This is especially true if someone they trust has sexually abused them. They may think it is normal for a carer to touch their private parts.

People can be particularly vulnerable if they have communication difficulties. If they do summon up the courage to report the incident, they may not be listened to, as was the case for Fiona Pilkington.

Case Study – Fiona Pilkington

In October 2007, Fiona Pilkington drove her 18-year-old daughter, who had learning disabilities, to a quiet spot, poured petrol in the car and set fire to them both. She had had enough.

'The jury heard Pilkington contacted police on no fewer than 33 occasions in seven years in which youths throwing stones and shouting abuse had kept her a virtual prisoner in her home.'
Source: www.guardian.co.uk/ uk/2010/mar/16/police-under- investiation-fiona-pilkington

In July 2006, a report found that in Kent and Medway NHS and Social Care Partnership Trust, people with learning disabilities living in Greenacres home were being abused.

- 'People were being physically abused by staff supposed to be caring for them. They were punched, kicked and dragged along the floor.
- People were forced to go without food and have cold showers.
- People were having their money taken.
- One person spent 16 hours a day tied to their bed or wheelchair.
- Medication was used to keep people easily controlled.'
Source: www.mencap.org.uk

This abuse was undetected by inspectors who did not look at learning disability services. Senior managers did not check what was happening. This report led to a full investigation of learning disability services across the country.

Did you know...

Mencap is a charity that works to promote the rights of people with learning disabilities.

⬭ Case Study

Miss W moved into Sunnydale retirement home when she could no longer cope at home alone. She has a small appetite and is easily put off eating if she is given too much food. The manager of Sunnydale believes all residents should eat well. Miss W is given a plate piled high with meat and vegetables and told she must finish it. The manager stands over her to make sure she eats it. This is bullying.

Privacy and invasion of privacy are issues for Miss W. She is a very private person, likes her own company and is happy reading a book or listening to the radio in her room. The carers are told that everyone must have a bath everyday. Miss W is quietly reading a book in her room when Maggie, the carer, walks in without knocking and says it is time for her bath. Maggie leaves the door to the corridor open, goes into the bathroom, turns on the taps and shouts to Miss W that she had better use the toilet before she gets in the bath, not like last time. Walking in without knocking is invading Miss W's privacy. Shouting about her toilet habits is another breach of privacy.

Did you know...

Age Concern and Help the Aged are now called Age UK.

People who may abuse

Unfortunately anyone may abuse. There is no category of person who might not, at some point, become an abuser. Health or care professionals and those working in health or care environments do not usually set out to become abusive, but sometimes being exhausted and stressed from working long hours can lead to a carer becoming an abuser.

According to a Department of Health study quoted in *Nursing Times*, neglect is the most common form of abuse, followed by financial abuse. Risk factors for neglect include being over 85, female, in poor health, depressed and in receipt of health or care services. Those living alone, lonely, in receipt of services and in poor health are more at risk of financial abuse.

The old, the sick and the lonely are vulnerable to abuse

The same study found that:

> 'Most often, the perpetrator of mistreatment was a partner or spouse (51% of cases), closely followed by another family member (49%), then by a care worker (13%) and by a close friend (5%). Some people reported abuse from more than one person.'
>
> Source: www.nursingtimes.net

Strangers may be abusers, as in the case of Fiona Pilkington quoted earlier. The effect of abuse is serious. In the study quoted in *Nursing Times*, 'Around three-quarters of the people questioned said that the effect on them was either serious (43%) or very serious (33%)'.

Activity 3 P3 M1 D1

In pairs, write down the factors that may lead to abusive situations. Write the name of the factor on one side of a Post It note and the explanation of that factor on the other side. Put the Post It notes on a desk with the explanation uppermost. Take turns to identify each factor from the explanation. When you are confident you can explain each factor, write up your own notes.

For M1 and D1, focus on two different types of abuse and prepare a presentation in which you assess the immediate effects of abuse on the individuals concerned, and then evaluate the potential long-term effects. Your evaluation may suggest that the long-term effects are severe and disabling or they may be judged as minimal, but you must explain how you reach this evaluation.

3 Know legislation and regulations which govern the safeguarding of adults

Legislation (laws) change, so it is important to keep up to date by checking government websites (e.g. Department of Health) and reading reliable newspapers (e.g. the *Guardian* and e-journals such as *Community Care* and *Nursing Times*).

Relevant legislation and regulations

These are current but may change, especially when a new government is elected:

1 The Safeguarding Vulnerable Groups Act

2 The Rehabilitation of Offenders Act
3 The Police Act
4 The Sexual Offences Act
5 The Care Standards Act
6 The Care Homes (Adult Placements) (Amendment) Regulations
7 The Mental Health Act
8 The Mental Capacity Act
9 The Disability Discrimination Act
10 The Race Relations Act
11 The Human Rights Act
12 The Data Protection Act

The Safeguarding Vulnerable Groups Act

The Safeguarding Vulnerable Groups Act 2006 was passed following the Bichard enquiry into the Soham Murders of 2002, when Ian Huntley, who was a school caretaker, murdered two girls at the school where he worked. The report called for a single agency to vet all individuals who want to work or volunteer with children or vulnerable adults and to bar unsuitable people from doing so. This act created the Independent Safeguarding Authority, which vets and bars unsuitable people from working in England, Wales and Northern Ireland.

The Rehabilitation of Offenders Act

The Rehabilitation of Offenders Act 1974 enables criminal convictions, with some exceptions, to become 'spent' or ignored after a rehabilitation period. This act is under review and may change. The Crime and Disorder Act 1998 introduced a new custodial sentence for young people with different rehabilitation periods. Currently, cautions, final warnings and reprimands are not sentences with rehabilitation periods, but this may change. Enhanced criminal record checks show everything, even cautions, and employers in certain areas must request enhanced criminal records checks where people work with children and vulnerable adults, in professions such as health, pharmacy and the law (www.nacro.org.uk).

Did you know...

NACRO is the charity that works with ex-offenders to resettle them in the community.

The Police Act

There are several acts that regulate police activity. The Criminal Justice and Police Act 2001 allows the taking of fingerprints and DNA samples in an effort to crack down on anti-social behaviour. The taking and keeping of DNA samples of innocent people was controversial and was found to be in breach of Article 8 of the European Convention of Human Rights.

The Police Act 1997 makes provision in relation to applications for criminal record certificates and enhanced criminal record certificates. It has been amended several times to allow for changes in the CRB (Criminal Record Bureau) process.

It is important to recognise that under the Health Act 1999, statuary agencies such as health, social services and the community justice services and police must work together in partnership, sharing information. Fiona Pilkington had reported abuse several times to the police but they did not share this information with social services. As a result of this failure, she did not get the support she needed and killed herself and her daughter.

Some types of abuse are criminal offences. Physical and sexual assault, rape, theft, fraud, and racial and gender discrimination are all criminal offences and must be dealt with by the police and the Crown Prosecution Service. These complaints must be referred to the police as a matter of urgency.

The Sexual Offences Act

The Sexual Offences Act 2003 created new provisions concerning sexual offences, their prevention and protection of children from harm.

Among other things, the act:

- classified any sexual intercourse with a child aged 12 or younger as rape
- created a number of offences related to 'intent', including a new offence targeting drinks spiking
- redefined sexual assault as intentional sexual touching without consent, which includes touching any part of the body, clothed or unclothed, by either a body part or an object.

The Care Standards Act

The Care Standards Act 2000 set out a regulatory framework for social care to ensure high standards of care and improve the protection of vulnerable people. The act established the independent National Care Standards Commission (NCSC), which links to National Standards.

The Care Homes (Adult Placements) (Amendment) Regulations

The Care Homes (Adult Placements) (Amendment) Regulations 2003 are an amendment of the Care Homes Regulations 2001 – principal regulations, made under the Care Standards Act 2000. When short-term breaks are provided, the care provider does not have to ensure that a GP is provided.

The Mental Health Act

The Mental Health Act 1983 sets out how a person can be admitted, detained and treated in hospital against their wishes. The act covers the rights of people while they are detained, how they can be discharged from hospital and what aftercare they can expect to receive. The act applies in England and Wales. The Mental Health Act 1983 was recently amended by the Mental Health Act 2007. Mental Health Act commissioners visit and protect people whose rights are restricted in hospital.

The Mental Capacity Act

The Mental Capacity Act 2005 was fully implemented in 2009. It outlines what should happen when adults are unable to make decisions for themselves, perhaps because of a learning disability, dementia or mental health problems. According to the Care Quality Commission (www.cqc.org.uk), the act sets out:

- how a person's capacity to take a decision should be assessed
- who can take particular decisions on someone else's behalf
- when and how a decision can be taken
- when and how people who lack capacity to take decisions about their care and welfare can be deprived of their liberty to get the care they need in a hospital or care home.

The final point in the list above was introduced in April 2009.

Did you know...

The Equality and Human Rights Commission 'has the responsibility to protect, enforce and promote equality across the seven "protected" grounds – age, disability, gender, race, religion and belief, sexual orientation and gender reassignment'.
Source: www.equalityhumanrights.com/our-job/

The Disability Discrimination Act

The Disability Discrimination Act 1995, amended in 2005, promotes the rights of people with disabilities and protects them from discrimination.

The Race Relations Act

The Race Relations Act 1976, amended in 2000, makes it unlawful to treat a person less favourably than another on racial grounds. This includes race, colour, nationality (including citizenship), and national or ethnic origin.

The Human Rights Act

- The Human Rights Act 1998 protects rights given under the European Convention on Human Rights.

Source: adapted from www.liberty-human-rights.org.uk/issues/human-rights-act

The Data Protection Act

The Data Protection Act 1998 repealed (replaced) the Data Protection Act 1984, Access to Personal Files Act 1987, and most of the Access to Health Records Act 1990.

The working of the act is regulated by the Information Commission Officer (ICO). The Data Protection Act is designed to maintain the confidentiality of information, but in safeguarding situations, it is important that professionals share information.

Protocols exist that say what information can be shared between partner organisations in safeguarding situations. Information must be shared where a criminal act may be involved.

Disclosure should be only for the purpose stated and have regard to the Human Rights Act and the Data Protection Act. Disclosure may occur when someone has a history of violence or is on the sex offenders' register and might present a threat – for example, to a vulnerable person or a professional visiting a vulnerable person (www.dh.gov.uk).

Activity 4 **P4**

Make a booklet for new care staff outlining the key legislation and regulations governing safeguarding adults.

4 Know working strategies and procedures to reduce the risk of abuse of adults

In the previous section, we looked at laws that say *what* we must do. In this section, we look at *how* we must do it. Strategies are plans, so working strategies are working plans. Like any plans, we may need to amend them if we find they do not work. Procedures are the actions we must take to put the plan into practice. Strategies alone are no good – they need actions to make them happen. This is why you may see the words 'strategies' and 'procedures' together, but be clear that they mean different things.

Key terms

Strategies – plans.
Procedures – a set of actions or steps that meets the requirements of the policy or strategy

In this section, we will look at some of the strategies to reduce the risk abuse.

Recruitment of staff

Having the correct strategy in place when recruiting staff is vital for reducing the risks of abuse. It involves running several checks.

The first procedure is to check the job applicant against the adults' barred list. The Vetting and Barring Scheme has two lists, the Children's Barred List and the Adults' Barred list. These replace, in England and Wales, List 99, the Protection of Children's Act List (POCA) and the Protection of Vulnerable Adults List (POVA) and, in Northern Ireland, the Disqualification from Working with Children List, the Unsuitable Persons List and the Disqualification from Working with Vulnerable Adults List, as well as the current system of disqualification orders that is operated by the criminal justice system.

The two lists have details of people that the Independent Safeguarding Authority (ISA) has decided it is appropriate to bar from working with children or vulnerable adults. If someone's name is on the list, they cannot work or volunteer to work with vulnerable children or adults.

The Independent Safeguarding Authority (ISA) is part of the government's Vetting and Barring Scheme (VBS) and works with the Criminal Records Bureau (CRB). The ISA's role is to make independent barring decisions and place or remove individuals on either or both the Children's Barred List or the Vulnerable Adults' Barred List.

The role of the CRB is to provide a checking service for organisations. Two levels of checks are available – a standard and an enhanced check. Health and social care workers are required to have enhanced checks. ISA maintains the barred lists, which are checked for certain types of employment.

Sector guidance

Employers are guided by the Protection of Vulnerable Adults Scheme in England and Wales for Adult Placement Schemes, Domiciliary Care Agencies and Care Homes 2006 (updated publication 2009). Although the ISA makes decisions on who is and who is not able to work with vulnerable adults, employers have a duty to obtain an ISA check before a new person starts work and they now have a duty to refer anything that may subsequently put an employee on the list.

The ISA and CRB provide national guidance. Other guidance relates to what should happen at a regional level.

The Department of Health's 'No Secrets' guidance is a key document that sets out guidance for inter-agency working led by social services. It gives practical suggestions for sharing of policies and procedures to prevent the abuse of adults. 'In Safe Hands', published in 2000 and amended in 2009, is the Welsh equivalent of the English 'No Secrets' guidance for prevention of abuse. It provides examples of good financial practice when supporting vulnerable people in their own homes (www.scie-socialcareonline.org.uk).

'Safeguarding Adults: a national framework of standards for good practice and outcomes in adult protection work' (2005) followed on from 'No Secrets'. It suggested the introduction of local Safeguarding Adults Committees, with senior members from each organisation championing this work in their own organisation and feeding back to the joint committee.

The Dignity in Care Initiative, started by the Department of Health, aims to put dignity at the heart of care services with its ten-point challenge to services. This topic is covered in Unit 28 Caring for older people (available online, see inside front cover for details).

Human Rights in Healthcare – A Framework for Local Action (2008) outlines human rights and what they mean in health care for frontline staff. It looks at the legal obligations of the NHS under human rights legislation and suggests how to improve services (www.dh.gov.uk).

Organisational policies give specific guidance. Mencap are clear about what they do and what they want to achieve. Read their manifesto 'Making Rights a Reality' at www.mencap.org.uk.

Birmingham adult social services put their policies online, as do most local authorities. There is a clear procedure for reporting abuse using a multi-agency alert form, and a link to policies and procedures and information-sharing protocols (www.birmingham.gov.uk/safeguardingadults).

Local and regional guidelines for staff and volunteers working with vulnerable adults are also available. For example, Dignity Champions are encouraged to share examples of good practice.

Guidelines for volunteer champions are provided on their website and at local and regional levels (www.dhcarenetworks.org.uk/dignityincare/Topics/championresources/ToolkitForAction/Public/).

The codes of practice for nursing and social work provide guidance on preventing abuse and protecting vulnerable people from harm. These codes are explained in detail in Unit 28 Caring for older people (available online).

Strategies

Strategies to reduce the risk of abuse include:

- partnership working
- multi-agency working
- working in partnership with adults using services, families and informal carers
- decision-making processes and forums
- staff training and induction
- role of Care Quality Commission.

Partnership working

Partnership working is working together across organisations. It brings different skills and resources together to deal with a common problem and implies an equal respect for each other's strengths. The Redbridge Learning Disability Partnership was established in December 2002, bringing together health and social care commissioning and provision on behalf of four organisations, Redbridge and Waltham Forest councils and primary care trusts. Benefits include sharing of information and a more holistic approach to care.

Multi-agency working

This differs from partnership working in that it implies working with many other organisations, with one taking the lead.

Case Study

Mr Z is 80 years old and diabetic. He lives alone and is fiercely independent. He has care from his GP and from the community nurse for his diabetes, and his social worker has arranged for domiciliary support once a day from a private agency.

The case study above shows health services, social services and private care working together. If they worked in isolation, Mr Z would get poorer quality of care than if they worked together. His GP might not be aware that he is increasingly forgetting to take his insulin. The carer who comes to give him his breakfast may think he is unusually tired and reluctant to get up in the morning. She may not recognise the signs of hyperglycaemia. The social worker may think it is time Mr Z moved to residential care as he is so much slower. A multi-agency approach, where each agency is represented at a case review and where Mr Z can have his say either by himself or through an advocate, may find a different solution from residential care.

Working in partnership with adults using services, families and informal carers

Sometimes abuse happens when carers are exhausted. See the case study below.

Case Study

Mr Y cares for his wife of 40 years. She has dementia and often gets up in the middle of the night and wanders about the house. She turns on the gas but forgets to light it. Mr Y has to get up and persuade her to go back to bed. He has no support and is very tired. He starts to get irritated with his wife. She becomes angry and he lashes out and hits her.

By working in partnership with families and carers, social workers could pick up on such situations and abuse could be avoided. Mr Y needs help. He should not get to the point of abuse before help arrives.

Decision-making processes and forums

These are most useful when they involve different agencies and when service users are represented. The policies developed are then known to all and used by all. Examples of good practice in social work training can be found at www.scie.org.uk

Staff training and induction

This provides frontline workers with the knowledge to prevent abuse but also, if it happens, to recognise and report abuse. Skills for Care, the Sector Skills Council for Social Care, provides online knowledge sets for induction and continuous professional development on topics such as Safeguarding of Vulnerable Adults. Read some of the information at: www.skillsforcare.org.uk/developing_skills/knowledge_sets/safeguarding_of_vulnerable_adults.aspx.

The role of the Care Quality Commission

The role of the Care Quality Commission (CQC) is to regulate health and social care services provided by the NHS, local authorities, private companies and voluntary organisations. The CQC make sure there is better care for all, in hospitals, care homes and people's own homes. If you have a complaint about care, the CQC will look into it.

Procedures for protection

The first line of defence against abuse is to be alert. Abuse can happen anywhere – at home, at a day centre, in a residential home or in

Case Study – University of Plymouth, B.Sc. Hons Health and Social Care Management

The consultative group of users, carers, academics and practitioners meets regularly. It has been involved in planning the new award and continues to play a significant role in all aspects of delivery and development. In addition to involvement in assessment, it contributes to partnership learning in a number of ways.

- People who use services and their carers are involved in the substantial two-week induction at the beginning of the course, which includes a session explaining why users are involved. This emphasis on the contribution of users defines the culture of the whole course.
- People who use services take part in teaching sessions. While there has been positive feedback from students, this involvement takes a lot of time, both during the session and in preparation.
- At the selection stage, users are involved as observers in the group interview and also play an equal part in individual interviews.

hospital. The abuser may be in a position of trust and have responsibility for the care of the individual. Most abusers are known to their victims.

Signs of abuse may be difficult to spot – for example, bruises hidden by clothing and gradual loss of weight. Some signs are obvious – a dirty, smelly environment and soiled, unchanged bed sheets may indicate neglect. Emotional withdrawal or unexplained anger may indicate psychological abuse. Where a family is abusing a relative, the person may not be allowed to speak to a professional alone. An older person may deny there is anything wrong because they feel embarrassed that someone they care for could do such a thing and they may wish to protect the abuser.

Referral

If you suspect abuse of an older person, you should let them know that help is available. They can report the abuse themselves if they are able, by contacting the charity Action on Elder Abuse, a national free helpline in UK and Ireland, on the following numbers:

UK: 0808 808 8141

Republic of Ireland: 1800 940 010

Did you know...

Action on Elder Abuse also runs the helpline for Southern Cross, one of the largest private providers of care in England and they provide an email service for advocates (www. elderabuse.org.uk).

Victim Support is a charity that gives free, confidential help to victims of crime, witnesses, their family, friends and anyone else affected across England and Wales. They can be contacted by telephone or by email. The Victim Supportline is 0845 30 30 900 (www.victimsupport.org.uk).

Although Action on Elder Abuse and Victim Support can advise, referrals should be made to the statutory organisations. The government website www.direct.gov.uk can help you find your local council. Referral should be to the social services or social work department's adult protection unit.

In England, the guidance professionals follow is 'No Secrets' and, in Wales, it is 'In Safe Hands', but the process is the same. In Scotland, there is a legal duty to respond to your referral. There is no guidance in Northern Ireland but there is a process for adult protection referral. Whichever of these countries you are in, talk to the adult protection team. In the Republic of Ireland, the health boards deal with elder abuse referrals.

A person does not need to be getting care support to report abuse. Whether they are paying for their care or receiving it free, they are entitled to be free from abuse. It is a basic human right.

Did you know...

If a crime has been committed such as assault, theft or rape, the referral must be made to the police/Gardai at once, using 999 if an emergency or to the local police station – find it on www. police.uk (click on the 'Police Forces' tab) or www.direct.gov.uk.

The organisation that receives the referral must pass this on to the appropriate inspection body and inform other agencies that may be involved and any other authority that may be using the service provider.

> 'Residential care homes are required under the Registered Homes Act 1984 (as amended in 1991) to notify the Registration Authority not later than 24 hours from the time of its occurrence [...] of any event in the home which affects the well-being of any resident, and specifically of:
>
> - any serious injury to any person residing in the home (Regulation 14(1)(b)); and
> - any event in the home which affects the well-being of any resident (Regulation 14 (1) (d)).'
>
> Source: 'No Secrets', Section 3

Abuse in care homes and domiciliary services should be reported to social care inspection bodies:

- In England, the Care Quality Commission, tel.: 03000 616161, www.cqc.org.uk.
- In Scotland, the Scottish Care Commission, tel.: 0845 603 0890, www.carecommission.com.
- In Wales, the Care and Social Services Inspectorate for Wales, tel.: 01443 848450, http://wales.gov.uk/cssiwsubsite.
- In Northern Ireland, the Northern Ireland Department of Health, Social Services and Public Safety – Social Services Inspectorate, tel.: 0289 052 0500, www.dhsspsni.gov.uk/hss/ssi/index.asp.

Any professional, such as a GP, dentist, practice nurse or community nurse, will help if you are concerned.

Investigations should be coordinated. The stages of an investigation are as follows:

- Reporting to a single referral point. This happens once a referral has been made.
- Recording, *with sensitivity to the abused person*, the precise factual details of the alleged abuse.
- Initial coordination involving all agencies which might have a role in a subsequent investigation.
- Investigation within a jointly agreed framework to determine the facts of the case.
- Decision-making which may take place at a shared forum such as a case conference.

Investigation

The initial assessment should evaluate whether the person is suffering harm or exploitation and whether the intervention is in the best interests of the vulnerable adult. According to 'No Secrets' guidance, when assessing the seriousness of a case, the factors that need to be considered are the vulnerability of the individual, the nature and extent of the abuse, the length of time it has been occurring, the impact on the individual, and the risk of repeated or increasingly serious acts involving this or other vulnerable adults (source: 'No Secrets', section 2.19).

The alleged abuser must be made aware of their rights. If they are a service user and a vulnerable adult themselves, they have the right to have an appropriate adult with them while being questioned by the police.

Decision-making

When investigations are completed, the lead agency should be notified of the outcome and they determine what, if any, further action is necessary. The standard of proof for prosecution is 'beyond reasonable doubt', whereas the standard of proof for internal discipline is 'on the balance of probabilities'.

Decisions should set out:

- what steps are to be taken to assure the person's safety in future
- what treatment or therapy he or she can access
- modifications in the way services are provided (e.g. same-gender care or placement)
- how best to support the individual through any action he or she takes to seek justice or redress
- any on-going risk management strategy required.

Assessment planning for the person's future protection must respect the rights of individuals to make choices. This may at times be difficult for care workers to understand if a victim returns to live with an abuser or fails to press charges where evidence is clear.

> 'If someone has "capacity" and declines assistance this limits the help that he or she may be given. It will not however limit the action that may be required to protect others who are at risk of harm.'
> Source: 'No Secrets', section 6

Record-keeping

All agencies should keep clear and accurate records and bring together all relevant agency and service user records into a file to record all action taken. These records must be available to inspectors.

The situation must be monitored and reviewed to ensure that actions have been carried out and changes made to improve the service.

A complaints procedure should be available to service users and complaints should be dealt with promptly.

Whistle-blowing

Whistle-blowing or making a disclosure in the public interest means that, if you believe there is wrongdoing in your organisation, you can report it following correct processes. You should not suffer as a result of this. The government website www. direct.gov.uk has a section on whistle-blowing.

Activity 5   P5   M2

Make a second booklet for a carer new to health and social care to add to the one you completed in Activity 4. Outline the working strategies and procedures used in health and social care to reduce the risk of abuse.

To cover M2, describe your work for P4 and P5 in depth.

---

5 Understand the role of supportive relationships to promote the rights, independence and well-being of adults using health and social care services

When care goes well, it rarely makes the headlines. When it goes wrong, it is often front-page news. In this section, we look at when it goes well and when it does not.

⬭ Case Study – Sheffield Expert Elders Network

The Expert Elders Network comprises 105 older people who volunteer their time to advise the NHS and local authority on the planning, design and delivery of local services.

The Expert Elders Network is about the empowerment of older people to ensure that they have a strong voice in how services are shaped to meet their needs. This is not just health and social care services but the everyday services that help people go about their lives, such as public transport, building design, parks and open spaces, housing and libraries. It is part of the 'Strategy for an Ageing Population'.

Older people can register their specific interests, ranging from commenting on draft policies, to sitting on service modernisation boards, to helping to write job descriptions. The coordinators promote the availability of this 'well' of knowledge, and encourage organisations to register requests for older people's participation. They act as brokers, ensuring there is a match between levels of interest, knowledge and time required. A training programme enables older people to develop their skill.

Source: www.dhcarenetworks.org.uk

Case Study – Coventry and Warwickshire Partnership NHS Trust

The 2008 Health and Social Care Award for Dignity in Care (West Midlands region) went to Coventry and Warwickshire Partnership NHS Trust – Community Learning Disability Service. This project is developing personal history records of individuals for whom there may previously have been no informal records. The project involves the creation of a Life Story book, into which a wide variety of information and items can be saved for future study.

Source: www.dhcarenetworks.org. uk/dignityincare/awards/HSCawards/ regionalwinners/westmids

Core principles of care

The Coventry and Warwickshire Partnership NHS Trust and the Sheffield Experts Elders Network are just two examples of good practice. You can find more on the Dignity in Care website. What they have in common with all examples of good practice are that they are based on the core principles of care.

The core principles of care are dignity, equality, respect, fairness and privacy. Both examples respect people as individuals and treat them fairly, with dignity, equality and respect.

Build effective relationships

In both examples above, the adult is at the centre of planning. They are listened to and their methods of communication are respected. There is a respect for culture and beliefs, respect of lifestyle and choices, and recognition of needs. Their preferences are taken into account and, where relevant, confidentiality is maintained.

Working practices

Working practices are person centred. In the Coventry and Warwickshire Partnership example, needs are assessed and the care planning cycle highlighted a gap in information. Person-centred practices focused on the lack of personal history records. Using face-to-face communication, carers worked with people to develop 'life story' books to fill the gap in their lives. This shows inclusive practice, which is anti-discriminatory and anti-oppressive. It is aimed at empowering individuals. In a safe and secure environment, people are encouraged to share information appropriately. This is then shared, with their permission, with others who care for them, which works towards a better service for them.

Supportive practice

Both the Coventry and the Sheffield examples show supportive practice using a humanistic approach: empowering, promoting rights and giving choice. They use preferred methods of communication to include all, meeting needs, across health, social care, mental health and special needs. They are responsive to needs – for example, the needs of older people and the needs of those with learning disabilities. They are working with individuals, families and carers.

When care goes wrong – the Bournewood case

The Bournewood case started in July 1997 when a 49-year-old severely autistic man, known as HL, who could not speak, was admitted to Bournewood psychiatric hospital, Surrey, after becoming distressed at a day centre. When the day centre staff were unable to contact HL's carers (Mr and Mrs E) and could not contain the situation, a GP tried to calm him down with medication. When this didn't work, the GP referred him to the local hospital where he was seen by a psychiatrist. The psychiatrist couldn't tell whether HL had a psychiatric condition or behavioural problem, so decided to admit him for observation. When he was discharged just over four months later, his carers claimed HL looked like 'someone out of Belsen'.

This was not deliberate abuse but it was a failure of care. Mr and Mrs E took the case to court, lost at the High Court, but won at the Court of Appeal. The informal admission to hospital was deemed unlawful, but the House of Lords overturned this decision. The case then went to the European Court of Human Rights where the verdict was:

> 'that HL had been deprived of his right to liberty under article 5 of the human rights convention. HL had not been detained under the Mental Health Act 1983, instead he was accommodated in his own "best interests" under the common law doctrine of "necessity". The European court held that this doctrine was too arbitrary and lacked the safeguards provided to those sectioned under the Mental Health Act.'

Source: www.communitycare.co.uk/ Articles/2009/09/02/112480/The-Bournewood-Case.htm

A serious care review found that HL's detention had 'resulted in an adverse effect upon his physical condition'; his detention was unnecessarily long and community-based alternatives had not been considered; and that the 'system' did not allow it to be challenged. Today, under new safeguarding procedures, it would be seen as potential professional abuse 'due to alleged misuse of therapeutic powers'.

Although people acted with good intentions, the core principles of care were not met. There was failure in building effective relationships. HL was not at the centre of planning. He was not listened to and his methods of communication were not respected. There was little respect for choice and the predominant need seemed to be institutional. Working practices were unsatisfactory. HL could have been released earlier with a community care plan in place. There was little duty of care and no evidence of advocacy involved, except that of Mr and Mrs E.

Supportive practice was not evident; in fact it was the opposite. HL was deprived of liberty. There was a lack of a humanistic approach, lack of empowerment, and failure to promote rights or choice. The system was not responsive to his needs and failed to meet them. There was little evidence of working with the individual or his carers. You can read more about the case at:

www.communitycare.co.uk/Articles/2009/09/02/ 112480/The-Bournewood-Case.htm.

Bournewood was a landmark case because it made people look at the legal aspects of care for an individual. In the next example, we see poor quality care across the whole service.

When care goes wrong – Sutton and Merton Primary Care Trust investigation

In 2006, the Healthcare Commission was called in to investigate the service for people with a learning disability at Sutton and Merton Primary Care Trust (PCT) following serious allegations of physical and sexual abuse. They looked at the quality and safety of care at Orchard Hill Hospital, community homes in Sutton and Merton, and at Osborne House in Hastings. They also looked at how the PCT worked with people with learning disabilities, their carers and their families, and whether they were involved in decisions relating to care and treatment. Here are their conclusions:

- Institutional abuse occurs when the rituals and routines of a service result in the lifestyles and needs of individuals being sacrificed in favour of the needs of the institution. This abuse was found to be prevalent in most parts of the learning disability service.
- People were unable to go out into the community.
- Environments that people lived in were unsatisfactory with inadequate access for disabled people, poor decoration and furnishings, and insufficient space in bathrooms for hoists.
- Short break care was unacceptable. For example, one person requiring short breaks had behaviour that challenged, and as a result of that behaviour other people living in that house stayed in their bedrooms for long periods because they were frightened.
- There were serious deficiencies in record-keeping. In particular, the requirement for people to have a person-centred care plan based on the principles of Valuing People was not adequately met.
- The overall model of care provided by the learning disability service was one that promoted dependency.

- People with learning disabilities were not supported and encouraged to develop new skills.
- There was inadequate specialist support for people with behaviour that challenges. For three years, the psychologist had repeatedly asked for more resources but had not been supported in this request.
- Due to the absence of a policy about restraint and lack of training, staff were restraining people inappropriately without giving sufficient consideration to alternative approaches. Items such as straps on wheelchairs and splints on limbs were used to restrict movement, and their use was not regularly reviewed to determine whether they were still required.
- Staff appeared to be unaware of their duty to protect adults less able to look after themselves.
- The views of people with learning disabilities were seldom heard.
- Some staff believed incorrectly that if a person could not talk, he or she could not communicate.
- Relatives, carers and advocates were not treated as partners in the process of planning care.

The interactions between staff and people who lived in the learning disability service were generally kind in nature. People were cared for, rather than supported by staff to be as independent as possible.

Source: www.cqc.org.uk/_db/_documents/Sutton_and_Merton_inv_sum_Tag.pdf

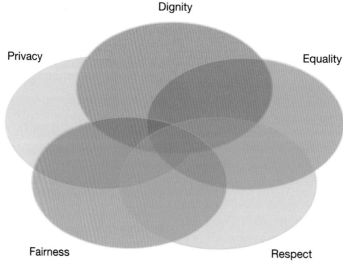

Core principles of care

Activity 6

Look again at the Bournewood and the Sutton and Merton Primary Care Trust cases.

Can you find evidence of core principles of care in either case? Remember the core principles of care are dignity, equality, respect, fairness and privacy.

- Can you find evidence of building effective relationships?
- Can you find evidence of effective working practices?
- Can you find evidence of supportive practice?

Perhaps you can now explain and discuss the role of supportive relationships in reducing the risk of abuse and neglect.

Activity 7   P6   M3   D2

Research examples of good practice from the Dignity in Care website (www. dhcarenetworks.org.uk/dignityincare/awards/HSCawards). For two of the case studies, find evidence of the following:

- Core principles of care
- Building effective relationships
- Effective working practices
- Supportive practice.

For M3, discuss the role of supportive relationships in reducing the risk of abuse and neglect, using examples.

For D2, evaluate the role of multi-agency working to reduce the risk of abuse of adults, with reference to legal frameworks, regulations, working strategies and procedures. You will need to look beyond the two case studies and draw on the 'No Secrets' guidance.

Summary

In this unit, we looked at how we can safeguard vulnerable adults and promote their independence. In order to do this, we looked at types of abuse and the indicators of such abuse. We then looked at what factors may cause people to abuse others.

The laws and regulations governing the safeguarding of adults were examined, as well as the role of the new Independent Safeguarding Authority in relation to criminal record checks.

We looked at strategies and procedures to reduce the risk of abuse, drawing on the 'No Secrets' and 'In Safe Hands' guidance. Finally, we looked at two examples where supportive relationships promoted rights, independence and well-being, and two examples where supportive practice was not achieved.

Assessment and grading criteria

In order to pass this unit, the evidence that the learner presents for assessment needs to demonstrate that they can meet all the learning outcomes for the unit. The assessment criteria for a pass grade describe the level of achievement required to pass this unit.

To achieve a pass grade the evidence must show that the learner is able to:	To achieve a merit grade the evidence must show that, in addition to the pass criteria, the learner is able to:	To achieve a distinction grade the evidence must show that, in addition to the pass and merit criteria, the learner is able to:
P1 describe forms of abuse which may be experienced by adults	**M1** assess the likely immediate effects of two different forms of abuse on the health and well-being of adults	**D1** evaluate the potential long-term effects of these two types of abuse on the health and well-being of adults
P2 describe indicators that abuse may be happening to adults		
P3 explain factors that may lead to abusive situations		
P4 outline key legislation and regulations which govern safeguarding adults work	**M2** describe legislation and regulations, working strategies and procedures used in health and social care to reduce the risk of two types of abuse	
P5 outline working strategies and procedures used in health and social care to reduce the risk of abuse		
P6 explain the role of supportive relationships in reducing the risk of abuse and neglect.	**M3** discuss the role of supportive relationships in reducing the risk of abuse and neglect, using examples.	**D2** evaluate the role of multi-agency working to reduce the risk of abuse of adults, with reference to legal frameworks, regulations, working strategies and procedures.

Resources

Department of Health (2000) *No Secrets: guidance on developing and implementing multi-agency policies and procedures to protect vulnerable adults from abuse.*

Department of Health (2005) *A National Framework of Standards for Good Practice and Outcomes in Adult Protection Work.*

Goffman, E. (1961) *Asylums: Essays on the Social Situation of Mental Patients and Other Inmates*, New York: Doubleday.

Nursing Times (2007) 'Recognising and preventing the abuse of older people', *Nursing Times*, 103(27): 21.

Sutton and Merton Primary Care Trust (2007) *Investigation into the Service for People with Learning Disabilities.*

Welsh Assembly (2009) *In Safe Hands: the protection of vulnerable adults from financial abuse in their own homes.*

Weblinks

http://wales.gov.uk:
Welsh Government Assembly

www.ageconcern.org.uk:
Age Concern

www.alzheimers.org.uk:
Alzheimer's Society

www.birmingham.gov.uk/safeguardingadults:
Birmingham local government safeguarding policy

www.carecommission.com:
Scottish Care Commission

www.community-care.co.uk:
Community Care

www.cqc.org.uk:
Care Quality Commission

www.dh.gov.uk:
Department of Health

www.dhcarenetworks.org.uk/dignityincare:
Dignity in Care

www.direct.gov.uk:
Government information website

www.dh.gov.uk/en/Publicationsand statistics/Publications/PublicationsPolicyAndGuidance/DH_4008486:
'No Secrets'

www.elderabuse.org.uk:
Action on Elder Abuse

www.equalityhumanrights.com:
Equality and Human Rights Commission

www.guardian.co.uk:
Guardian newspaper – a reliable source of information

www.isa-gov.org.uk:
Independent Safeguarding Authority

www.liberty-human-rights.org.uk:
Liberty – human rights pressure group

www.mencap.org.uk:
Mencap – charity for people with learning disabilities

www.mind.org.uk:
Mind

www.nacro.org.uk:
National Association For Care And Resettlement Of Offenders

www.nhs.uk:
National Health Service

www.nursingtimes.net:
Nursing Times

www.dhsspsni.gov.uk/hss/ssi/index.asp:
Northern Ireland Department of Health, Social Services and Public Safety – Social Services Inspectorate

www.police.uk:
Police website (click on 'Police Forces' tab to find local police stations)

www.redbridge.gov.uk:
Redbridge local government

www.scie-socialcareonline.org.uk:
Social Care Institute for Excellence

www.skillsforcare.org.uk:
Sector Skills Council for Care and Development

www.skillsforhealth.org.uk:
Sector Skills Council for the UK Health Sector

www.victimsupport.org.uk:
Victim Support – charity that supports victims of crime and runs the witness support scheme

www.womensaid.org.uk:
Women's Aid charity

Introduction

Nutrition is essential for health and well-being. If you are working within health and social care and have a responsibility for the well-being of others, it is important to have a thorough understanding of nutrition and diet.

Service users have various needs that we have to be aware of and, in this unit, you will investigate how we can tailor diets to meet those specific needs, such as those due to religion, culture, medical conditions or age.

This unit will explain how to plan specific diets and what a balanced diet consists of. It will also allow you to investigate an individual's diet and, from findings, prepare and make appropriate and realistic recommendations for change.

Learning outcomes:

On completion of this unit, you should:

1 Understand concepts of nutritional health

2 Know the characteristics of nutrients

3 Understand influences on dietary intake and nutritional health

4 Be able to use dietary and other relevant information from an individual to make recommendations to improve nutritional health.

1 Understand concepts of nutritional health

Concepts

This section looks at definitions and different ways of describing food intake and diet.

Nutrition is the science of how we take in and use food in the body. DEFRA defines food as:

'any solids or liquid which can be swallowed and supply material from which the body can produce movement, heat or other forms of energy, material for growth and repair or reproduction or substances necessary to regulate the production of energy or the processes of growth and repair'.

Food

Food is classed as any solid or liquid that gives an individual energy.

Diet

This is food and drink taken into our body in varying amounts. How we eat this mixture of food is known as our diet. A good diet provides all our nutritional requirements from a broad range of foods. It can be said that there are no unhealthy foods; it is an imbalance of foods that makes a diet unhealthy.

Meals and snacks

A meal usually consists of a range of different nutrients and has taken some preparation time. Traditionally, meals are eaten at specific times of the day and at specific eating places. However, nowadays meals are eaten in less formal surroundings with the takeaway and fast-food culture being very popular. As meals are larger in proportion to snacks, they can be nutritionally poor.

Snacks are usually a single type of food taken with a drink between regular meals. They are often eaten in informal settings. Some snacks may be very low in nutritional content and, eaten often over a long period of time, can be unhealthy.

Nutrients

All foods have components, known as nutrients. Nutrients consist of:

- carbohydrates, which are necessary for energy and which may be turned into body fat
- fats, which provide energy, protect vital organs and help the absorption of certain vitamins
- proteins, which are essential for growth and repair of the body
- minerals and vitamins, which regulate the body's processes and some are used for growth and repair.

Water is also essential for health, although it is not defined as or considered to be a nutrient. Fibre is also not considered a nutrient as the body does not absorb it, but it is needed for healthy bowels. Sometimes substances are added to food to perform specific functions. These are known as additives. Additives may be used to prevent food spoilage or enhance the texture, flavour or appearance of food.

Nutritional health

Malnutrition

Malnutrition is the result of a long period of time with insufficient or excessive amounts of nutrients. This could be from inadequate amounts of specific

Key terms

Deficiency – when the body lacks a certain nutrient.
Marasmus – the result of poor weaning or inadequate breastfeeding, which usually occurs as a result of the mother not having sufficient nutrients to pass on through her milk. Marasmus can cause poor muscle development, stunted growth and learning difficulties through poor brain development.

nutrients or lack of a combination of nutrients, or an excessive intake of high-energy foods, resulting in health problems.

Under-nutrition

Under-nutrition results when someone consumes less than is needed for a healthy diet. This can result in the individual becoming ill or more at risk from developing certain conditions. Under-nutrition may be caused when not enough food is provided or when there is a deficiency of a specific nutrient. It can also be caused if the body is unable to use or absorb nutrients.

Overweight and obesity

Weight problems and obesity are usually caused by an energy imbalance. This means that the number of calories consumed is higher than the number of calories used (for example, through movement or exercise). This imbalance may be caused by eating too many calories or by not doing enough exercise. In other words, the intake of calories is higher than those which the body is using up.

People who are obese stand a greater risk of developing dangerous conditions such as high blood pressure. This can lead to problems such as diabetes, or problems with the cardiovascular system. Obesity can be determined by calculating the body mass index (BMI) of an individual (see below).

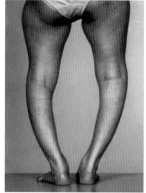 

Rickets   Beri Beri

Nutritional measures

Nutritional and energy balance

Food and drink provide us with varying amounts of energy and our intake should realistically balance our output. If there is an imbalance either way, then over a prolonged period of time this can lead to health problems, which are discussed later in this unit.

Different individuals require differing amounts of energy and this depends on our age, health status and activity level. It is important to balance the amount of energy we eat with the amount we use up. We require energy not just for physical activities but also for activities that are not under our control – for example, digesting food, healing, and hair and nail growth.

Activity 1

Working in pairs or groups, research one of the following conditions. What is lacking in the diet to cause them?

- Scurvy
- Beri Beri
- Kwashiorkor
- Rickets
- Anaemia
- Pellagra.

Growth charts

Growth charts are used to plot the average growth of children from birth to the age of four. They are designed specifically to be used in Personal Child Health Records (PCHRs). There are different charts for use with low birth-weight infants.

The new UK-WHO growth charts for children from birth to four years are now available. The charts have been developed as a project undertaken within the Science and Research Department led by Professor Charlotte Wright from the University of Glasgow and funded by the Department of Health. The charts are available in A4 format and there are six separate charts for insertion into PCHRs. There is also a new specialist low birth-weight chart for births from 23 weeks gestation. See www.rcpch.ac.uk/Research/UK-WHO-Growth-Charts. This link also provides ten reasons why these charts should now be used

Weight for height and gender

As there are many different types of body frame, there are no hard-and-fast rules as to average height and weight according to gender. Many factors must be taken into consideration before this is calculated. For example, genetics can play a part in body size, as can health status and age. The link below provides average heights and weights for gender and also accounts for your life stage: http://kidshealth.org/teen/food_fitness/dieting/weight_height.html#.

Body mass index (BMI)

Key term

Body mass index (BMI) – BMI looks at the relationship between height and weight and is a good indicator of whether someone is the right weight for their height.

The calculation for BMI is body weight (kg) divided by height $(m)^2$.

BMI is measured like this:
Underweight: below 20
Normal: 20–25
Overweight: 25–30
Obese: 30+.

Therefore someone who weighs 65 kg and is 1.72 m tall would have a BMI of 22 (rounded up) and would be in the normal weight range.

The calculation is as follows:
1.72^2 (i.e. 1.72 x 1.72) = 2.96
65 divided by 2.96 = 21.9

Activity 2

Work out the BMI for the following people:

1 Jim is 1.70 m and weighs 57 kg.

2 Billy is 1.83 m and weighs 121 kg.

3 Sian is 1.62 m and weighs 45 kg.

4 Sam is 1.55 m and weighs 70 kg.

Actual food intake and recommended food intakes

Individuals have differing dietary patterns around the world; major factors being availability and culture. Most people have what is known as a staple diet; this is usually a cereal or root food. Secondary foods then accompany this, which are usually high in protein (e.g. meat and fish). Lastly, other foods may not be nutritionally essential but a pleasure to eat; these may contain sugar and additives.

When asked to look at our food intake, many of us would know our likes and dislikes and how often we have eaten, but we would be less likely to understand the exact nutritional content of our food.

Tables 21.1, 21.2 and 21.3 detail the recommended intakes for the population.

Dietary reference values

Dietary reference values (DRVs) were developed by the Department of Health in 1991 to replace recommended daily amounts (RDAs). DRVs are benchmark intakes of energy and nutrients – they can be used for guidance but should not be seen as exact recommendations. They show the amount of energy or an individual nutrient that a group of people of a certain age range (and sometimes sex) needs for good health.

Although DRVs are given as daily intakes, people often eat quite different foods from one day to the next and their appetite can change so, in practice, the intake of energy and nutrients needs to be averaged over several days. Also DRVs apply only to healthy people. DRV is a general term used to cover:

- estimated average requirement (EAR) – this is the average amount of energy or a nutrient needed by a group of people
- reference nutrient intake (RNI) – this is the amount of a nutrient that is enough to meet the dietary needs of about 97 per cent of a group of people

- lower reference nutrient intake (LRNI) – this is the amount of a nutrient that is enough for a small number of people in a group with the smallest needs; most people will need more than this
- safe intake – this is used when there isn't enough evidence to set an EAR, RNI or LRNI. The safe intake is the amount judged to be enough for almost everyone, but below a level which could have undesirable effects.

Activity 3

Plot a graph that shows the energy requirements shown in Table 21.1. What do you notice? Why might this be the case?

Reference nutrient intakes

Tables 21.2 and 21.3 show the number of nutrients sufficient for almost every individual. It tends to be higher than most people need.

Table 21.1 Estimated average requirements for energy

Age	Males		Females		Age	Males		Females	
	(MJ)	(kcal)	(MJ)	(kcal)		(MJ)	(kcal)	(MJ)	(kcal)
0–3 mo	2.28	(545)	2.16	(515)	11–14 yr	9.27	(2220)	7.72	(1845)
4–6 mo	2.89	(690)	2.69	(645)	15–18 yr	11.51	(2755)	8.83	(2110)
7–9 mo	3.44	(825)	3.20	(765)	19–50 yr	10.60	(2550)	8.10	(1940)
10–12 mo	3.85	(920)	3.61	(865)	51–59 yr	10.60	(2550)	8.00	(1900)
1–3 yr	5.15	(1230)	4.86	(1165)	60–64 yr	9.93	(2380)	7.99	(1900)
4–6 yr	7.16	(1715)	6.46	(1545)	65–74 yr	9.71	(2330)	7.96	(1900)
7–10 yr	8.24	(1970)	7.28	(1740)	74+ yr	8.77	(2100)	7.61	(1810)

Source: www.nutrition.org.uk

Table 21.2 Reference nutrient intakes for vitamins

Age	Thiamin mg/d	Riboflavin mg/d	Niacin (nicotinic acid equivalent) mg/d	Vitamin B6 mg/d†	Vitamin B12 µg/d	Folate µg/d	Vitamin C mg/d	Vitamin A µg/d	Vitamin D µg/d
0–3 months	0.2	0.4	3	0.2	0.3	50	25	350	8.5
4–6 months	0.2	0.4	3	0.2	0.3	50	25	350	8.5
7–9 months	0.2	0.4	4	0.3	0.4	50	25	350	7
10–12 months	0.3	0.4	5	0.4	0.4	50	25	350	7
1–3 years	0.5	0.6	8	0.7	0.5	70	30	400	7
4–6 years	0.7	0.8	11	0.9	0.8	100	30	400	–
7–10 years	0.7	1.0	12	1.0	1.0	150	30	500	–
Males									
11–14 years	0.9	1.2	15	1.2	1.2	200	35	300	–
15–18 years	1.1	1.3	18	1.5	1.5	200	40	700	–
19–50 years	1.0	1.3	17	1.4	1.5	200	40	700	–
50+ years	0.9	1.3	16	1.4	1.5	200	40	700	**
Females									
11–14 years	0.7	1.1	12	1.0	1.2	200	35	600	–
15–18 years	0.8	1.1	14	1.2	1.5	200	40	600	–
19–50 years	0.8	1.1	13	1.2	1.5	200	40	600	–
50+ years	0.8	1.1	12	1.2	1.5	200	40	600	**
Pregnancy	+0.1***	+0.3	*	*	*	+100	+10	+10	10
Lactation									
0–4 months	+0.2	+0.5	+2	*	+0.5	+60	+30	+350	10
4+ months	+0.2	+0.5	+2	*	+0.5	+60	+30	+350	10

Source: www.nutrition.org.uk

Table 21.3 Reference nutrient intakes for minerals

Age	Calcium mg/d	Phosphorus mg/d	Magnesium mg/d	Sodium mg/d†	Potassium mg/d	Chloride mg/d	Iron mg/d	Copper mg/d	Selenium µg/d	Iodine µg/d
0–3 months	525	400	55	210	800	320	1.7	0.2	10	50
4–6 months	525	400	60	280	850	400	4.3	0.3	13	60
7–9 months	525	400	75	320	700	500	7.8	0.3	10	60
10–12 months	525	400	80	350	700	500	7.8	0.3	10	60
1–3 years	350	270	85	500	800	800	6.9	0.4	15	70
4–6 years	450	350	120	700	1100	1100	6.1	0.6	20	100
7–10 years	550	450	200	1200	2000	1800	8.7	0.7	30	110
Males										
11–14 years	1000	775	280	1600	3100	2500	11.3	0.8	45	130
15–18 years	1000	775	300	1600	3500	2500	11.3	1.0	70	140
19–50 years	700	550	300	1600	3500	2500	8.7	1.2	75	140
50+ years	700	550	300	1600	3500	2500	8.7	1.2	75	140
Females										
11–14 years	800	625	280	1600	3100	2500	14.8**	0.8	45	130
15–18 years	800	625	300	1600	3500	2500	14.8**	1.0	60	140
19–50 years	700	550	270	1600	3500	2500	14.8**	1.2	60	140
50+ years	700	550	270	1600	3500	2500	8.7	1.2	60	140
Pregnancy	*	*	*	*	*	*	*	*	*	*
Lactation										
0–4 months	+550	+440	+50	*	*	*	*	+0.3	+15	*
4+ months	+550	+440	+50	*	*	*	*	+0.3	+15	*

Source: www.nutrition.org.uk

Activity 4

Look at Tables 21.2 and 21.3.

What do you notice about iron levels? Why might this be the case?

When is more calcium needed? Why?

Nutrients per portion and per 100 g of food

Manufacturers are not legally obliged to provide nutritional information unless a nutritional claim is made. For those that do provide this information, they must state the energy value in kilojoules and kilocalories, as well as the amount of protein, carbohydrate and fat in grams. The amount of sugars, saturates, fibre and sodium can be optionally provided unless a claim is made about these levels. Information must be given as values per 100 g or 100 ml of food. Values for a portion can be given too, as long as the number of portions is given.

Dietary intake guidelines

The eatwell plate

The eatwell plate shows the recommended daily food groups, including drinks and snacks. You should aim for a good balance over a week.

The eatwell plate is based on the five food groups:

- bread, rice, potatoes, pasta and other starchy foods
- fruit and vegetables
- milk and dairy foods
- meat, fish, eggs, beans and other non-dairy sources of protein
- foods and drinks high in fat and/or sugar.

The eatwell plate encourages you to choose different foods from the first four groups every day, so your body receives all the nutrients it needs to function properly and stay healthy. Foods and drinks high in fat and/or sugar are not essential to a healthy diet.

The guidance given on the eatwell plate is suitable for most people, including people of all ethnic origins and people who are of a healthy weight or who are overweight. It is also suitable for vegetarians. It does not apply to children under two years of age because they have different nutritional needs. Anyone under medical supervision or with special dietary needs should check with their GP or a dietician to find out whether it is suitable for them (source: www.food.gov.uk/healthiereating/eatwellplate).

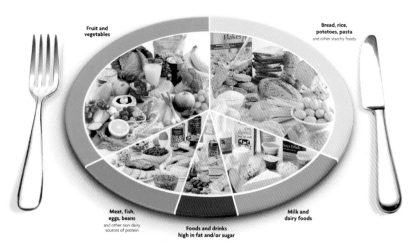

The eatwell plate

Activity 5

Make a list of your own food intake over the last two days.

1   Identify which food groups each item belongs to.

2   Which food group appears most?

3   Do your meals have a good balance?

4   Which group does not appear enough?

amounts of fruit and vegetables count as one portion.

Have a look at www.5aday.nhs.uk. Eating a healthy diet of fruit and vegetables provides a range of vitamins and minerals and can reduce the risk of heart disease and strokes.

Activity 6

Ask a range of people about their intake of fruit and vegetables. Are they all eating their five a day? Who is getting more? Who is getting less?

Food groups

Food pyramid

This concept of looking at foods and the amounts that should be eaten was developed in the USA based on nutritional requirements.

This has since been further developed with different types of pyramids depending on life stage and activity levels. For more information, go to www.mypyramid.gov.

The 5 A Day campaign aims to change the way people think about fruit and vegetables and to encourage people to eat more of them. Different

Effect of food preparation/processing methods

During preparation and processing, foods may lose some of their nutritional value. See the nutrients section on page 271 for more information.

Foods that are processed and sealed in cans are heated to a very high temperature and may be said to be less nutritious, but canned foods do not deteriorate for a long time so may be convenient for some service users who are unable to get to the shops or do not have storage facilities. It may also be a cheap way to have an easy meal.

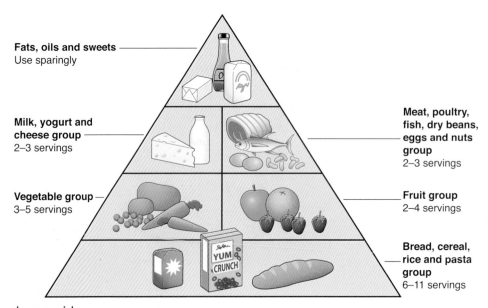

Fats, oils and sweets
Use sparingly

Milk, yogurt and cheese group
2–3 servings

Meat, poultry, fish, dry beans, eggs and nuts group
2–3 servings

Vegetable group
3–5 servings

Fruit group
2–4 servings

Bread, cereal, rice and pasta group
6–11 servings

The food pyramid

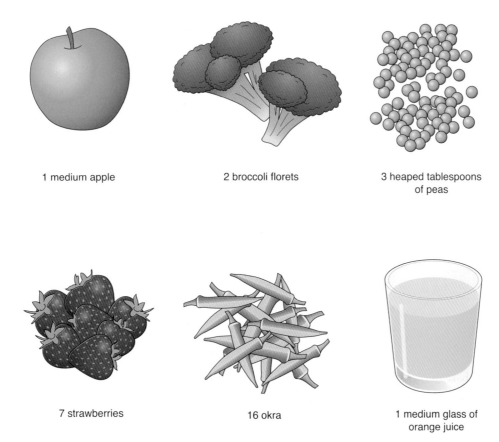

1 medium apple   2 broccoli florets   3 heaped tablespoons
                                                    of peas

7 strawberries   16 okra   1 medium glass of
                                                    orange juice

Examples of 5 A Day fruit and vegetables

Canned or ready meals can have high salt and sugar content so it is important to check the food label prior to purchase or serving, particularly if the service user is on a specific diet. Manufacturers, however, are responding to consumer worries, and processed food can now be purchased in natural juices, spring water and with reduced sugar and salt content.

Many vitamins and minerals are destroyed in the boiling process so making a sauce or gravy with the vegetable water will help to retain some of those valuable nutrients. Casseroling and stir-frying are good cooking methods for retaining nutrients. Also serving food immediately and not re-heating or keeping warm will retain the best part of the nutrients.

Current nutritional issues

Issues in the nutrition world are ever changing and are a source of great discussion.

Activity 7

In small groups, take one of the topics below and use the weblinks to formulate a news report to deliver to your colleagues.

Food labelling

By law, all foods, other than loose foods, should be labelled and show their nutritional content so the consumer can compare products. The recent traffic light system has been employed by some manufacturers and supermarkets to assist the consumer with healthy choices. Look at the links below to see the legislation behind food labelling and then search for some recent news articles around this topic:

- www.food.gov.uk/foodlabelling/
- http://news.bbc.co.uk/1/hi/uk/6228469.stm
- www.independent.co.uk/life-style/ food-and-drink/news/convenience-food-labelling-misleading-1868583.html.

Organic food

Organic food means that it has been produced without the use of pesticides or artificial ferti- lisers. Organic foods should not contain additives or preservatives. Meat that claims to be organic should have been reared in a free-range environment without the use of antibiotics or hormones.

Look at the weblinks below to understand why consumers may choose organically produced food and the regulations around this topic. Search for some recent news articles about this issue:

- www.food.gov.uk/foodindustry/farmingfood/ organicfood/
- http://news.bbc.co.uk/1/hi/8174482.stm
- www.meateat.co.uk/organic-meat-better-for-you.html.

Genetically modified foods

With the help of technology, food and animal characteristics can be changed to enhance specific properties to make them more desirable to the consumer. For example, disease resistance, enhanced nutrient levels and longer shelf lives. Some controversy has been raised as to whether new genes in our food may cause adverse effects in humans.

Have a look in you local supermarket at some foods with added nutrients. Think about the advantages and disadvantages of this. Look at these weblinks to investigate this topic further:

- www.eatwell.gov.uk/healthissues/ factsbehindissues/gmfood/
- www.greenpeace.org.uk/gm
- news.bbc.co.uk/1/hi/sci/tech/5098468.stm
- www.who.int/foodsafety/publications/ biotech/20questions/en/.

Environmental aspects of food production

When purchasing food, we need to consider where it has been produced and also, with landfill sites becoming full, we need to consider how foods are packaged and stored.

See if you can find out any tips about recycling or packaging that you want to share with your colleagues. Visit the weblinks below to investigate this topic further:

- www.nfumutual.co.uk/lifestyle/issue-one/ reducing-food-miles.htm
- www.packagingnews.co.uk/news/992142/ Unilever-tops-food-drink-sustainability-ranking/
- www.telegraph.co.uk/news/uknews/7552265/ British-households-throw-out-almost-half-a-ton-of-food-related-waste.html.

Self-prescribed health supplements

Health or dietary supplements refer to a range of products commonly consumed for the purpose of supplementing the diet and enhancing health. They are usually presented in dosage form, such as capsules, soft gels, tablets and liquids. Some examples of health supplements include vitamins, minerals (e.g. calcium, iron, magnesium) and herbal supplements (e.g. Echinacea, Guarana). These products typically contain ingredients from natural sources. They are not medicinal products meant to prevent, treat, cure or alleviate the symptoms of medical diseases or conditions and are generally considered low-risk.

Visit the following weblinks to investigate the benefits and controversy of self-prescribed health supplements:

- www.ehow.com/about_4672439_what-dietary-supplement.html
- www.cancer.org/docroot/ETO/content/ ETO_5_3x_How_to_Know_What_Is_Safe_ Choosing_and_Using_Dietary_Supplements. asp
- www.online-ambulance.com/articles/doc/4/ grp/Healthy/art/Fav_Vitamin.htm.

Treatments for obesity

Treatments for obesity range from diet changes to surgery and behaviour modification programmes. As obesity is a growing trend in our society, treatments are readily available and becoming more common. Visit the weblinks below to look at treatments available and news items that raise contemporary issues around obesity treatment. See if you can find more news articles about the treatment of obesity.

- www.nhs.uk/Conditions/Obesity/Pages/ Treatment.aspx
- www.bmi-calculator.net/treatment/obesity-treatment.php
- http://news.bbc.co.uk/1/hi/health/1372832. stm.

Advertising food

Food advertising can be a controversial issue because adverts have to meet specific legal require-ments so they are aimed at the right consumer for the right reasons. Some adverts have been banned because of their content, because they promote unhealthy eating habits – to children, for example – or even because they make untrue or unrealistic claims.

Visit the weblinks below to look at the legal requirements for food adverts and some news issues around the topic:

- http://news.bbc.co.uk/1/hi/6154600.stm
- www.adassoc.org.uk/aa/index.cfm/fau/
- www.food.gov.uk/healthiereating/.

Global food inequalities

The World Health Organisation is responsible for providing leadership on global health matters, shaping the health research agenda, setting norms and standards, articulating evidence-based policy options, providing technical support to countries and monitoring and assessing health trends. Visit the following weblinks to understand the work of the WHO in addressing global food inequalities:

- www.who.int/countries/nga/reports/ foodcrisis.pdf
- www.who.int/food_crisis/fact_sheet/en/
- www.thirdworldtraveler.com/Globalization/ Globalization_FactsFigures.html.

Activity 8 **P1**

In a booklet, explain the basic concepts of nutritional health terminology. Your booklet should contain five sections:

- **Concepts**
- **Nutritional health**
- **Nutritional measures**
- **Dietary intake guidelines**
- **Explanation of one current nutritional issue.**

2 Know the characteristics of nutrients

This section looks at:

- nutrients and their sources (where we obtain them from)
- the function of nutrients in the body (why we need them)
- nutritional requirements (how much we need)
- the effects of processing (what happens to the nutrients when heated, stored or frozen).

Key terms

Macro nutrient – these are nutrients required in large quantities – for example, carbohydrates, proteins and fats.
Micro nutrient – these are nutrients which are needed in small amounts – for example, vitamins and minerals.

Characteristics

Nutrients are available to the body through digestion or sunlight. During digestion, nutrients enter the small intestine and pass into the blood-stream. The liver then controls the distribution around the body. Some nutrients, such as vitamin

D, are obtained through sunlight acting on substances within the skin.

Carbohydrates

Carbohydrates are macro nutrients. They are the body's source of energy. Carbohydrates contain the elements of oxygen, hydrogen and carbon. When carbohydrates are heated, the sugar dissolves, caramelises, then burns in water. Starch forms a paste or becomes dextrin.

Monosaccharides

These are also known as 'simple sugars' and are soluble in water. There are three types:

- fructose: occurs in fruit and vegetables and especially honey and is very sweet
- glucose: what the body uses for energy; found in fruit and plant juices; other carbohydrates are converted to glucose in digestion
- glactose: found in milk of mammals as lactose (milk sugar).

Disaccharides

These are sometimes known as double sugars and are soluble in water. These are two monosaccharides joined together. There are three main types:

- sucrose: occurs in sugar cane and sugar beet and in some fruits – it is glucose and fructose
- lactose: found only in milk (including human) – made up of glucose and galactose
- maltose: this is two glucoses joined together; occurs when starch is broken down; sometimes known as malt sugar.

Polysaccharides

Poly means many – these are many saccharides joined together. Polysaccharides are insoluble in water and there are a number of types, including starch and non-starch polysaccharides (NSPs). Starch is by far the most important of the polysaccharides. It is found in corn, bread, pasta and rice and is also supplied by traditional staple foods such as cereals, roots and tubers. Humans cannot digest polysaccharides if they are eaten raw in foods such as flour and potatoes. When eaten, they are broken down within the body into glucose and absorbed. NSPs are found in the cell walls of vegetables and fruits. They are classed as fibre and are necessary for healthy bowel function.

Sugar substitutes – natural and artificial

These substitutes taste sweet, unsurprisingly! Sorbitol is one example of a natural sugar substitute often used in diabetic foods as it is absorbed into the body more slowly. It is also used in diet foods (including diet drinks) and sugar-free chewing gum. Other sweeteners are made up of artificial sugar substitutes, such as saccharin or aspartame. A sugar substitute, or artificial sweetener, is a food additive which attempts to duplicate the taste of sugar in taste, but often with less food energy or, in other words, fewer calories.

Proteins

Proteins are necessary for the growth and repair of the body and can also be used for energy. Proteins are large molecules made up of smaller units called amino acids. There are 20 amino acids commonly found in plant and animal proteins and there are therefore numerous combinations. Amino acids are often divided into two categories, indispensable (or essential) and dispensable (or non-essential). Indispensable amino acids cannot be made in the body.

Good sources of protein include meat, cheese, fish and dairy products such as milk and eggs. When amino acids are linked together, they are known as peptides. Longer chains are polypeptides.

The reference nutrient intake for a 16-year-old male is 55.2 g a day and, for a female, 45 g a day. Can you work out your own daily intake of protein?

Lipids

> ## Key term
>
> Lipids – fats and oils.

Fats and oils have the same chemical structure but the main difference is that fats are solid at room temperature and oils are liquid. The main functions of fats are as a source of energy, to protect vital organs, to provide insulation, to preserve body heat, as a source of fat-soluble vitamins (A, D, E, K) and to add texture and flavour in food.

Fats are made up of carbon, oxygen and hydrogen. The difference between these and carbohydrates is that fats contain less oxygen. Fats are a mixture of triglycerides. These are a combination of three fatty acids and a unit of glycerol. There are around 40 different fatty acids and they differ in the number of carbon and hydrogen atoms.

Saturated fatty acids have atoms with single bonds joined together:

$$
\begin{array}{ccc}
H & H & H \\
| & | & | \\
C & C & C
\end{array}
$$

Unsaturated fats have double bonds:

$$
\begin{array}{c}
H \\
| \\
C = C \\
| \\
H
\end{array}
$$

Unsaturated fatty acids come in two shapes. They may be 'cis' or 'trans' fatty acids depending on how the atoms are arranged. 'Cis' fats are considered better for health and can be found in unmodified dietary sources such as olive oil.

Vitamins

Vitamins are chemical substances that the body needs in only fairly small amounts. They are generally obtained through food as the body cannot make them itself. They can be divided into two groups depending on the substance in which they dissolve (either fat or water). Fat-soluble vitamins are A, D, E and K and water-soluble vitamins are B and C.

Minerals

Minerals are essential for the normal functioning of the body. They may be either bulk minerals (needed in quite large amounts) or trace minerals (needed in tiny amounts). They tend to be unaffected by heat processing and may leak into cooking water and processing as a result.

Iron

Iron is needed to form haemoglobin, which is used to transport oxygen in the blood to all parts of the body. Iron is found in foods like liver and other red meat, breakfast cereals, bread and dark green vegetables such as spinach and watercress. Vitamin C can help the absorption of iron. Pregnant women may need more iron due to the baby's needs and menstruating women may need more iron due to the loss of blood. A lack of iron may lead to anaemia.

Calcium

Calcium has a number of important functions. It helps build strong bones and teeth, it regulates muscle contraction, including the heartbeat, and it ensures that blood clots normally. Good sources of the mineral calcium include milk, cheese and other dairy foods, along with green leafy vegetables. Too little calcium can cause rickets or osteoporosis; too much can lead to stomach pain and diarrhoea, or can lead to calcium deposits forming.

Zinc

Zinc is necessary to help wound healing and helps with enzyme functioning. Meat and dairy products are good sources.

Sodium

Sodium is essential to maintain a fluid balance in the body and to help muscle and nerve function. Too little can cause muscle cramps, but too much is a concern as it can lead to high blood pressure and strokes.

Potassium

Potassium assists sodium in helping cells to function. It occurs in a wide variety of foods, such as citrus fruits and bananas.

Magnesium

Magnesium is present in bones and enzymes involved in energy functioning. It is found in a variety of foods, including cereal, bread, fruit, vegetables and milk. Deficiency is rare but can cause tiredness and depression.

Selenium

This enzyme is necessary for red blood cells. It is found in meat, fish and cereals.

Activity 9

Write a list of all the meals you had yesterday. Break down what you have eaten in terms of the nutrients.

Other diet-related consumption

Water is important to the body and the body's functions. It makes up the body's fluids, helps the bodily processes which need water, regulates body temperature and helps excretion. Water needs replacing every day and the amount you need depends on activities undertaken – you will need more water if you do more exercise.

Fibre is made up of a number of complex carbo-hydrates. There are two types of fibre, soluble and insoluble. There are no calories, vitamins or minerals in fibre and it is not digested when we eat it. When fibre passes through the bowel, it absorbs a lot of water and increases the bulk of the waste matter, so it is necessary for healthy bowel movements and prevents constipation. It also protects against bowel diseases, such as bowel cancer. Fibre is only found in the cell walls of plants. Foods such as meat, fish and dairy products contain no fibre at all.

Alcohol contains calories but no nutrients. It negatively impacts upon the content of B vitamins in the body. For more information, go to www.alcoholconcern.org.uk.

There is much debate over supplements and whether or not they are necessary and safe. People may take them for a variety of reasons. For example, vegans may take vitamin B12 as it is found only in food from animals.

Energy

The rate at which energy is used in the body is called the metabolic rate, so even a person who is resting needs energy to carry out internal activities.

Energy is measured in a laboratory with a piece of apparatus called a 'bomb calorimeter'. The food is heated and a small explosion occurs. The amount of heat released by this burning process is then measured. This is said to be equivalent to the energy released in the body when the food is completely broken down.

Energy yields of nutrients

1g protein provides 17 kJ (4 kcal).
1g carbohydrate provides 16 kJ (3.75 kcal).
1g fat provides 37 kJ (9 kcal).
1g alcohol provides 29 kJ (7 kcal).

Physiological context

For more on the physiological principles of digestion, see Unit 5: Anatomy and Physiology for Health and Social Care.

Groups

Different groups of the population need different nutrients for a variety of reasons.

DEFRA provides information on diets needed by different groups. This is summarised below.

Children and young people

Newborn infants rely on milk for their nutritional needs. Human breast milk contains all the nutrients necessary for an infant and it also provides immunity from certain diseases. It also requires no preparation. Breast milk is ideal for at least the first four months of life as babies cannot process solid foods before this time. Introducing babies to solid foods is known as weaning.

Children need a balanced diet with fruit, vegetables, protein and carbohydrates. Milk is a good source of protein and calcium, and foods such as fish, liver, eggs, fruit, green vegetables and potatoes provide a wide range of nutrients. Children should avoid eating junk food, such as biscuits, sweets and crisps.

As children grow into adolescence, they tend to have bigger appetites and should be encouraged to eat as healthily as possible.

Table 21.4 Vitamin sources, functions and requirements

Vitamin	Sources	Function in the body	Requirements for the average 16-year-old male and female	Effect of processing (Source: DEFRA)
A (Retinol)	Animal foods, milk, cheese, eggs, oily fish, fruit and vegetables.	Essential for vision in dim light. A prolonged lack can lead to night blindness. It helps with the maintenance of healthy skin and keeps mucous membranes (such as eyes and throat) free from infection, supple and smooth. It also assists in the growth of bones and teeth and helps the body fight infection. Too much vitamin A can lead to a toxic effect as the liver cannot process it. There is also a link between too much vitamin A and birth defects. As a consequence pregnant women are advised not to take nutritional substances which contain vitamin A.	Male – 700µg Female – 600µg	Stable in most cooking, some loss may occur from prolonged storage. If canned or cooked in margarines then there may be some loss.
D (Cholecalciferol)	Found in fish liver oils, oily fish, eggs and dairy produce and is added to margarine by law. It is also found in the UV rays in sunlight. Vitamin D is stored in the liver and can be used as required.	Required for bones and teeth – these contain large amounts of calcium and phosphorus. Vitamin D helps the absorption of calcium. People are unlikely to be deficient in vitamin D unless they have limited exposure to the sun. Lack of vitamin D can cause weak bones and teeth. Bones may then bend which can cause rickets in children or ostemolacia in adults. Too much can lead to deposits of calcium in the joints which can damage organs.		Stable in most cooking.

Vitamin	Sources	Function in the body	Requirements for the average 16-year-old male and female	Effect of processing (Source: DEFRA)
C (Ascorbic acid)	Fresh fruit and vegetables, fruit juices.	Aids absorption of iron and helps build bones and teeth. It aids vitamin E as an antioxidant and is necessary to build and maintain skin and the digestive system. Helps fight infection by protecting immune systems.	Males and females – 40mg	Can be destroyed through cooking, may dissolve in water or be lost in the presence of an alkali. Some loss in freezing.
B1 – Thiamin	Milk, eggs, vegetables, fruit.	Helps release energy from carbohydrates.	See www.nutrition.org.uk	Cooking and/or freezing may cause a loss of this nutrient.
B2 – Riboflavin	Milk and milk products.	Helps utilise energy from foods.		
Niacin	Cheese, meat (especially chicken).	Helps utilise food energy.		All B vitamins are water soluble which means there may be some loss. B6 is sensitive to heat.
B6 – Pyridoxine	Meat, fish, eggs.	Metabolism of amino acids and helps form haemoglobin.		
B12 – Cyanocobalamin	Meat (especially liver), milk, eggs, cheese. Does not occur in vegetables.	Needed by cells that divide rapidly. One example is bone marrow which helps make red blood cells.		
Folate		Helps vitamin B12 with rapidly dividing cells.		

Vitamin	Sources	Function in the body	Requirements for the average 16-year-old male and female	Effect of processing (Source: DEFRA)
E (Tocopherol)	Vegetable oils, nuts and egg yolk.	Major role as an antioxidant. Stored in the body to protect body cells from free radicals (unstable compounds that damage healthy body cells). It also maintains a healthy reproductive system, nerve and muscles.	See www.nutrition.org.uk	Not soluble in water. Stable in heat and oxidised in air.
K	Widespread in many foods including leafy vegetables such as spinach and cauliflower. It can be produced in the body by bacteria. Babies tend to be given an injection of vitamin K at birth.	Essential for blood clotting.	See www.nutrition.org.uk	

Adults

Adults need to eat a well-balanced diet high in starchy foods, fruit and vegetables and low in foods with high concentrations of sugar and fat. Alcohol should be limited to current guidelines (currently 21 units per week for men and 14 units per week for women). It is also important to regulate salt intake and adults should ensure their intake is less than 6 g a day.

Older people

Older people should be encouraged to eat a balanced diet and maintain a good energy intake. They also require foods which contain good sources of protein, vitamins and minerals.

Pregnant women

Good nutrition during pregnancy helps to keep a developing baby and its mother healthy. The diet of pregnant women should contain energy, protein, iron, calcium, folate and vitamins C and D. These are nutrients needed to build the baby's tissue, bones and teeth and to make haemoglobin. Mothers should also take a supplement of folic acid to prevent neural defects. Pregnant women are advised not to take supplements of vitamin A as it can lead to birth defects. Overall, it is important to choose a wide variety of foods to ensure the nutritional needs of both mother and baby are met.

Women who are breastfeeding

Women who are breastfeeding require adequate amounts of food containing energy, protein, vitamins and minerals due to the extra demands of the baby. Women should also ensure they drink plenty of fluids.

Activity 10

Choose one of the above groups and produce a healthy one-day meal plan for them. Ensure you include all meals and drinks. Explain what foods you have chosen and why these are suitable for them.

Activity 11   P2   M1

For P2, in a table, list all the macro nutrients and micro nutrients and describe their benefits to the body. You could highlight particular nutrients and their benefits to certain population groups and also show what effects excessive or deficient amounts of these nutrients may have.

For M1, choose two population groups and discuss similarities and differences in their nutritional needs. For example, high-protein diets are required for both young children and older service users to ensure growth and repair of new cells, but amounts of carbohydrates will vary according to their activity levels.

3 Understand influences on dietary intake and nutritional health

Nutritional health is based on a number of measurements. This includes body mass index (BMI), which looks at the relationship between an individual's weight and height. Nutritional health should also take into account any specific nutritional needs of individuals and any other factors affecting their food intake, such as diabetes, restricted movement or breastfeeding. A healthy diet should reflect a balance of good health with the right combinations of nutrients. Also, when considering a healthy diet, you should be aware of the presence of any diet-related diseases.

There are many influences on the food that people consume. Some of these are described below.

Health factors

Non-insulin dependent diabetes

This is sometimes referred to as type 2 diabetes. This occurs when the pancreas does not secrete sufficient insulin (the hormone responsible for regulating blood glucose) and the amount of blood glucose increases until excess glucose is excreted by the kidneys into the urine. This can be avoided by dietary regulation and avoiding large rises in glucose. Generally, a diabetic diet should be low in fat and sugar. An individual with diabetes may need to take tablets. For more information, see www.diabetes.org.uk or www.bda.uk.com.

Coeliac disease

Coeliac disease is an autoimmune disease. Gluten, which is found in wheat, barley and rye, triggers an immune reaction in people with coeliac disease. This means that eating gluten damages the lining of the small intestine so absorption of food is incomplete, resulting in weight loss, diarrhoea and vomiting. Other parts of the body may be affected. In babies, symptoms may only develop during the weaning process.

Service users have to stick to a strict gluten-free diet to avoid symptoms.

Irritable bowel syndrome

Irritable bowel syndrome (IBS) affects a large number of the population. It is more common in young adults and twice as common in women. IBS is a functional disorder of the bowel. No abnormality is seen in the structure of the bowel, so diagnosis may be quite difficult.

Service users with IBS may suffer spasmodic abdominal pain, wind, bloating, swelling and a changing stool pattern. There are conflicting views on the best treatment. Various research studies have shown that a high-fibre diet can, in some cases, make IBS worse, and a recent guideline stated that 'high-fibre diets are not recommended for people with IBS'. However, since that guideline was published, a review of treatments for IBS concluded that fibre was good at easing symptoms in some people with the condition (source: www.patient.co.uk/health/Irritable-Bowel-Syndrome.htm).

Lactose intolerance

Some people are 'intolerant' of certain foods. This can be due to a variety of reasons but it is not normally an immune reaction. An example is someone who is lactose intolerant. Strictly speaking, lactose intolerance is the inability to absorb lactose – the predominant sugar in milk – into the digestive system. If lactose is not absorbed properly, it ferments and this results in abdominal pain, a bloated stomach and diarrhoea. It is treated by avoiding foods with lactose in them, although it is still important to eat products containing calcium in order to avoid a calcium deficiency.

Food allergies

People may be allergic to certain foods, which means their immune system reacts in a certain way when these food substances are absorbed. Foods that may cause this reaction include milk, eggs, peanuts and shellfish.

Loss of ability to feed independently

If service users are unable to feed independently because of a stroke, which can cause paralysis or difficulty swallowing, they may need supervision with meals or meals that are easy to swallow, or it may be necessary to give parenteral feeding. 'Parenteral feeding' describes the intravenous administration of nutrients. This may be supplemental to oral or tube feeding or it may provide the only source of nutrition as total parenteral nutrition (TPN). (See www.patient.co.uk/doctor/Parenteral-Feeding.htm for more information.)

Dietary habits

People tend to eat the foods they like and this has implications for their health. For example, if people eat a lot of fatty foods, they are putting themselves at risk of cardiovascular disease. People also tend to follow a specific pattern of eating – this may be cereal for breakfast or a sandwich for lunch. These patterns may vary according to cultures. Finally, the availability of food has a big impact on dietary influences. If food is not available then people cannot buy it. Time is often cited as a factor in the purchase of convenience foods, such as people saying 'I just never have time to cook'. In more rural areas, the distance to larger supermarkets can affect the availability of foods.

Lifestyle influences

The lifestyle people lead can impact on their health. A person with a very busy occupation may find it easier to buy 'ready meals' rather than cooking every day. People in jobs requiring more activity or those who do a lot of exercise require more energy-dense foods because they use up more energy. Social eating and peer pressure can also influence the food we eat.

Other values may impact upon the food people eat. For example, some people may choose to buy free-range eggs or dolphin-friendly tuna. Others may choose not to eat any meat and fish (vegetarian) or not to eat any animal products at all (vegan). The way in which we are socialised, our culture, families and communities has an impact upon the food we eat and the way in which we eat it. Some families place importance on sitting down and having a meal together, whereas others may not.

Education and nutritional knowledge also play a big part in the choices we make about our food. People who are aware of healthy eating tend to choose healthier foods. This awareness may come from public health campaigns, such as the 5 A Day campaign (see page 268), through education at school, from package labelling or from health professionals.

Economic influences

Economic factors can affect food production. These include the way food is processed and sold and what is available within local outlets. The cost of food has a significant impact upon purchasing and availability, and economy impacts on access to shopping areas and ability to store food.

Socio-cultural influences

People's beliefs can have an impact on the food that they eat. Jewish people, for example, do not eat shellfish, pork, rabbit or derivatives of these animals, and meat and dairy products are not eaten in the same meal.

Activity 12

Look at one of the following religions. What impact or dietary rules does this religion have on the diet of its followers?

- **Buddhism**
- **Rastafarian**
- **Sikhism**
- **Judaism**
- **Islam**
- **Christian.**

Educational influences

Health education plays a major role in our dietary habits. We may be persuaded to eat particular brands of foods because of the media. We may also be advised to eat or avoid certain foods by education through the media. What adverts can you think of that have made you aware of the benefits or drawbacks of a certain food or drink type?

Activity 13

Choose one of the following health professionals. What role would they have in promoting good nutritional health?

- **Dieticians**
- **Public health nutritionists**
- **Doctors**
- **Nurses**
- **Carers**
- **Sports nutritionists**
- **Health and fitness instructors.**

Social policy

Recently there have been three important pieces of legislation that have had an impact on the food children eat. These are the Children Act 2004, Every Child Matters and Nutritional Standards for School Lunches and Other School Food 2006.

The Children Act 2004 emphasises the importance of children's services working together. This includes physical and mental health and emotional well-being. See Part 2, Section 10 of the act on www.opsi.gov.uk/acts/acts2004/ukpga_20040031_en_3. This, therefore, includes food and nutrition.

The Every Child Matters legislation explores the health and well-being of children from birth to 19 years. There are five strands which look at 'being healthy, staying safe, enjoying and achieving, making a positive contribution and achieving economic wellbeing'. Childhood obesity is one of the issues discussed in the 'being healthy' section. For more information, go to www.everychildmatters.gov.uk.

The Nutritional Standards for School Lunches and Other School Food was announced in May 2006. It was in response to a survey of meals in UK secondary schools and the increasing concern over the food given to children. The recommendations consisted of two standards:

1 The types and frequency of food children have.
2 The proportion of nutrients that children and young people have.

These nutritional standards mean that no confectionery is sold in schools, no savoury snacks other than nuts and seeds are offered and a variety of fruit and vegetables are available. Also, children should have access to free, fresh drinking water. For more information, go to www.dfes.gov.uk/schoollunches.

Other initiatives are outlined below.

Healthy Schools

This is a national initiative which encourages schools to develop a healthy approach to health promotion. It looks at the school curriculum to encourage healthy habits – for example, eating, exercise and emotional well-being. Find out if your local school is involved in this initiative and how they are implementing it.

National Minimum Standards for Care Home Catering

The National Minimum Standards for Care Homes for Older People form the basis on which the new National Care Standards Commission will determine whether care homes meet the needs and secure the welfare and social inclusion of the people who live there. Follow this weblink to investigate what standards are set regarding feeding and mealtimes: www.dh.gov.uk/prod_consum_dh/groups/dh_digitalassets/@dh/@en/documents/digitalasset/dh_4054007.pdf.

Activity 14   P3   M2   D1

Write a report on a service user or case study and include the following:

For P3, introduce your service user, explaining what influences their dietary intake.

For M2, assess how these influences may affect their nutritional health.

For D1, conclude your report by making recommendations to reduce the negative influences in their diet.

4 Be able to use dietary and other relevant information from an individual to make recommendations to improve nutritional health

This section looks at how to examine the diet of individuals by using quantitative analysis. It also looks at how an individual's lifestyle will affect their dietary needs. Any imbalance within the diet may result in under- or over-nutrition. Recommendations can then be made on changing an individual's diet to improve their health. This may include restricting the amount of calories consumed or increasing nutrients required (for example, iron or other minerals).

Record of food intake

A record of food intake is necessary to examine the diet of an individual. To analyse this successfully, it is essential to gather as much information as possible. This should include types of food eaten, including brands if possible. This is because different brands may contain different nutrients. Cooking methods should also be included – fried chicken, for example, is much higher in fat than grilled skinless chicken. Portion sizes should be included; you could show the individual a typical portion size and ask them to assess theirs in relation to the example. The individual should record all drinks they consume, as well as all snacks, all confectionery and any supplements they take. How this information is recorded can be tailored to meet the needs of the individual, but you could use Table 21.5 as a template. The daily diet record sheets should be completed for three days.

Sources of nutritional information

The diet of the individual can be examined using food analysis databases or printed tables. Remember that each food can contain different nutrients. The nutrients obtained from the food can then be compared with the dietary reference values (see page 264).

Quantitative analysis

Each of the foods can be analysed for their nutritional content, to work out energy, protein, fat, iron, vitamin C, fibre and the proportion of energy from fat.

For example:
Weetabix per 100 g contains:
Energy 354 kcal/1482 kJ
Protein 10.7 g
Fat 2 g (20% sat)
Fibre 8.5 g
Iron 6.0 mg
Vitamin C 0 mg

An average serving of Weetabix is 40 g. Therefore, two Weetabix contain the following: energy 141.6 kcal, protein 4.28 g, fat 0.8 g, fibre 3.4 g, iron 2.4 mg, vitamin C 0 mg. These can then be compared with the recommended nutritional requirements. A 17-year-old man, for example, needs 11.2 mg of iron. Two Weetabix provide 21 per cent of this.

Activity 15

Write down the foods you had yesterday and analyse their content using a database or tables. What proportions of nutrients are you getting from your food?

Each individual's lifestyle choices should be taken into account – for example, their activity levels, how much they sleep, walk and exercise. Energy requirements are based on the amount that is needed to keep the body going (known as the basal metabolic rate) and extra energy needed for any physical activity. Depending on the level of activity and the time spent doing it, different amounts of energy are required. Resting, for example, exerts 60–80 kcals per hour, while jogging can exert 360 kcals an hour. So if you spend 30 minutes jogging, you will need an extra 180 kcals.

Table 21.5 Record of food intake

Day	Food and drink consumed *Identify food preparation type*	Mark the nutritional groups included in this meal		Activity / inactivity
Breakfast		☐ Carbohydrate ☐ Protein ☐ Fat ☐ Water ☐ Fibre ☐ Calcium	☐ Vitamin A ☐ Vitamin B ☐ Vitamin C ☐ Vitamin D ☐ Iron	
Lunch		☐ Carbohydrate ☐ Protein ☐ Fat ☐ Water ☐ Fibre ☐ Calcium	☐ Vitamin A ☐ Vitamin B ☐ Vitamin C ☐ Vitamin D ☐ Iron	
Dinner		☐ Carbohydrate ☐ Protein ☐ Fat ☐ Water ☐ Fibre ☐ Calcium	☐ Vitamin A ☐ Vitamin B ☐ Vitamin C ☐ Vitamin D ☐ Iron	
Snacks		☐ Carbohydrate ☐ Protein ☐ Fat ☐ Water ☐ Fibre ☐ Calcium	☐ Vitamin A ☐ Vitamin B ☐ Vitamin C ☐ Vitamin D ☐ Iron	

Please comment in the box below about RNIs, food groups, 5 a day and amount of activity taken. This should highlight areas for change.

Findings from today's food diary:

◊

◊

◊

◊

◊

◊

Activity 16   P4 P5 M3 D2

Choose a friend, family member or yourself for this next activity.

For P4, using a chart like the one in Table 21.5, carry out a quantitative analysis over a three-day period.

For P5, using the information you have collected, prepare a one week plan that will improve the health of your chosen individual.

For M3, in a report, assess how the plan will meet the needs of your chosen individual. For example, 'I have chosen an easy-to-prepare evening meal as this person has a busy lifestyle and needs to visit the gym after work'.

For D2, continue in a report format and evaluate how the plan might improve the health of your chosen individual. For example, by changing cooking processes from frying to grilling, saturated fats in the diet will be significantly reduced. You may like to suggest what health implications may occur if this individual were not to make recommended changes.

A dietary plan for an individual should take into account the nutritional needs and the amount needed to fuel the body for energy needs.

As well as nutritional and lifestyle choices, other factors should be taken into account. These include:

- Personal preferences – you are unlikely to persuade someone to eat something they do not like!
- Economic circumstances – how much money an individual can afford to spend.
- Social and cultural factors – such as family meal times, religious beliefs, how much time someone has to prepare meals.

Summary

Good nutrition is essential for health and well-being. A balanced diet consists of a range of nutrients, each with different functions within the body. Too few nutrients can lead to deficiencies and too many can have adverse effects.

There are many social, cultural and economic factors which can impact on the food that we eat. In-depth nutritional analysis can be carried out on diets, after which recommendations for improvements can be made, taking into account factors such as an individual's lifestyle choices.

Assessment and grading criteria

In order to pass this unit, the evidence that the learner presents for assessment needs to demonstrate that they can meet all the learning outcomes for the unit. The assessment criteria for a pass grade describe the level of achievement required to pass this unit.

To achieve a pass grade the evidence must show that the learner is able to:	To achieve a merit grade the evidence must show that, in addition to the pass criteria, the learner is able to:	To achieve a distinction grade the evidence must show that, in addition to the pass and merit criteria, the learner is able to:
P1 explain concepts associated with nutritional health		
P2 describe the characteristics of nutrients and their benefits to the body	**M1** discuss similarities and differences in the nutritional and energy requirements of two groups of individuals	
P3 explain possible influences on dietary intake	**M2** assess how influences on dietary intake may affect the nutritional health of individuals	**D1** make realistic recommendations for minimising negative influences on individuals in a specific health and social care setting
P4 carry out a quantitative analysis of the daily intake of nutrients and energy by one individual	**M3** assess how the plan will meet the nutritional needs of the chosen individual.	
P5 prepare a one-week plan to improve the nutritional health of the chosen individual.		**D2** evaluate how the nutritional plan might improve the health of the chosen individual.

Resources

Aldworth, C. (2008) *Knowledge Set for Nutrition and Well-being*, Oxford: Heinemann Educational Publishing.

Barasi, M. (2003) *Human Nutrition: A Health Perspective*, London: Hodder Arnold.

Blades, M. (2005) *Intermediate Nutrition and Health*, Doncaster: Highfield Publications.

Lean, M. (2006) *Fox and Cameron's Food Science, Nutrition and Health*, London: Hodder Arnold.

Weblinks

www.dh.gov.uk:
Department of Health
www.fdf.org.uk:
Food and Drink Federation
www.nutrition.org.uk:
British Nutrition Foundation
There are several commercially available food analysis databases; these should be UK based as they may be linked automatically to the DRVs used in the UK. American sites will relate to American recommended intakes not used in the UK. A few weblinks to food analysis databases are given here:

www.buzzle.com/articles/vitamins-and-minerals-chart.html:
Buzzle – vitamins and minerals chart
www.nutritiondata.com:
Nutrition Data
www.food.gov.uk:
Food Standards Agency
http://users.rcn.com/jkimball.ma.ultranet/BiologyPages/N/Nutrition.html#carbohydrates:
Human Nutrition

22: Research Methodology for Health and Social Care

Introduction

Some people think research is difficult and worry they will not understand it. This unit will help you realise that you already know a lot about research. Consider an everyday activity, such as choosing a meal. When you choose lunch, you consider what is available, the food taste, cost and so on. You do this through research, asking questions and reading information. You look at the evidence, compare findings and make recommendations to friends based on this.

Health and social care practitioners must have evidence from research upon which to base practice; 'evidence-based practice'. Health and social care practitioners need to be 'research minded'.

This unit will help you understand why and how research is conducted. You will learn about the different types and methods of research used in health and social care, examine the ethical issues involved and some implications of research. You will identify a suitable topic, produce a plan for a research proposal, conduct the research, present the findings and evaluate the research project.

Key terms

Evidence-based practice – work based on research findings.
Ethical – moral.
Implications – suggestions or consequences.
Evaluate – assess the value of something.

In this unit, learners can show initiative, take responsibility and manage their time effectively, providing opportunities for the assessment of personal, learning and thinking skills.

Learning outcomes:

On completion of this unit, you should:

1 Understand the function of research in health and social care

2 Understand ethical issues relating to research in health and social care

3 Understand research methodologies relevant to health and social care

4 Be able to plan for a research project

5 Be able to conduct research relevant to a health and social care context

6 Be able to interpret research findings.

1 Understand the function of research in health and social care

Research is used in many areas, from space science to computer games, helping to produce better products, avoid mistakes and to identify need. Research is used in health and social care to:

- identify need
- plan provision and highlight gaps
- inform and improve policy or practice
- extend knowledge, understanding and reflection
- monitor progress
- examine topics of importance.

Identifying need

How do we know where there is a need for health and social care? Do we need more hospitals or more care in people's own homes? Do we need more care for the elderly? What health and social care services do young people need? Research can help us answer these questions.

An example of research is the report carried out by the National Care Advisory Service for the Social Exclusion Unit 'What makes the difference? Care leavers and benefits'. It tells us there is a need to support young people leaving care and recommends the introduction of an information page, the government website, to guide young care leavers through the benefits system. It also recommends allowing them to study for more hours each week than normally permitted while on income support (www.cabinetoffice.gov.uk).

Highlighting gaps in provision

Research by Shipman *et al.* (2008) looked at the provision, commissioning, research, and use of generalist end of life care. (www.bmj.com/ cgi/content/abstract/337/oct01_1/a1720#other articles). A national survey of healthcare practitioners, commissioners, academics, and representatives of user and voluntary groups and organisations were asked for information. Out of the 285 invited, 210 participated.

Results showed that 'end of life care' was understood in various ways, from a period of more than a year to the last few days of life, and there were concerns about skill levels of those caring for people dying from illnesses other than cancer. The researchers concluded that 'definitions of end of life care need clarification and standardisation and more needs to be known about the context of provision and the influence of competing priorities and incentives'. This shows the gap in provision of end of life care.

Planning provision

Young runaways sleeping rough need care because, with no fixed address, it is very difficult to find work. Sleeping in a doorway on a rainy December night is not healthy so young runaways get sick, tired and hungry. They are unlikely to see a general practitioner or be sick enough to go to an Accident and Emergency department.

Did you know...

'One quarter of runaways will sleep in unsafe places, putting them at serious risk of harm. As many as 1 in 14 children and young people who run away, around 5,000 a year, survive through stealing, begging, drug dealing and prostitution. Runaways with the most problems are likely to run to city centres and spend time on the streets, sleep outside, or stay in other unsafe places, such as with adults who may exploit them.'

Source: Young Runaways, report by the Social Exclusion Unit, November 2002 (www.cabinetoffice.gov.uk/media/cabinetoffice/social_exclusion_task_force/assets/publications_1997_to_2006/young_runaways_sum.pdf)

Research by the Social Exclusion Unit showed the need to plan provision for homeless young people: 'These young people will need more intensive support – services that can locate and make contact with them, and then either help from social services, a safe place to sleep and/or help negotiating a return to home or care.'

Table 22.1 Government spending on health, education and social protection

Total expenditure (£ billions)	1999–2000 outturn	2000–2001 outturn	2001–2002 outturn	2002–2003 outturn	2003–2004 outturn	2004–2005 outturn	2005–2006 estimated outturn
Health	57.2	61.8	66.5	71.4	78.2	84.1	88.6
Education and training	48.6	52.2	56.4	58.7	63.2	65.8	69.7
Of which is education	47.0	50.5	54.8	56.8	61.3	63.9	67.7
Social protection	141.3	145.5	151.8	156.0	162.7	167.1	170.3

Source: adapted from www.hm-treasury.gov.uk

Activity 1   P1

Look at government spending in Table 22.1.

1 From the items in the table, on what item did the government spend most money?

2 What was the next biggest expense?

3 What has happened to spending on all these items since 1999–2000?

Answers:

1 The biggest spending in this table was on social protection. (Social protection includes benefits.)

2 The next biggest expense was health.

3 Spending has increased on all these items in the period shown, from 1999–2000 to 2005–2006.

Research shows we need to spend more on supporting those who are on low incomes, sick, unable to work, elderly, retired or homeless. We spend an estimated £170.3 billion on this and an estimated £88.6 billion on health care. Research helps the government know where money is needed.

Informing policy or practice

Research informs health and social care practitioners on how best to care for people. Here is an example of how research can inform policy and practice. In December 2006, the Department for Health published a policy paper by Professor Roger Boyle, National Director for Heart Disease and Stroke (see www.dh.gov.uk). Key points showed that:

1 Cardiovascular disease (heart disease, stroke and related conditions) causes two-thirds of all premature deaths in England. If strokes were treated as an emergency at specialist centres, then over 1,000 stroke victims a year would regain independence rather than die or become dependent.

2 Clot-busting treatment for stroke needs to be delivered by skilled professionals in settings with facilities open 24 hours a day, seven days a week. This means concentrating services in centres of excellence rather than spreading resources over too many sites.

3 For both heart disease and stroke, paramedics assess where patients should be treated, taking some heart patients directly to specialist treatment centres or pre-alerting stroke units about suspected stroke patients to speed direct admission.

4 Improved support after early discharge provides a better service for heart attack and stroke survivors in the community.

5 Improvements in heart and stroke services will increase the efficient use of resources, save lives and reduce disability.

Instead of these patients being taken to the nearest hospital, patients should be taken to specialist centres that are always open, staffed by specialists with the right resources. Because time can mean the difference between life and death for the patient, paramedics should assess where the patient should go, calling and warning the nearest stroke unit about a suspected stroke patient in advance. Such changes to practice means patients recover earlier, returning home after a few days, rather than weeks. We would need more community nurses to care for them while at home, but reducing the expensive hospital stay would save money and lives.

Activity 2

If you know someone who has had a heart attack or stroke, ask them what they liked about the service they were given and what could be improved. Do they agree with these suggestions in the report?

Extending knowledge and understanding

For many years, patients with peptic ulcers (a type of stomach ulcer) were given antacids but did not improve. In 1984, two doctors, Barry J. Marshall and J. Robin Warren, noticed that people with ulcers had an organism called Helicobacter pylori in their stomach. This organism was only in the stomachs of those with gastritis. Marshall, who was healthy, tested the research by swallowing the organisms and developed the symptoms of gastritis. Fortunately, they had also discovered a cure – a course of antibiotics, which he took and was cured. Since then, most doctors treat these ulcers with antibiotics.

This research extended knowledge and under-standing of the cause and treatment of stomach ulcers, improving practice. Marshall and Warren were given the Nobel Prize in 2005 for this research. See their PowerPoint presentation (and watch out for the cartoons) on http://nobelprize.org/nobel_prizes/medicine/laureates/2005/marshall-slides.pdf.

Research extends knowledge by asking questions e.g. 'what makes children happy?'. It seems that toys do not; more important is a secure attachment to parents or primary caregiver, gaining skills and being appreciated by their parents or carer. However, up to half of this is down to genetic inheritance. Find out more on www.open2.net/healthliving/family_childdevelopment/children_happiness2.html.

Improving practice

In February 2010, the Ofsted report 'An evalu-ation of the provision of mental health services for looked after young people over the age of 16 accommodated in residential settings' drew on visits to 27 children's homes and looked at how the mental health needs of young people aged 16+ in care are met.

Key term

Looked after children – the legal term for children and young people in public care. It refers to children who are subject to care orders and those who are accommodated.

The Department of Health set National Minimum Standards for Children's Homes. Standard 2.1 states:

'On admission, all children and young people who are looked after should have their needs effectively and comprehensively assessed, including their emotional and healthcare needs.'

All children's homes in the Ofsted research had assessed young people's needs before admission, but only 4 of the 27 children's homes involved young people in their assessment. The report identified good practice in some local authorities and recommended that all adopt it, emphasising the importance of agencies working together to improve and develop services for young people (www.ofsted.gov.uk/Ofsted-home/Publications-and-research/Browse-all-by/Documents-by-type/Thematic-reports/An-evaluation-of-the-provision-of-mental-health-services-for-looked-after-young-people-over-the-age-of-16-accommodated-in-residential-settings).

Aiding reflection

Care workers need to reflect on how they cope with power relationships in their work because some carers can become hardened and cease to care, leading to abuse.

Philip Zimbardo

Philip Zimbardo, Professor Emeritus of Psychology at Stanford University, carried out a classic piece of research in 1971. He conducted an experiment having implications for all those in charge of others. He asked: 'What happens when you put good people in an evil place? Does humanity win over evil, or does evil triumph?'

In the Stanford prison experiment, undergraduate volunteers were divided into guards or inmates and put into a prison situation. The guards were assigned uniforms and power over the inmates. The inmates, who had done nothing wrong, were locked up, stripped, shaved, given prison clothes and allowed no privileges. The experiment was designed to last two weeks but was stopped after six days because the guards became brutal and the inmates showed high stress levels.

Here is a discussion point from the website www. prisonexp.org, where you can find out more about the experiment:

> 'In the encounter sessions, all the prisoners were happy the experiment was over, but most of the guards were upset that the study was terminated prematurely. Why do you think the guards reacted this way?'

Remember, 'an evil place' could be a care home or children's home where abuse happens and no one tells.

Erving Goffman (1922–1982) was a sociologist and writer. In 1961, Goffman published his famous research *Asylums: Essays on the Social Situation of Mental Patients and Other Inmates*. He worked and researched in an institution for mentally ill people, finding that people survive in the system by giving in, taking on the inmate role and accepting the regime (see www.sociology.org.uk/methpo6d.htm).

This research shows what can happen when patients and individuals are not respected, and how carers can become abusive if they are not held accountable. They are important pieces of research to aid reflection because they deal with a key issue in care – that of power and control. Good carers empower vulnerable service users; bad carers abuse them. It is important to reflect on this in order to recognise good and bad care.

Allowing progress to be monitored

According to research by Duffy (2010), for every woman over-diagnosed by breast screening, two deaths are prevented. This research was partly funded by Cancer Research UK and shows how we are making progress by reducing deaths from breast cancer.

Examining topics of importance

Crime and anti-social behaviour are two contemporary topics that research can help us clarify.

> ### Key term
>
> **Contemporary** – current, up to date.

Is crime increasing? According to the British Crime Survey (2008–2009), which is carried out by the government:

- all household crime is down by 14 per cent
- all personal crime is down by 17 per cent
- all crime surveyed is down by 15 per cent.

Source: www.homeoffice.gov.uk/rds/crimeew0809. html.

Do anti-social behaviour orders (ASBOs) work or are there better ways of managing anti-social behaviour? Research may be able to tell us.

'Tackling anti-social behaviour' published in December 2006 by the Home Office, examined three interventions – warning letters, acceptable behaviour contracts and ASBOs. They found that warning letters and acceptable behaviour contracts were equally effective. Around two-thirds of people received just one intervention, and had no further anti-social behaviour.

However, more than half of those who received ASBOs breached them. Furthermore, 40 per cent of people who received an ASBO had received an earlier anti-social behaviour intervention and 80 per cent had previous criminal convictions (source: www.nao.org.uk/pn/06-07/060799.htm).

Activity 3   P1   M1

Prepare notes for a talk explaining the function of research for health and social care. Your audience, unenthusiastic students, will need convincing that research is essential for this area, so you will need to include interesting examples of research to support what you say.

2 Understand ethical issues relating to research in health and social care

Ethical principles

Ethical principles include:

- Protection from harm – research should not harm those who take part.
- Informed consent (voluntary) – participants should know exactly what is involved before they take part, they should not be forced and should give their consent only when they are fully informed.
- Confidentiality – any information about participants must not be shared with others.
- Obtaining ethical approval – no research should happen without approval from the ethics committee. If staff want to conduct a survey on patient treatment, they must submit an outline of their research. Only when the ethics committee has given approval can the research begin.

Ethical principles are especially important in drug trials. All drugs must be tested before they can be prescribed, first in the laboratory, then in the final stages, tested on humans. In March 2006, a group of healthy male volunteers participated in a trial of a new drug, TGN1412. The trial had approval and the participants were informed about what to expect. Unfortunately, the trial went badly wrong. The participants unexpectedly became ill almost immediately, requiring intensive care. This shows the difficulty researchers have in giving full information and obtaining informed consent.

The researchers were criticised because, allegedly, they failed to provide access to all the information and fully inform volunteers about the risks.

Ethical issues

One of the criticisms of the Stanford prison experiment was that participant's human rights were ignored. Research should provide protection from harm and do no harm. Both the Stanford prison experiment and the drug trial harmed participants. The Medicines and Healthcare Products Regulatory Agency stopped the TGN1412 experiment because they had an immediate priority to ensure that no further patients were harmed.

The role of the media is important in reporting research. The media includes radio, television, the popular press, the internet and specialist research journals, e.g. *New Scientist* (www.newscientist.com) and *Nurse Researcher* (http://nurseresearcher. rcnpublishing.co.uk).

When the TGN1412 trial went wrong, the popular press looked not at the scientific background but at the emotional aspect of the story. The headline from the *Daily Mail* read: 'Tighter controls needed to prevent Elephant Man drug trial horror' (www. dailymail.co.uk).

The role of the media was to raise awareness of the risks in volunteering for drug trials, but the media can also be used to announce new discoveries, such as a vaccine against cervical cancer.

Data can be used or misused. When findings are presented, there are ethical considerations. Results should be presented as a whole, even if

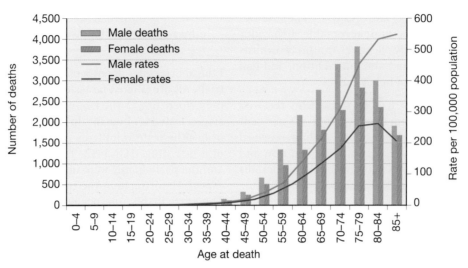

Number of deaths and age-specific mortality rates, lung cancer, by sex, UK, 2005
Source: http://info.cancerresearchuk.org/cancerstats/types/lung/mortality/?a=5441#trends

they do not show the picture you expected, so that people will not be misled. Huff's *How to Lie with Statistics* (1954), explains how statistics can be used to mislead people.

Here are some examples. Cancer Research UK provides the above graph, which clearly illustrates data on lung cancer and mortality rates.

The male death rate is still rising but the female death rate is less. After 75, the difference between male and female death rates increases.

The adapted graph below shows differences between male and female rates. We will use this to show how data can be presented to mislead people.

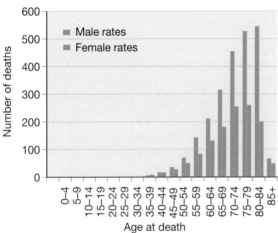

Differences between male and female death rates

If you cover everything below 300 on the left axis, it looks as though there are no female deaths. Sometimes data is presented like this to mislead people. An unscrupulous cigarette salesman might be tempted to say 'Women do not die from lung cancer – look at the graph!' and show it starting from 300. This is unlikely to happen now because advertising is heavily regulated.

The graph on page 295 does not start from zero – for good reasons. Why not?

In this example, the y axis (the left-hand, vertical line) does not start at zero so we can see the detail of deaths and temperature. Changing the starting point (origin) is not always done to mislead.

See if you can spot what has been done with the next graphs on page 295. The data is fictitious (made up) so that you can concentrate on the graph. The first graph clearly shows that younger people watch more television.

Look at the second graph. Did you spot what had happened to the scale on the y axis? If you change the scale, the difference between age groups is not so obvious.

Using a different type of graph can disguise links.

The last graph on page 295 shows a link between two things that can vary (variables). It seems to suggest that, as one increases, the other increases.

Why would a soft drinks manufacturer be unhappy with this graph? Perhaps parents who saw the

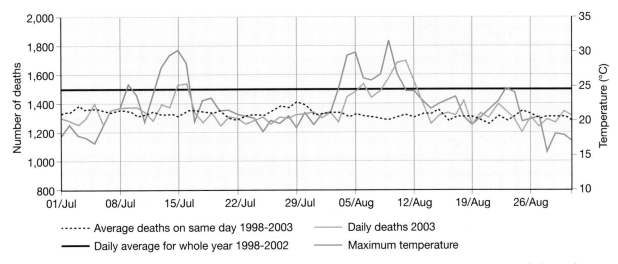

Daily deaths in England and Wales, and maximum Central England temperature, July and August 2003
Source: www.statistics.gov.uk/downloads/theme_health/auxiliary_data_summer_mortality_2003.xls

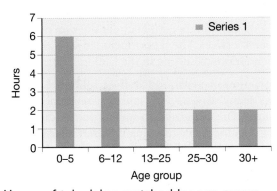

Hours of television watched by age group

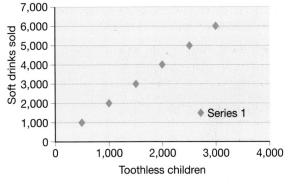

Toothless children and soft drinks sold

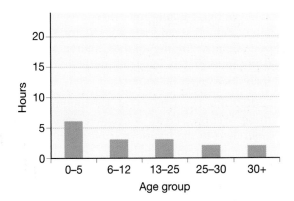

Hours of television watched by age group

graph would stop buying soft drinks for their children. An unscrupulous drinks manufacturer might prefer to present the graph as shown on page 296.

Using this type of graph, the drinks manufacturer might argue that they are selling a lot more drinks but that the rate of toothless children is not increasing as fast. You have to be good at statistics to spot misrepresentation!

When we research, we must consider the vulnerability of different groups. In the TGN1412 research, healthy young men were tempted to participate by the payment of £2,000. They were able to decide for themselves whether to take the risk, as did the participants in the Stanford prison

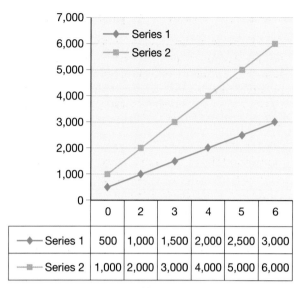

	0	2	3	4	5	6
Series 1	500	1,000	1,500	2,000	2,500	3,000
Series 2	1,000	2,000	3,000	4,000	5,000	6,000

Number of data sets

Soft drinks consumed by children compared with number of toothless children. Series 1 = toothless children; Series 2 = soft drinks sold.

experiment. People with mental health issues or learning disabilities and people in residential care may be more vulnerable and feel they have no choice but to participate. It is unethical to involve vulnerable people in research.

Implications

The implications of using research in health and social care must be considered. Look at who commissions the research. An independent charity such as Cancer Research UK has an obvious bias in that they are only interested in cancer-related issues. But who do you think sponsors the Drinkaware trust, which provides information on responsible drinking? Drinks manufacturers such as Carlsberg and Bacardi! (source: www.drink aware trust.org.uk).

Look at the *authenticity* of the research. If it is genuine, it will have been peer-reviewed and published in a reputable academic journal.

Consider the research's *validity*. Does it test what it is supposed to test? Or is there a change of focus or hypothesis? If a researcher set out to measure the number of teenage pregnancies, do they include *all* teenage pregnancies, even those for under-16s? Or do they just look at over-16s?

How *reliable* is the research? If someone else did the same research with a similar sample, and got similar results, the research is reliable.

Key terms

Commission – order or authorise.
Peer-reviewed – read by other professionals with experience of research.
Validity – does it test what it says it tests?
Reliability – consistency.

The *impact* of key research reports on services and users of services is not always immediate. It takes time for the information to filter down to practitioners, and for service users to notice a difference.

One key report, 'Every Child Matters', followed the investigation into the death of Victoria Climbié, a young girl who died while under the supervision of social services. The report included several recommendations, resulting in the Children Act 2004.

Sometimes legislation like the Children Act 2004 has many aspects and must be implemented in stages. One requirement was for local authorities set up a local safeguarding children board (LSCB) to coordinate services across health, education, the police and social work. Practitioners must share information about vulnerable children, and training is needed.

When a report such as 'Every Child Matters' is followed by legislation, some recommendations are brought in immediately and others over time. The death of Baby P, seven years after Victoria's death, showed that the findings of the Children Act 2004 had not immediately impacted on practice (www. dcsf.gov.uk/everychildmatters).

In 2007, the Department of Health published, 'Putting People First: a shared vision and commitment to the transformation of adult social care', aiming to reform public services and provide high-quality services to meet individual needs. The impact was the personalisation of care, in which people with care needs are given a budget to employ carers themselves.

Occasionally, recommendations can be implemented immediately. For example, the National

Institute for Clinical Health Excellence (NICE) researches treatments to improve the effective use of NHS resources (www.nice.org.uk). One report, 'Depression in Children and Young People' (2005), found that antidepressants should not be used for the first treatment of children and young people with mild depression because many recover without any treatment and the drugs had unwanted side effects. The impact of this was to recommend that GPs refer people for counselling as the first treatment instead of prescriptions.

The consequences/benefits of findings

Looking at the consequences and benefits of 'Every Child Matters', joint working has improved and more children are being referred to social services. Sure Start centres support parents while providing childcare. Progress can be measured against the five outcomes of 'Every Child Matters': to be healthy, stay safe, enjoy and achieve, make a positive contribution and achieve economic well-being.

For the first time, there is also a focus on improving outcomes for looked after children and those with special educational needs or disabilities, reducing teenage pregnancies and the number of young people not in education, employment or training.

The consequences and benefits of 'Putting People First' include increasing independence for users of services and more appropriate care for those with care needs. New posts called personal assistants have been created. Charitable agencies, such as Penderels Trust, offer advice to people who may, for the first time in their lives, be employing someone as their own carer (www.penderelstrust.org.uk).

If we look at the consequences of the NICE example, Murray and Cartwright-Hatton (2006) identified an immediate need for additional training for psychotherapists using cognitive behavioural therapy with younger children. They also recommended more research to compare the effectiveness of waiting, of psychotherapy and of medication. A benefit of the NICE research is that young people with depression are no longer prescribed medication with harmful side effects.

The effect/influence of publications

The Department for Children, Schools and Families has published leaflets in a variety of languages to explain the advantages of Sure Start to parents and to encourage them to participate in these schemes (www.dcsf.gov.uk/everychildmatters/publications/leaflets).

NICE publications are intended to inform professionals and the public about more effective ways of using resources. The Royal College of Psychiatrists publishes a series of booklets for parents and young people to help them understand depression (www.rcpsych.ac.uk).

Although official publications are freely available on the internet, a wider audience might be influenced by Dr Miriam Stoppard, who writes a blog for the *Mirror* newspaper; she says that pills are useful only for severe depression (http://blogs.mirror.co.uk/dear-miriam/tag/depression).

Activity 4

Which publications do you think a GP is most likely to read?

Which publications do you think an ordinary member of the public will read?

Which will have a wider influence?

Access to information

Information is useful only when people can access it. Whilst the internet makes more information available, not everyone uses it or has the skills to find information. Even if they do, the writing style or jargon may make it inaccessible to all but a limited audience.

Who do you think is more likely to have access to online information – a GP or an elderly pensioner receiving state pension? A GP is more likely to have a computer and be able to afford internet access.

Information is available in health centres but not everyone attends a health centre. People who work long hours may not get time to see their GP. Homeless people cannot register with a GP.

> ## Did you know...
>
> **You need an address in order to register with a GP.**

Leaflets are a common way of giving information but not everyone reads – they may be dyslexic, or visually impaired. People who speak a language other than English may be unable to read either language.

NICE publications are available too, but not everyone with internet access is aware that NICE exists and the language of these publications may be difficult to understand.

Legislation and policy

The Human Rights Act 1998 came into force in 2000 and is based on articles from the European Convention on Human Rights. Articles 2, 3 and possibly 5 are likely to be the most relevant to aspects of research, although other articles may also be relevant. See details in Unit 2.

The Data Protection Act requires that any personal information held on research participants is 'obtained only for one or more specified and lawful purposes, and shall not be further processed in any manner incompatible with that purpose or those purposes' (principle 2). See Unit 2 for more details (also: www.ico.gov.uk).

Several professional bodies have codes of practice. The NHS has the National Patient Safety Agency, which is part of the National Research Ethics Service that advises researchers. Here is an extract from a leaflet to help researchers make sure they explain research and get informed consent.

> 'Part one should provide brief, clear information on the essential elements of the study: the condition or treatment under study; the voluntary nature of involvement; what will happen during and after the trial, what treatment may be withheld; the participant's responsibilities; the potential risks, inconvenience or restrictions, benefits, and the alternative(s).

Part two should contain additional information on factors such as confidentiality and data protection, communication with the GP, indemnity and compensation, and publication. This should be read and understood before the participant decides whether they want to participate.'

Source: www.nres.npsa.nhs.uk

Many different bodies have their own codes of practice for research. In an attempt to standardise them, the UK Research Integrity Office has produced a generic code for universities, the NHS and private organisations undertaking research. You can see this on their website www.ukrio.org.

Policies and procedures vary in different organisations but, in general, an ethics committee must approve any research before it can be done, and a code of conduct must be followed.

> ## Activity 5   P2
>
> **You are a local junior reporter and have interviewed health and care professionals about the ethical considerations when carrying out research in health and social care. Prepare a detailed report of your findings.**

3 Understand research methodologies relevant to health and social care

We can carry out research in different ways using different methodologies.

> ## Key term
>
> **Methodology** – method or way.

The types of research commonly used are as follows:

- Quantitative research – this involves numbers (think of 'quantity'). The Census occurs every ten years and information or data is collected from everyone in the country. This data tells us how many people are over 65 and how many people are under 16.

- Qualitative research – this refers to in-depth information about a few cases (think of 'quality'). A qualitative study of drinking habits of teenagers may include just one or two interviews of a few people in one area. We cannot say that they represent all teenagers across the country.

Both quantitative and qualitative research methods are used in primary research.

Primary research

Primary research is done by the researcher. You will be the researcher when you carry out your research project and it will be primary research. Erving Goffman was the primary researcher when he studied asylums.

Here is an example of primary research. In 1961, Dr Albert Bandura conducted an experiment to find out how children learn. An adult hit a Bobo doll while a child watched. Later, the same child copied the aggressive behaviour. You can see the experiment on several internet sites, including http://video.google.co.uk. Dr Bandura's research led to the development of the social cognitive theory of behaviour.

Dr Bandura did the primary research. Professionals such as social workers and teachers read about it (secondary research) and use his findings to help them with their own research, so a teacher wishing to improve classroom behaviour may use this theory in a practical situation. A social worker who works with young people will use this research to encourage young people to work with mentors on community projects and, in this way, the young person will copy the mentor's behaviour.

Primary sources include:

- questionnaires
- structured and unstructured interviews
- scientific experiments
- formal and informal observations
- measurements.

Questionnaires

Questionnaires are used when the researcher wants to get the views of many people. Questionnaires are quick, relatively cheap and, if they are well planned, the information is easy to process. Questionnaires cannot give us the in-depth views of individuals. They do not usually give scope for answers outside a set range.

The questions must be carefully planned. They must be valid (test what they are supposed to test). If you want to find out how a person feels about social workers, it is no good asking them what they think of teachers. When you devise a set of questions, always ask yourself 'Do they test what they are supposed to test?'.

Questions must be reliable. This means that anyone asking the question to the same person is likely to get the same result. 'Do you play football?' is likely to get the same response each time. 'What did you think of the last match?' is likely to get different answers, depending on the outcome of the last match.

Questions may be open. For example, 'What do you think of the food in the home?'. This might get a long answer, describing every meal they had eaten and their view of it. Open questions are good for interviews when you are trying to get people's views but do not make for easy analysis in a questionnaire.

Questions may be closed. For example, 'Did you like the mashed potato at dinner?'. This requires a yes/no/don't know response. Closed questions are useful in questionnaires when you want to restrict the data for easier analysis.

The Census, held every ten years, is a long questionnaire. It provides valuable information for planners. It is usually several pages long. Some people do not want to fill it in. Why do you think people might not want to fill in a survey that is several pages long?

Did you know...

Between 1991 and 2001, older people tended to move to the countryside, whereas younger people tended to move to cities.
Source: www.sasi.group.shef.ac.uk

Table 22.2 Survey of diet using a Likert scale

Q1 Which is your age group?	0–25	26–50	51–75	76+
Q2 How often do you eat fresh fruit?	Every day	Every week	Every month	Never
Q3 How often do you eat fish?	Every day	Every week	Every month	Never

Table 22.3 Summary sheet

Student number	Question 1				Question 2				Question 3			
	1	2	3	4	1	2	3	4	1	2	3	4
1				✓		✓						✓
2			✓		✓					✓		
3												
4												
5												
6 etc												

The layout of a questionnaire is important. Too long and people will not fill it in. Too short and you will not get the information you need.

You may wish to find out detailed information. In this case, you may want to use a Likert scale (see Table 22.2).

You can process the information using a summary sheet or a tally chart, which makes it easy to process the information.

Table 22.3 shows an example of a summary sheet.

Interviews

These are used to gain detailed information about people's views. They may be structured and follow a set pattern led by the interviewer, or unstructured using open questions such as 'Tell me about your childhood'. Interviews provide the opportunity to ask extra questions and give the interviewee (the person being interviewed) a chance to say what they really think. The same validity and reliability must apply to these questions.

Avoid leading questions. 'People are very rude today, aren't they?' is an example of a leading question. It assumes the interviewee shares this view. A better question would be 'Do you think manners have changed?'. This allows the interviewee to give their views without being influenced by the interviewer. Interviews take time and it can be complicated to record and to process the information. The success of the interview depends on the skill of the interviewer. If the interviewer talks all the time, they will not get much information. If the interviewer is unfriendly, their subject may not want to talk. Constant interruptions will distract both interviewer and interviewee.

Activity 6

If you wish to interview someone, how can you encourage them to talk? What facial expressions might you use? What would your body language be like? What background noise would distract them? Where would you interview them?

Interviews are useful for small-scale research or to explore in depth one aspect of a bigger piece of research. Researchers on 'The experiences of young care leavers from different ethnic groups' by the Joseph Rowntree Foundation surveyed 261 young people and interviewed 36 of them. They did not try to interview everyone. It would take a long time to process the information if they had done so (www.jrf.org.uk/KNOWLEDGE/findings/socialpolicy/0285.asp).

Scientific experiments

These are used in specialist areas, such as university departments or the pharmaceutical industry. In the scientific method, a research proposal is submitted to an ethics committee and may be approved, or changes may be suggested. The proposal must say what has already been done in that area, what they are trying to find out (the hypothesis), what methods they will use and how long the research will take.

Scientists want to grow stem cells into nerves and tissues and help people with Alzheimer's, Parkinson's and cystic fibrosis. This is an example of a scientific experiment. They want to create animal–human embryos to understand the molecular minutiae behind such conditions. The researchers would pluck a cell from a patient and insert it into a hollowed cow or rabbit egg and stimulate it with a jolt of electricity. The two cells then fuse to make an embryo which is 99.9 per cent human and 0.1 per cent animal. Embryonic stem cells extracted from the embryo could be grown into nerves and other tissues, giving scientists insight into how the disease develops. Under existing laws, the embryos must be destroyed no later than 14 days old and cannot be implanted (source: www.guardian.co.uk/science/story/0,,2050279,00.html). Many people think this is a disturbing or even shocking experiment. What do you think? This raises ethical issues such as whether an embryo has rights.

Research is expensive and takes time. No one wants to waste resources repeating something but findings must be checked.

Look at the case study below for the drug trial for TGN1412 in March 2006 to show how the research process works in this experiment.

Case Study – countdown to disaster

January 27, 2006: Medicines and Healthcare products Regulatory Agency (MHRA) gives permission for human trials of antibody drug TGN1412.

February 22: volunteers selected for trial.

March 13: TGN1412 administered in trials at Northwick Park Hospital, London. The six men's immune systems react to drug with disastrous 'cytokine storm', resulting in agonising, life-threatening injuries.

May 25: MHRA inquiry finds 'unexpected biological effect' most likely cause of incident.

June 27: Ryan Wilson, most seriously injured victim, leaves hospital.

July 19: Wilson returns to hospital to have toes amputated.

Source: www.channel4.com/news/articles/dispatches/reckless+error+left+men+fighting+for+life/158065

Ryan Wilson, a 20-year-old trainee plumber lost fingers and toes as a result of the experiment.

Of course, scientific experiments are often successful. We owe our lives to antibiotics such as penicillin and to anaesthetics, which make operations possible. These were developed using scientific experiments.

Observations

Observations may be formal or informal. Formal observation is when the observer is noticeable – for example, an inspector may sit in a class and make notes. Informal observation occurs where the observed person does not realise they are being observed. An advantage of observation is that it gives a snapshot view of an activity. Unfortunately, observers can sometimes influence what they are observing. This is called the 'Hawthorne effect'. Some observers avoid this by working alongside the person they observe as a participant observer. This is a good way to observe children and many child psychologists use this method.

Erving Goffman used participant observation in his classic study on asylums. He worked at the asylum as a member of staff. His research role was mostly covert, or hidden. Most staff and inmates did not know he was a researcher. Only a few knew his real purpose and saw him as an overt researcher.

> **Did you know...**
>
> **Interviews and observations are useful methods for qualitative research where detailed information about a limited number of subjects is needed.**

Measurements

Measurements vary, depending on the type of research and methods used. In quantitative research, such as scientific research, measurements may need to be highly accurate – for example, when measuring levels of a drug in the blood. You are more likely to be measuring opinions or views

in your own research. It is important to design questions so that the results can be measured and later analysed. For example, you may use a Likert scale for questionnaires (see page 300) so people can indicate how far they agree with something.

Interview notes require content analysis. This means going through the notes and counting how many times a person raises a topic.

Observation checklists are useful to record findings, and sociograms can be used to measure observed social interactions. For example, Daisy observed social interaction at a day centre for older people and found Person A interacted more with other attendees than with support workers:

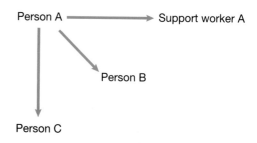

You can find out more about sociograms and find templates on the internet. Whether you use a checklist or a sociogram, it is important to have it with you before you start an observation so that you do not miss anything and so that measurements are accurate.

Case Study

Jay interviews two residents in a care home about their views of residential care. Jay counts how many times Person A talks about the food, the activities and the carers. He does the same for Person B. He finds that Person A mentions food five times, activities or the lack of them ten times and the carers seven times. Person B mentions food three times, activities or the lack of them twelve times and the carers five times.

From this Jay, concludes that the most important thing for residents is activities, next is the carers and last of all is food. Jay found this by measuring the content of the interview responses.

Secondary research

Secondary research uses research done by someone else. When you use http://neighbour hood.statistics.gov.uk to find out how many people under 16 live in your area, you are undertaking secondary research. Someone else did the research (probably for the Census) and you are using their findings. This is not cheating! It is good practice to find out what someone else has done before you research a topic. This is called a literature search. It saves duplication and you can build on their findings, thus adding to the total stock of knowledge. You should use it to help you understand a topic before doing your own research.

There are three aspects to secondary research:

1 Information literacy – e.g. using websites, journals, media, books, and e-resources.

2 Literature reviews – these require the ability to extract, interpret, analyse and synthesise information.
3 Understanding data – e.g. graphs, tables and statistics.

> ## Key terms
>
> **Information literacy** – 'is knowing when and why you need information, where to find it, and how to evaluate, use and communicate it in an ethical manner' (Chartered Institute of Library and Information Professionals).
> **Analyse** – break down into different parts.
> **Synthesise** – to combine, usually ideas from difference sources.

Information literacy is increasingly important. Being able to use websites, journals, media, books and e-resources effectively is important because information is available to help you in your everyday life, not just in research, if you know how to use it.

Most students can use a search engine such as Google and find a website with information on a chosen topic, but that is sometimes as far as it goes. Some then cut and paste the information into their own work, perhaps changing a word or two but effectively copying other people's work, whether from websites, books or journals. This is called plagiarism; stealing someone else's work and passing it off as one's own. All universities and most colleges check students' work for plagiarism and it is dealt with very seriously.

The correct way to use secondary research is to read it, understand it, extract the relevant parts and make notes. When you have found one article on a topic, look for another one, read it, extract the relevant information and make notes. Look at both articles and analyse them. Are they saying the same thing or do they contradict each other? Can you combine or synthesise the ideas or can you contrast the ideas? This process is hard work. It requires thinking skills and a lot more effort than cutting and pasting, but it will help you understand a topic before you begin to research it. Remember to note the reference for every article

you read for secondary research. You will need these references when you write up your own research. When writing a reference list, you should use the Harvard system of referencing.

> ## Key term
>
> **Plagiarism** – illegal use of someone else's work, copying, stealing work.

We will look at some of the sources you may use for secondary research. Websites are quick and make it easy to find information, but caution is needed. Some websites can be trusted and are relevant and some are not. Sam is researching 'health care' using a search engine. It takes her to a page that talks about President Obama and health care. The website has information about health care, which is what Sam wanted, but she realises that this site refers to American health care, which is different from English health care so it was not relevant for her topic.

> ## Did you know...
>
> **E-journals are much quicker to search than paper copies of journals.**

Journals in hard copy may have research that is relevant for your chosen topic, but you may spend a lot of time finding it, or the journal you need may be missing. A much easier way is to use e-resources, such as e-journals, especially if you are in a college or university where they use the shared online library system Athens (www.athens.ac.uk). Your librarian will show you how to use e-journals, which you can search quickly for your chosen topic. There is a wider range of journals online than can be stocked by any library. A quick search for 'social work' in an online library should bring up the *British Journal of Social Work*, with all copies available since it was first published, and the *Journal of Family Social Work*, for example.

The media can also provide secondary research, including newspaper articles and television documentaries. A reliable newspaper source for social issues is the *Guardian*. The Society section provides responsible, investigative journalism and

Activity 7   P3   M2   D1

Compile a report that describes different research methods, and then compare them by looking at the advantages and drawbacks of each. Assess each method to make sure the method gives validity of findings. Start by making some notes, using the table format below.

Method	Advantages	Drawbacks	Best for qualitative or quantitative research?	Best for primary or secondary research?	Will it ensure validity of findings?
Questionnaires					
Structured interviews					
Unstructured interviews					
Scientific experiments					
Formal observations					
Informal observations					
Measurements					
Information literacy					
Literature review					
Data					

can raise important issues. However, make sure that the articles are valid, reliable and relevant. And remember, if you use it, reference it.

Data in the form of graphs, tables and statistics must be read with caution. Check the source. A reliable source of data is the government website www.statistics.gov.uk. Here, you can find data such as the causes of death by age and sex as a table. You can then extract and interpret it as part of your literature review. Earlier in this unit, we looked at the use of data and how graphs can either inform or mislead. Be alert when reading statistics and when presenting your own.

4 Be able to plan for a research project

The key to successful research is planning. Make an action plan with definite timescales. Be realistic – allow roughly three times as much time to process the results as it takes to do the questionnaires, interviews or observations.

Shazia is unused to carrying out research so decides to undertake a practice research with friends, to help her sort out any problems and prepare for her main research project. She chooses to look at how many people in her class smoke. Shazia found that she was not very clear with her questions on her questionnaire. Her plan went something like this:

- A question or hypothesis for study – how many in my class smoke?
- Aims and objectives of the research – to find out how many from a target group of 16-year-olds ignore health warnings on cigarette packets.
- Rationale – a government target is to cut the number of deaths from smoking. This research aims to find out if government health warnings are having any effect.
- Proposed methodology of data collection – interviews to get in-depth information and questionnaires to get data from a large group.
- Proposed secondary resources – online data for smoking-related diseases.
- People involved – my class.
- Breakdown/timing – week 1: write questionnaire and give it out to class, do secondary research on internet; week 2: follow up with two interviews; week 3: analyse results.

Other considerations were that some people in her class were off sick when she planned to do the questionnaire – should she include them? There are more girls than boys in her class – would that mean she could not claim her class is truly representative of all classes in school?

An ethical issue was that some people smoked but did not want their parents to know. How could she make sure information was confidential? And how could she get consent – verbally or written?

A potential problem was how to record the interviews. Another problem was what questions to ask, both in the interviews and in the questionnaires. The more she thought about it, the more she realised that the topic was getting bigger and bigger.

See if you can spot any problems with her questionnaire:

Aim – to find out how many people smoke.
1 *Do you smoke?*
2 *How much do you spend on cigarettes?*
3 *When do you smoke?*
4 *Why do you smoke?*
5 *Where do you smoke?*
6 *When did you start smoking?*

7 *Why did you start smoking?*
8 *Have you seen the government health warnings on cigarette packets?*
9 *Do you intend to stop smoking?*
10 *Do you know anyone who has lung cancer?*

Shazia asked her friend Sarah to look at her questionnaire. Sarah pointed out a few things:

- The aim – who is the target group? Is this how many people in the whole world, or in our class?
- If they say 'no' to the first question, they do not need to do any more questions.
- Does Question 2 refer to per day, per week, per month?
- Question 3 – do you expect a time of day or a situation such as 'when stressed'?
- Questions 4 and 7 are open ended. How will you show the answers for them?
- Most questions are not relevant to the aim.

After some discussion, Shazia changed her questionnaire to this:

Aim – to find out how many people in our class smoke.
1 *Do you smoke?*

Shazia then received yes or no answers that she could put into a table and present as a line graph for quantitative data. She then interviewed one person who did smoke and one who did not to find out why they behaved as they did for qualitative information.

Now it's your turn. You will need to produce an outline of your planned research and then develop your plan in more detail. Decide on the research question and how you are going to research it. You may wish to research the social habits of 16-year-olds. If so, what do you mean by 'the social habits'? Does it include saying good morning to the neighbour as you leave your home? Or do you mean 'social habits' such as clubbing? Perhaps you are really interested in how many units of alcohol are consumed each week by a sample of students.

Clarify your thoughts and talk to people. They may have suggestions which will help. You could do this research quantitatively by surveying 20 or 30 people. You could also do this qualitatively by interviewing three students. Researchers often think of how they are going to process the information when they get it and this helps them decide which approach they will use.

Activity 8   P4   M2

Choose a topic to practice research in your own class, using interviews or observations and questionnaires. Here are some suggestions for topics, but you may use other ideas:

- leisure activities of teenagers
- what people spend money on
- diet of teenagers
- career ambitions
- sleeping patterns of teenagers
- role models for teenagers
- hours spent on part-time work.

Make a plan that includes:

- a question or hypothesis for study
- aims and objectives of the research
- rationale
- proposed methods of data collection and reasons why you chose these methods
- proposed secondary resources
- people involved
- breakdown/timing
- other considerations, e.g. ethical issues, potential problems or risks.

Keep a log – a record of progress and investigations.

Reflect on what you have learned before you start your main project. Were the questionnaires clear and did they ask what you needed to know? How did you record the interviews? Did you have any bias in your questions?

5 Be able to conduct research relevant to a health and social care context

If you have carried out a practice piece of research, you will know some of the difficulties that may occur.

Topic

Topic selection is important. Choose a subject in health and social care that interests you. If you want to know more about young people, choose a topic relevant to that age group. Will you be able to gather the information you need? If you do not know anyone who uses sign language, it may be difficult for you to research the use of British Sign Language. Clarify the question. Think carefully how you might approach a topic and whether you have access to that information. Choose a topic where you have access to that subject group.

The rationale
- Is the topic suitable?
- Is it interesting to you?
- Do you have access to that group?
- How will you approach sensitive topics? If you are researching drinking habits, will people trust you enough to tell you the truth?
- How will you maintain confidentiality?
- How will you manage the ethics? If you ask about previous painful experiences, how do you know that the person will not be upset?
- How will you gain informed consent?

> **Key term**
>
> Rationale – motivation or basis for choosing a subject to research.

Is your topic SMART?

- Specific – you cannot research all the views of all 16-year-olds in your town.
- Measurable – will you know when you have done it?
- Achievable – is it do-able?
- Realistic – will you *really* be able to interview

five people and process the information? Are the subject and your questions relevant to health and social care?
- Timed – will you get it done in the time you have?

Research fails because the researcher did not think enough before starting. Successful researchers spend a lot of time planning to eliminate problems before they start. Judith Bell's book *Doing Your Research Project* has plenty of practical advice for researchers in education and social science. Here is a checklist for planning your project. It is adapted from the book to suit the needs of BTEC students:

1 Draw up a short list of topics.
2 Select a topic for investigation.
3 Establish the precise focus of the investigation (choose the question carefully).
4 Decide on the aims and objectives of the study or formulate a hypothesis.
5 Draw up an initial project outline.
6 Read enough to enable you to decide if you are on the right lines.
7 Devise a timetable to enable you to check that all stages will be covered and time allowed for writing.
8 Consult your tutor.
9 Keep a brief record of what has been discussed in tutorials.
10 Check guidelines on plagiarism.

Hypothesis

> **Did you know...**
>
> 'Hypothesis' is singular. When we have more than one, the plural is hypotheses.

> **Key term**
>
> Hypothesis – an assumption, a guess or a supposition.

'Hypothesis' is a term often used in the scientific method of research. It is less used in social science research. A hypothesis is a suggested explanation for something – for example, students who eat chips get fat.

The scientific method requires that one can test a scientific hypothesis. Scientists try to get rid of any other variables that might interfere with the experiment. Of course, this hypothesis could not be tested on students for ethical reasons. It would harm them to be deprived of a balanced diet, and would make them unhealthy; therefore, it would not be approved as a proposal for a research topic.

In social science, as in health and social care, we cannot usually carry out an experiment to test a hypothesis; rather we use observation, interviews and questionnaires to test our hypotheses.

Conduct research

When you have decided on your hypothesis and methods, you are almost ready to conduct research, but first you have to look at secondary sources. What research has already been done in this area? You need to carry out a literature search.

Often people make modifications to their hypothesis after looking at secondary sources. They may find the original topic they chose is too big, or the topic is no longer relevant. It is much better to modify your research before you start, rather than halfway through.

Data collection is only the first part of research. Monitor your research. Keep a journal and note any difficulties you have. Check you are on time and following your plan. Once you have the data, whether as checklists, interview notes, completed questionnaires or observation sociograms, you have not finished. Research is only useful when it tells us something and, for that to happen, we have to analyse the data.

6 Be able to interpret research findings

Once you have collected your data, you can start on the analysis. Present your work logically. You may wish to use the following headings:

- Introduction
- Method
- Results
- Conclusion.

Introduction

Give a summary of current research in the field with relation to chosen topic. This is what you find out from your literature search. Evaluate the

---

Activity 9   P5   M3   D2

Discuss your research ideas with your teacher, then make a plan for your research project using these headings:

- **A question or hypothesis for study**
- **Aims and objectives of the research**
- **Rationale**
- **Proposed methods of data collection – use interviews and questionnaires**
- **Proposed secondary resources**
- **People involved**
- **Breakdown/timing**
- **Other considerations, e.g. ethical issues, potential problems or risks.**

Carry out your research following the plan. Keep a journal of any changes or modifications you have to make to your research.

articles you read or the programmes you watch. What did you learn from them?

Method

Present your hypothesis or research focus. Explain your primary research methods, and any secondary research. Say how you recorded data, e.g. a tally chart, or transcribing (writing out) taped interviews. You may have used notes you made at the time of the interview.

Triangulation means 'checking one set of findings by using another method'. Explain how you triangulate your findings. In your research, use two methods to triangulate findings. A frequently used way of triangulating is to use a survey and then interview a smaller number of people from that sample. This triangulates when people interviewed support what was said on the survey forms.

Key term

Triangulation – checking one set of results using a different method. Ideally, the findings should be the same using two different methods.

Results

You will need to compile data and present it so that is can be understood easily. If you have quantitative data, use an Excel spreadsheet or any other ICT software to compile a table and then a graph of your findings. Present data in an understandable way.

For statistical information, produce percentages and work out the mean, median and mode. (Statistical significance is only reliable if the sample is over 30.)

Using the data in Table 22.4, we can work out the mean: 1,237 + 1,172 + 787 + 696 + 362 divided by 5 = 851. We can interpret this information by saying that Greater Manchester and Greater London issue more ASBOs than other areas.

The median is the middle value, 787, so we can say that Greater Manchester and Greater London issue more than the median number.

The mode is the most frequent value. There is no mode here but if you conduct a questionnaire and ask how many times people go clubbing each month, you might get a series of numbers such as

1   2   2   5   2   4   5

The mode would be the most frequently occurring, which is 2, so according to these findings most people go clubbing twice a month.

Per cent means per hundred, written as %. One per cent is written 1% and means one in every hundred, 5% is the same as saying five in every hundred. If we want to know the percentage values for the most ASBOs, we add up all the values, which makes a total of 4,254. We then take 1,237 and divide it by 4,254 and multiply by 100 to give the percentage.

Table 22.4 Number of anti-social behaviour orders by area, 1999–2005

Area	Number of ASBOs
Greater Manchester	1,237
Greater London	1,172
West Midlands	787
West Yorkshire	696
Lancashire	362

Source: Home Office

Table 22.5 Number and percentage of antisocial behaviour orders by area 1999 – 2005

Area	Number of ASBOs	Percentage of ASBOs
Greater Manchester	1,237	29%
Greater London	1,172	28%
West Midlands	787	18.5%
West Yorkshire	696	16%
Lancashire	362	8.5%
Total	4,254	100%

From these percentages, you can see that the West Midlands issues twice as many ASBOs as Lancashire (because 18.5 per cent is just over twice Lancashire's 8.5 per cent).

This is the same information as a column graph.

It can also be presented in a pie chart.

The pie chart and graph show the same information and can be presented quickly and easily. Which do you prefer?

Here is some different information about ASBOs.

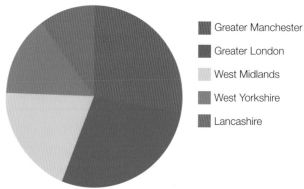

Most ASBOs 1999–2005, by area

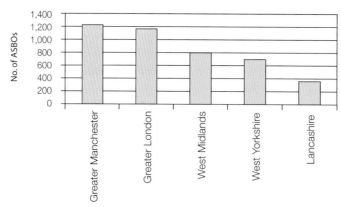

Most ASBOs 1999–2005, by area

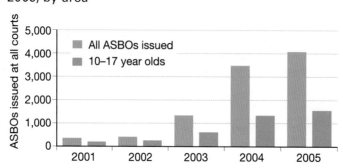

ASBOs issued at all courts
Source: Home Office

From this graph, you can see that the number of ASBOs issued has increased. The number of ASBOs given to 10–17 year olds has also increased but not at the same rate.

Use the most appropriate methods of presentation for your data, whether bar charts, histograms, graphs, pie charts or tables. Most people use a computer to produce these easily and quickly. A large study of 1,000 participants would require IT software for processing statistical information. SPSS for Windows is a program used by academic researchers. Of course, if you do not have sensible data, you will not have sensible conclusions. Statisticians use these programs to manage very complex data and research projects. You are unlikely to use such a package until you get to university.

When you present findings, results should be presented as a whole, even if they do not show the picture you expected. The results should be presented clearly so that people will not be misled.

Conclusions

In drawing conclusions, make sure you are aware of any bias. For example, 'What music do you like?' assumes the person likes music. They may not. Good researchers conduct a pilot test to get rid of any biased questions before they give out the main questionnaire or conduct the interviews. Another source of bias is where the interviewer hears what they want to hear and disregards the rest. This is why tape recordings are often used – so the interviewer can check what really was said.

Research is never perfect. Often at the end of a research project, more questions are raised than there were at the beginning. A common recommendation is that a further research study should be conducted. If your research project raises more questions than it answers, do not despair! Evaluate your project. To what extent did it answer the question or test the hypothesis? Did you find out everything you intended or did you only find out part of it? Did you have to change your research focus?

How do the results of your research link to current research? Do they support or contradict the findings? If you research how many of your fellow students smoke, you might find that your results are similar to national statistics or you may find that your sample is not typical.

It is important to identify the limitations of your research. For example, if you looked at a small sample and used interviews to produce qualitative research, it may not be possible to generalise. Your results are reliable only for your sample, not for the whole country because your sample may be biased. This is not 'wrong'; it is just a limitation of your research. You may find that only 10 question-naires were returned, even though you sent out 50. The findings are therefore not fully repre-sentative of your sample.

Your research might highlight potential areas for further research. If you research the smoking habits of college students, you might find that people do not know all the health risks linked to smoking. Further research might be needed to identify health risks.

You should also look at ethical considerations. Were people fully informed before they consented to become involved? Professor Zimbardo had to stop his prison experiment because people were getting hurt, physically and psychologically. What ethical issues were there in your research? Check that confidentiality was maintained and that data was fully protected and destroyed after use. Were human rights respected? The prison experiment did not respect the rights of the 'prisoners' and had to be stopped.

What are the implications for the sector based on your research findings? Include a section on recommendations. Focus on who will read the research. A smoking cessation nurse might be interested in your findings about smoking at college. If you write your recommendations for health and social care policy-makers, your research might highlight gaps in provision, such as a lack of activities for residents in care homes.

Activity 10 · P6 · M4 · M3 · D2

Analyse your findings and present them as a table or graph. You may find it useful to use an Excel spreadsheet. Explain your findings and conclusions and how they relate to what you set out to explore. How far do your findings relate to the aims? Perhaps you drifted from the original topic and did not ask the questions you needed. Include this in your evaluation.

Summary

This is a long unit but one which will provide you with the basic research skills you will need if you intend to study at a higher level. We looked at the function of, or reasons why we use, research in health and social care. We need research to help us provide better care. We looked at some of the ethical issues relating to research and especially the need for confidentiality and informed choice. The TGN1412 drugs trial showed what can go wrong, even when permission has been given for the research to go ahead. Practical research methods were explained. Guidelines were given for planning and conducting the research. Finally we looked at how to present and interpret research findings.

Assessment and grading criteria

In order to pass this unit, the evidence that the learner presents for assessment needs to demonstrate that they can meet all the learning outcomes for the unit. The assessment criteria for a pass grade describe the level of achievement required to pass this unit.

To achieve a pass grade the evidence must show that the learner is able to:	To achieve a merit grade the evidence must show that, in addition to the pass criteria, the learner is able to:	To achieve a distinction grade the evidence must show that, in addition to the pass and merit criteria, the learner is able to:
P1 explain the function of research in health and social care	**M1** discuss the function of research in a chosen area of interest	
P2 discuss ethical issues relating to research in the health and social care sectors		**D1** assess research methodologies with regard to ensuring validity of findings

To achieve a pass grade the evidence must show that the learner is able to:	To achieve a merit grade the evidence must show that, in addition to the pass criteria, the learner is able to:	To achieve a distinction grade the evidence must show that, in addition to the pass and merit criteria, the learner is able to:
P3 compare different research methodologies for health and social care	**M2** justify the research methodologies chosen for the project	
P4 plan a research project		
P5 carry out the planned research project	**M3** assess strengths and weaknesses of the research project in meeting the aims or hypothesis	**D2** evaluate how the research project could have been improved.
P6 report findings and conclusions from the research project.	**M4** assess findings of the research project in relation to the original hypothesis.	

Resources

Barn, R., Andrew, L. and Mantovani, N. (2005) 'The experiences of young care leavers from different ethnic groups' (available at www.jrf.org.uk/KNOWLEDGE/findings/socialpolicy/0285.asp).

Bell, J. (2005) *Doing Your Research Project: A Guide for First-time Researchers in Education, Health and Social Science*, New York: Open University Press.

Department of Health (2002) 'Children's homes: national minimum standards, children's homes regulations' (available at www.dh.gov.uk/en/Pub licationsandstatistics/Publications/Publications PolicyAnd Guidance/DH_4010076).

Department of Health (2007) 'Putting People First: a shared vision and commitment to the transformation of adult social care' (available at www.dh.gov.uk/en/Publications andstatistics/Publications/Publications PolicyAndGuidance/DH_081118).

Duffy, S., Tabar, L., Olsen, A., Vitak, B., Allgood, P., Chen, T., Yen, A. and Smith, R. (2010) 'Absolute numbers of lives saved and over diagnosis in breast cancer screening, from a randomised trial and from the Breast Screening Programme in England', *Journal of Medical Screening*, 17(1): 25–30.

Goffman, E. (1961) *Asylums: Essays on the Social Situation of Mental Patients and Other Inmates*, New York: Doubleday.

Huff, D. (1954) *How to Lie with Statistics*, New York: Norton.

Leece, J. and Peace, S. (2010) 'Developing new understandings of independence and autonomy in the personalised relationship', *British Journal of Social Work* (in press) (available at http://dx.doi.org/doi:10.1093/bjsw/bcp105).

Marshall, B.J. and Warren, J.R. (1984) 'Unidentified curved bacilli in the stomach of patients with gastritis and peptic ulceration', *Lancet*, 1(8390): 1311–1315.

Murray, J. and Cartwright-Hatton, S. (2006)

'NICE guidelines on treatment of depression in childhood and adolescence: implications from a CBT perspective', *Behavioural and Cognitive Psychotherapy*, 34: 129–137.

NICE (2005) 'Depression in children and young people: identification and management in primary, community and secondary care', NICE clinical guidelines CG28.

Ofsted (2010) 'An evaluation of the provision of mental health services for looked after young people over the age of 16 accommodated in residential settings' (available at www.ofsted.gov.uk/Ofsted-home/Publications-and-research/Browse-all-by/Documents-by-type/Thematic-reports/An-evaluation-of-the-provision-of-mental-health-services-for-looked-after-young-people-over-the-age-of-16-accommodated-in-residential-settings).

Shipman, C. et al. (2008) 'Improving generalist end of life care: national consultation with practitioners, commissioners, academics, and service user groups', BMJ, 337:a1720 (available at www.bmj.com/cgi/content/abstract/337/oct01_1/a1720#otherarticles).

Social Exclusion Task Force (2002) *Young Runaways – Summary of the Social Exclusion Unit Report*, London: Stationery Office.

Weblinks

www.dcsf.gov.uk/everychildmatters:
Every Child Matters

www.ic.nhs.uk/statistics-and-data-collect ions/social-care/adult-social-care-infor mation/community-care-statistics-2008:- supported-residents-adults-england:
Community Care Statistics 2008

www.ico.gov.uk:
Information Commissioner's Office

www.nres.npsa.nhs.uk:
National Research Ethics Office

www.open2.net/healthliving/family_child development/children_happiness2.html:
Children and happiness – what makes children happy?

www.statistics.gov.uk:
UK National Statistics

www.ukrio.org:
UK Research Integrity Office

Glossary

Please note that Unit 12, Unit 14, Unit 20, Unit 28, Unit 29, Unit 40 and Unit 47 are available online. See the inside front cover for details.

Abuse: a violation of an individual's human and civil rights by any other person or persons. Neglect or mistreatment of individuals, generally those who are vulnerable, and can be sexual, physical, emotional or financial. UNITS 2 and 11

Acupuncture: the procedure of inserting and manipulating needles into various points on the body to relieve pain for therapeutic purposes. UNIT 14

Ageing: the process of growing older. We are all ageing from the minute we are born! UNIT 4

Analyse: break down into different parts. UNIT 22

Anatomy: the study of the body's structure and how each part relates to others. UNIT 5

Anti-discriminatory practice: discrimination is against the law and as a care worker, it is essential not only that you uphold the law yourself, but that you ensure the service users you deal with are not subjected to discrimination or unfair practice from others. This may mean challenging others if you witness discriminatory behaviour, either by other service users or by colleagues. Discriminatory practice means treating someone unfavourably compared to others in relation to the provision of goods or services, buying, renting or selling land or property or within employment. UNIT 2

Aromatherapy: the use of fragrant substances (usually 'essential' oils distilled from flowers, resins, woods and roots) to treat emotional disorders such as stress and anxiety, as well as a wide range of other ailments. UNIT 14

Behaviourist: focuses on behaviour as a learned response. UNIT 8

Beliefs/values: these are things you hold to be true. They inform your attitude and how you live your life – your values. They are important to a person and are generally based on what was learnt during someone's upbringing or through experience. It is important to remember not to treat someone differently because they do not share your views. Beliefs and values help to inform a person's sense of self. UNIT 2

Biological: how the physical body influences behaviour – for example, through genetic inheritance. UNIT 8

Biopsy: removal and examination of a piece of tissue to analyse disease. UNIT 14

Body mass index (BMI): BMI looks at the relationship between height and weight and is a good indicator of whether someone is the right weight for their height. UNIT 21

Capacity: the ability to make a decision about a particular matter at the time the decision needs to be made. UNIT 40

Capitalism: an economic and social system in which the means of production are privately owned. Labour, goods and services are bought and sold and the profits distributed to the owners. UNIT 7

Catheter: a flexible tube which is inserted into the body to allow passage of fluids. UNIT 14

Coalition: a government made up of more than one political party, who have formally agreed to work together. This usually happens when no party has a majority of seats to govern overall. UNIT 47

Coeliac disease: coeliac disease is an autoimmune disease, where the body's immune system attacks its own tissues. This immune reaction is triggered by gluten, a collective name for a type of protein found in the cereals wheat, rye and barley. A few people are also sensitive to oats. UNIT 14

Cognitive/information processing: how we understand the world. Cognitive refers to our thinking processes. A child starts by calling everything red, but as they develop cognitively, they can tell the difference between red, pink and orange. UNIT 8

Collectivism: emphasises 'rights to', e.g. health care – positive liberties. UNIT 7

Colostomy: surgical operation allowing part of

the bowel to exit onto the abdomen. The exit is called a stoma. UNIT 14

Commission: order or authorise. UNIT 22

Commodified: turned into something that can be bought and sold. UNIT 7

Communication: an interactive, two-way process of giving and receiving a message, such as exchanging ideas or information. UNIT 1

Communication cycle: the sending, receiving and decoding of messages. UNIT 1

Complementary: this means they go together, like 'fish and chips'. UNIT 29

Conditioning: a learned response to a stimulus. UNIT 8

Conserve number: the understanding that the number of items stay the same whether they are crowded together or spread out. UNIT 29

Constituency: a geographical area in the UK that is represented by one MP in the House of Commons. People living in that area are called constituents. UNIT 47

Contemporary: current, up to date. UNIT 22

Contrasting: in the context of studying different perspectives, this means they have opposite approaches. UNIT 29

Creatinine: a normal waste product present in the urine and used to measure kidney filtration. UNIT 14

Cytology: the study of cells. UNIT 5

Data: numerical information (e.g. how many deaths), usually expressed as a percentage. UNIT 12

Deficiency: when the body lacks a certain nutrient. UNIT 21

Dementia: an ongoing decline of the brain and its abilities. UNIT 40

Demography: the study of populations. UNIT 28

Development: an increase in skills. Babies learn to talk and to smile. Teenagers learn to use MP3 players. An older person may learn a new language before going on holiday abroad. UNIT 4

Developmental norms: there are stages of development which people pass through in a certain order. So a baby starts to coo and babble before forming words. Some people think babies should reach developmental milestones at certain ages, or there is something wrong. In fact this is a complex subject. Each child is unique. UNIT 4

Developmental psychology: the study of how we develop psychologically, in our thoughts and feelings. UNIT 29

Difference: this is the quality that makes someone unlike someone else. UNIT 2

Direct (overt) discrimination: one of two forms of discrimination. It is when you knowingly treat someone unfairly on the basis of race, gender, etc. UNIT 2

Disadvantage: this is a situation in which an individual is in a position of weakness relative to someone else. A disadvantage is something that will count against someone and put him or her in a weaker situation than someone else. UNIT 2

Diversity: we all have the right to different views and opinions and these must be respected. It is not just about being politically correct or being a good society; it is about creating social cohesion and harmony through challenging and changing people's attitudes towards different cultures. UNIT 2

Economic status: how wealthy, or not, someone is. UNIT 7

Efficacy: usefulness and effectiveness; value. UNIT 12

Empowerment: one of the fundamental principles of care work, empowerment is about enabling people to take control over their lives through choices and be as independent as possible. UNIT 2

Epidemiology: the study of the origin and spread of disease. UNIT 12

Equality: this is about ensuring that people have equal opportunities in life and a fair chance to fulfil their potential. In health and social care, equality is focused on equal access to health and social care and equal treatment for everyone, irrespective of race, ethnicity, sex, gender, religion, social class, age or any other difference. UNIT 2

Equity: this is a principle that all people should be treated fairly and impartially (in an unbiased way). This is not about everyone having the same wealth or power but about ensuring that everyone has the same rights under the law. It also means that individuals should not be discriminated against. It is based on a moral right that individuals have the right to be treated equally. UNIT 2

Ethical: moral. UNIT 22

Evaluate: assess the value of something. UNIT 22

Evidence-based practice: work based on research findings. UNIT 22

Experiential learning: learning by experience, not just learning from a book. UNITS 6 and 48

Family dynamics: the relationships within the family and how family members relate to one another, especially in relation to who has the power and control. UNIT 10

Feminist theory: focuses on how gender inequality has shaped the social world. UNIT 7

Fissure: a groove, natural division, deep furrow, cleft or tear in various parts of the body. UNIT 14

Fistulae: an abnormal canal between two organs or between an organ and the outside of the body. UNIT 14

Growth: an increase in physical size. Most babies grow bigger. UNIT 4

Hazard: something that can cause harm. UNIT 3

Hierarchy of needs: some needs are more important to our survival than others. We need food, water and oxygen. These are basic needs we must satisfy if we are to survive. Higher-level needs, such as the need for love and belonging, come only after basic needs have been met. UNIT 8

Histology: the study of tissues. UNIT 5

Hormone: a chemical messenger that travels throughout the body but may affect only certain cells. UNIT 5

Household: a person living alone, or a group of people living at the same address who have the address as their only or main residence and either share one main meal a day or share the living accommodation (or both). More people were living alone in 2004 than 40 years previously. UNIT 4

Humanistic: human behaviour is driven by needs. UNIT 8

Hypothesis: a theory or assumption, which needs to be proved or disproved by further research. UNITS 7 and 22

Immunisation: vaccination or inoculation against disease by introducing a harmless form of the disease to stimulate the individual's immune system defence. UNIT 12

Implications: suggestions or consequences. UNIT 22

Independence: this means that someone has the freedom to choose how they live their lives, to not be dependent or controlled by someone else, an organisation or the state. UNIT 2

Indicators: signs. UNIT 11

Indirect (covert) discrimination: this type of discrimination is subtler than direct discrimination – for example, applying criteria that only some people are able to meet. Although it may be unintentional, it is still unlawful. UNIT 2

Individualism: emphasises liberties in terms of 'freedom from', e.g. government control – negative liberties. UNIT 7

Industrial Revolution: the development of the machine-based manufacturing industry. UNIT 12

Information literacy: 'is knowing when and why you need information, where to find it, and how to evaluate, use and communicate it in an ethical manner' (Chartered Institute of Library and Information Professionals). UNIT 22

Information processing: how we make sense of all the stimuli around us. We see, hear, taste, touch and smell the world around us. Most people can filter out the information they do not need but people with autism have difficulty filtering and processing. They may get information overload, and crash out, just like a computer crashing. UNIT 8

Intelligence: comes from analysing data and identifying what it means (e.g. by comparing two sets of data you can tell if something has improved or not). UNIT 12

Interaction: an exchange of communication between two people. UNIT 1

Interaction analysis: the assessment of a communication exchange to see if meaning has been shared. UNIT 1

Interactionist: interactionist perspectives examine how shared meanings and social patterns develop through social interactions within a particular social context. UNIT 7

Interdependence: this is when people are dependent on each other. This may be through mutual assistance or cooperation. UNIT 2

Interpersonal: between people. UNIT 1

Jaundice: yellow tinge to the skin and whites of the eyes caused by excessive amounts of bilirubin in the bloodstream. UNIT 14

Keratinised: the process by which keratin is deposited in cells and the cells become hardened (as in nails and hair). UNIT 5

Laissez-faire: means to leave alone, not interfere. In politics, it means minimal regulation by government and minimal social welfare (government or state help for those in poverty/ need). UNIT 47

Labelling: by labelling someone, you are applying a stereotype to him or her. People are not seen as individuals but seen as whatever is implied by the label. For example, 'hoodie', rather than someone's older brother, 'queer', rather than a good worker, etc. From this, discrimination results. It is used to 'put people down'. Individuals or groups who fall within a negative stereotype start from a disadvantaged position and thus lack power and influence. UNIT 2

Lactose intolerance: lactose intolerance is the inability to absorb lactose into the digestive system. If lactose is not absorbed properly, it ferments and this results in abdominal pain, a bloated stomach and diarrhoea. UNIT 14

Learning: this means more than just accumulating facts; it means acquiring information and gaining new skills that change your behaviour. UNITS 6 and 48

Learning styles: the preferred way or ways that people learn. UNITS 6 and 48

Legislative authority: the right to make the law (legislation). UNIT 47

Life course: the events in a person's life. Sometimes it can be described as a river, starting in the hills as a small stream, running fast, then broadening and slowing as it gets bigger. As it matures and approaches the sea, it slows down. It may be deep and powerful but calm on the surface. Eventually it joins the sea, which is the end of the journey, and for humans, the end of life. Some people have an easy life, with no real problems. Other people have a rough journey, facing obstacles along the way. UNIT 4

Life expectancy: how long a person is expected to live. This varies depending on the individual. UNITS 4 and 28

Lipids: fats and oils. UNIT 21

Living wage: defined as sufficient income to provide adequate nutrition, physical activity, housing, social interaction, transport, medical care and hygiene for an average family. UNIT 7

Looked after children: the legal term for children and young people in public care. It refers to children who are subject to care orders and those who are accommodated. UNIT 22

Macro nutrient: these are nutrients required in large quantities – for example, carbohydrates, proteins and fats. UNIT 21

Makaton: a system of symbols and pictures that works like a language to help people make themselves understood. UNIT 1

Manual handling: lifting or moving objects or people without a mechanical aid or equipment. UNIT 3

Marasmus: the result of poor weaning or inadequate breastfeeding, which usually occurs as a result of the mother not having sufficient nutrients to pass on through her milk. Marasmus can cause poor muscle development, stunted growth and learning difficulties through poor brain development. UNIT 21

Maturation or maturity: this is a holistic process. It includes physical, social and emotional aspects. Emotional maturation comes with thinking about experiences. Some young people who have had a lot of responsibility may be very mature in their outlook. Adults are expected to be experienced and wise, but this is not always the case. An older person who has never had any responsibility may lack experience and be immature, even though they are physically old. UNIT 4

Maturational theory: this states that our brain has to mature to be able to shape behaviour. It is no good expecting a one-month-old baby to speak in sentences. The language part of their brain is not sufficiently developed to enable it to form words. UNIT 8

Metabolism: a continual process of chemical changes in cells which allows them to grow and function. It involves constant building of complex molecules (anabolism) and breaking them down (catabolism). These processes often release energy. The speed at which these reactions take place is called the metabolic rate. UNIT 5

Methodology: method or way. UNIT 22

Micro nutrient: these are nutrients which are needed in small amounts – for example, vitamins and minerals. UNIT 21

Mortality rate: the number of people who die of a particular disease or condition compared with those who could be expected to die of all other causes. UNIT 12

Nature: nature, in terms of developmental psychology, refers to the genes we inherit. UNIT 29

Nebuliser: a device used to administer medication to people in the form of a mist inhaled into the lungs. UNIT 14

Neuropathy: the condition is generally referred to as peripheral neuropathy and is most commonly due to damage to nerve axons. Neuropathy usually causes pain and numbness in the hands and feet. UNIT 14

Nurture: nurture, in terms of developmental psychology, refers to the influences from our environment. UNIT 29

Object permanence: the understanding that an object is still there even if you cannot see it. UNIT 29

Opportunity: if equality and diversity are enshrined within society, discrimination will eventually be eradicated and everyone should have an equal chance to achieve his or her potential in society. UNIT 2

Palliative: treatment that alleviates signs and symptoms without curing. UNIT 14

Palliative care: care for people who are not going to recover from their illness and for whom no further treatment is available. It consists of making sure they are pain-free and comfortable, enhancing the quality of life. UNIT 10

Paramount: of principal and supreme importance. UNIT 10

Paramountcy principle: when dealing with children and young people, their welfare, needs and rights must come first, before those of adults. UNIT 2

Pathogens: micro-organisms that are capable of causing disease. UNIT 3

Patriarchy: a form of society or social system, which is dominated and ruled by men, who are seen as being in authority. Power is passed from father to son. UNIT 7

Peer-reviewed: read by other professionals with experience of research. UNIT 22

Perspectives: views or approaches. There are six main psychological perspectives: behaviourist, social learning, psychodynamic, humanistic, cognitive/information processing and biological. UNIT 8

Phenomenology: the philosophical study of lived experience. UNIT 7

Physiological: the functioning of the different parts of the body and their relationship to the efficient functioning of the whole organism. UNIT 7

Physiology: the study of how the body works and functions within the organs and alongside other structures. UNITS 5 and 14

Plagiarism: illegal use of someone else's work, copying, stealing work. UNIT 22

Pluralistic: diverse, with multiple variations of reality (cultural differences). UNIT 7

Policy: a plan of action that has been adopted by the setting. UNIT 3

Political beliefs: known as ideology and these often form the basis of policy and legislation. UNIT 47

Political ideologies: these describe the beliefs that underpin political approaches and actions; political belief systems. UNIT 47

Political party: a group of people sharing the same beliefs and values. Members are chosen by political parties to stand for election to Parliament. They will represent a constituency. UNIT 47

Positivists: positivists believe that social processes should be studied in terms of cause and effect, using scientific methods. UNIT 7

Poverty line: the financial level below which people were considered poor. UNIT 12

Predictable event: a planned or chosen change. UNIT 4

Prejudice: having a pre-conceived idea about somebody or a group of people. Prejudice can take many different forms; it is often deep-seated and can lead to discrimination, preventing people having their needs addressed and, in extreme cases, can result in bullying and abuse. It is based on fear or lack of knowledge and can be a feature of unequal power relations. UNIT 2

Procedure: a set of actions or steps that meets the requirements of the policy or strategy. UNITS 3 and 11

Psychodynamic: our unconscious mind influences our behaviour. UNIT 8

Psychological: thinking skills. UNIT 4

Psychological development: developing mentally, learning new ways to think and feel. UNIT 4

Psychology: the study of how mental processes influence behaviour. UNIT 8

Puberty: the first phase of adolescence, the time when sexual maturity becomes evident. A large increase in hormones – oestrogen in girls and testosterone in boys – leads to a range of physical and emotional changes that are completely natural but sometimes hard to deal with. UNIT 4

Putting the patient/service user at the heart of service provision: this means to focus on what the person needs and provide it, giving them control and power over their lives, rather than telling them what services are available. People should be involved in decisions over things that affect their lives, so that they are as independent as possible. UNIT 2

Rationale: motivation or basis for choosing a subject to research. UNIT 22

Reflexology: treatment involving massage to reflex areas found in the feet. UNIT 14

Regulations: laws approved by Parliament. UNIT 3

Reinforcement: this causes behaviour to occur more often. UNIT 8

Reliability: consistency. UNIT 22

Rementia: the regaining of lost cognitive and functional abilities. UNIT 40

Remission: a temporary state where a disease's signs and symptoms disappear. UNIT 14

Rights: everyone has a right to care and practitioners have a duty and responsibility to uphold this right, otherwise you are not giving appropriate care. By not accepting that all people have the same rights, they are being denied their rights as human beings. UNIT 2

Risk: the effect of a hazard and the probability of a hazard occurring. UNIT 3

Role theory: the idea that certain behaviour is associated with certain roles, such as a doctor wears a white coat and has an air of authority. UNIT 8

Safeguarding: protecting. UNIT 11

Self-actualisation: self-fulfilment, meeting one's full potential. UNIT 1 and 8

Self-concept: our awareness of ourselves and our beliefs about ourselves. UNITS 7 and 8

Self-esteem: how much we value ourselves. UNIT 8

Self-fulfilling prophecy: if you believe something will happen, you sometimes make it happen. UNIT 8

Social determinants of health: the genetic, social, lifestyle, cultural and environmental factors that influence health and the likelihood of ill health and disease. UNIT 7

Social learning: we learn behaviour from others. UNIT 8

Socio-economic: social and economic. Social is to do with society and other people; economic is about money. UNIT 28

Speaker: the person whose role it is to maintain the smooth running of Parliament and discipline MPs. UNIT 47

Specific: precise, definite, not vague. UNIT 29

Standardised mortality rate: this is a calculation based on the number of actual deaths compared with the expected number of deaths in a particular group. UNIT 7 and UNIT 12

Stereotyping: this is based on prejudice (pre-judging) and means holding beliefs that all members of a group are the same. This information is often based on negative beliefs and is inaccurate. The person is not seen as an individual. Stereotypical remarks often start with 'They all…'. UNIT 2

Stigmatise: to label as socially undesirable. UNIT 10

Strategies: plans. UNIT 11

Synthesise: to combine, usually ideas from difference sources. UNIT 22

Tolerance: broadminded acceptance (of difference). UNIT 2

Triangulation: checking one set of results using a different method. Ideally, the findings should be the same using two different methods. UNIT 22

Unconscious mind: the part of our mind we are not aware of. UNIT 8

Universal services: those services within health and education that are provided for all children, e.g. immunisation and school services. UNIT 10

Unpredictable event: a sudden and unexpected change. UNIT 4

Urbanisation: the movement of people away from the countryside to live in the towns. UNIT 12

Urea: a normal waste product produced when the liver breaks down protein or amino acids. The kidneys then transfer the urea from the blood to the urine. UNIT 14

Validity: does it test what it says it tests? UNIT 22

Vulnerability: a psychological state of mind that can make someone more likely to suffer from danger, harm or abuse. Many people who use services are vulnerable because they are in a stressful situation as a result of ill health or an unforeseen crisis. UNIT 2

Welfare: action, usually by government, to improve the social, financial and basic well-being of people most in need. UNIT 47

Welfare services: these are universal; they are provided by the government, funded from individual contributions so individuals within a society can expect to benefit from them. This is an example of collectivism. UNIT 7

Welfare state: in the UK, this is the system for providing healthcare for all and basic financial assistance for those who are sick or unable to work. UNIT 12

Index